Quantitative Analysis for Business Decisions

IRWIN SERIES IN QUANTITATIVE ANALYSIS FOR BUSINESS

Consulting Editor

ROBERT B. FETTER *Yale University*

QUANTITATIVE ANALYSIS *for* BUSINESS DECISIONS

by

HAROLD BIERMAN, JR., Ph.D.

Professor of Accounting and Managerial Economics,
Graduate School of Business and Public Administration,
Cornell University

CHARLES P. BONINI, Ph.D.

Associate Professor of Statistics
Stanford University

LAWRENCE E. FOURAKER, Ph.D.

Professor, Graduate School of Business Administration
Harvard University

ROBERT K. JAEDICKE, Ph.D.

Associate Professor of Accounting,
Graduate School of Business,
Stanford University

REVISED EDITION · 1965

RICHARD D. IRWIN, INC.

HOMEWOOD, ILLINOIS

REVISED EDITION

First Printing, April, 1965

PRINTED IN THE UNITED STATES OF AMERICA
Library of Congress Catalog Card No. 65–17687

THE ADMINISTRATION of a modern business enterprise has become an enormously complex undertaking. During the past twenty years there has been an increasing tendency to turn to quantitative techniques and models as a potential means for solving many of the problems that arise in such an enterprise. Some of these techniques and models have been incorporated in the traditional courses in the business administration curriculum. However, many of them have not yet been included, though they are useful tools for solving many types of business problems. The purpose of this book is to describe a representative sample of the models and their related quantitative techniques that have not yet gained wide treatment in traditional courses. It is hoped that this book will serve as a basis for a course which will not encroach upon the established subject matter of functional areas, and that it may act as a connecting force between the mathematical courses on the one hand and the applied business courses on the other.

This course would be available for students of business or industrial administration who have had the equivalent of at least one full semester of academic work in the general areas of accounting, economics, statistics, and management, and who have had one or more mathematics courses at the college level.

This is an introductory work in the application of mathematics to problems of business. It is not an introductory work to the mathematics which are being applied. We have summarized—in a rather rough and ready manner by a mathematician's standards—some of the mathematical tools employed. Our purpose is to get our notation and a few basic relationships before the reader rather than to teach him mathematics. Basic background works include S. Goldberg, *Probability* (Prentice-Hall, 1960); E. Parzen, *Modern Probability Theory and its Applications* (Wiley, 1960); and W. Feller, *An Introduction to Probability Theory and Its Applications* (Wiley, 1950).

We have attempted to minimize the amount of mathematical training required to read this book. . . . Some previous exposure to probability and statistics would certainly facilitate the reading of many of the chapters, but a reader who does not have formal training in these areas should not think that this book is beyond his ability.

The book is an attempt to consider techniques which treat quite sophisticated and difficult problems; so, even though we tried to choose the simplest means of exposition—avoiding proofs and much of the characteristic rigor of such treatments—the essential subtlety of the techniques remains. These attributes can be understood only by patient application of effort over a protracted period of time. In this connection, we commend the exercises to the reader.

To a large extent the sequence of chapters in this book is arbitrary. The reader may prefer to start with decision making under conditions of certainty and study linear programming before beginning the study of probability and decision making under uncertainty. . . .

We have made no attempt to identify the originators of the ideas or techniques presented in this book. However, some relationships between this book and predecessors must be acknowledged. We have been strongly influenced by R. D. Luce's and H. Raiffa's *Games and Decisions* (Wiley, 1957) and Robert Schlaifer's *Probability and Statistics for Business Decisions* (McGraw-Hill, 1959). If our efforts induce readers to go on to these pioneering works, we will have achieved one of our major purposes.

In addition, we have also borrowed freely from the ideas presented by Samuel Goldberg, Ronald Howard, Howard Raiffa, and Allen Spivey during lectures at the Institute of Basic Mathematics for Application to Business.

One relationship that warrants the label "obvious" is that we are responsible for the errors that surely must be present in a work of this sort.

Thomas Mahoney, Jerome McCarthy, and Edgar Pessemier read an early draft and assisted us with detailed comments and criticisms. We are also indebted to the fellows and faculty of the Institute of Basic Mathematics for Application to Business for advice and consideration that went beyond the scholar's commitment, and to the Harvard Business School and Ford Foundation for providing a physical and financial harbor for such a program. In our specific cases we want to thank Cornell University, Harvard University, and the Pennsylvania State University for making this year of study a part of our experience rather than a part of our aspirations.

PREFACE: Revised Edition

THE REVISED EDITION of *Quantitative Analysis for Business Decisions* is considerably different from its predecessor. The material from four chapters has been dropped completely. Another three chapters have been cut back and combined with other surviving chapters. Eight new chapters dealing primarily with the area of decision making under uncertainty (statistical decision theory) have been added. A few chapters are changed very little, but most of the retained chapters have been extensively revised.

We have attempted to make changes which are consistent with the objectives described in the preface of the first edition. A prime continuing objective has been to make the material understandable to a reader who does not have an extensive mathematical background.

The list of persons who have offered us assistance continues to grow. We want especially to thank the many users of the first edition who bothered to point out errors that we had made, and to offer suggestions for improving the second edition. This assistance is greatly appreciated.

HAROLD BIERMAN, JR.
CHARLES BONINI
LAWRENCE E. FOURAKER
ROBERT K. JAEDICKE

April, 1965

TABLE OF CONTENTS

Chapter 1

INTRODUCTION TO QUANTITATIVE

ANALYSIS

THIS IS a book about business decision making. We consider business decision making to be a process whereby management, when confronted by a problem, selects a specific course of action, or "solution," from a set of possible courses of action. The process of making decisions in a business context has the same essential characteristics as problem-solving behavior in general; it is a part of a man's purposeful activity.

BUSINESS DECISIONS

The business manager wants to choose that course of action which is most effective in attaining the goals of the organization. In judging the effectiveness of different possible decisions, we must use some measuring unit. The most commonly used measure in making decisions is dollars, but we shall see in the following chapters that for many decisions the use of dollars in judging the relative merits of different courses of action would not be desirable.

The business manager is faced with a variety of different types of decision situations; but for our purposes, we shall classify decisions as follows:

1. Decisions under certainty (all the facts are known for sure); or uncertainty, where the event that will occur (the state of nature) is not known for sure but probabilities can be assigned to the possible occurrences (in this situation, we can say the process is stochastic).
2. Decisions where the opponent is nature (drilling an oil well) or a thinking opponent (setting an advertising budget where we have to consider the actions of competitors).
3. Decisions by an individual or by a group.

1

The following general process of solution is common to all types of decision situations:

1. Establish the criterion which will be used. For example, in a simple situation the criterion may be to choose the act which maximizes the expected profit. In a capital-budgeting decision involving several choices of equipment, we may choose the equipment with the largest net present value.
2. Determine the model which will be used, and the values of the parameters of the process. For example, we may decide that the algebraic expression of the model of total expenses is:

$$\text{Total Expenses} = a + b \text{ Units Sold}$$

The parameters are a and b, and their value would have to be determined in order to use the model.
3. Determine which decision optimizes, i.e., is consistent with, the criterion established above in item 1.

Example

We can sell 1,000 units of product to the government at a price of $50 per unit. Should the order be accepted? The firm has excess capacity.

1. We shall use the profit maximization criterion, i.e., accept the order if it increases profit, reject the order if it does not increase profit.
2. We need to know the incremental expenses of producing the 1,000 units. The relevant expense model is:

$$E = a + 1,000b.$$

Assume that special dies costing $5,000 will have to be bought (a is equal to $5,000$) and that the variable costs of producing a unit are $30 ($b$ is equal to 30). The total relevant expenses of filling the order are $35,000 (equal to $5,000 plus $30,000).
3. A comparison of the incremental revenues, $50,000, and incremental expenses indicates we should accept the order. Profit will be greater by $15,000 if we "accept" compared with the decision "refuse the order."

In the above example, we used basic knowledge and simple computational techniques. However, in dealing with more complex problems, we might need to use other tools of quantitative analysis, including calculus, probability, statistics, and programming (linear, nonlinear, and dynamic).

We shall now consider some aspects of model building.

ABSTRACTION

Every empirical (or "real-world") problem is enormously complex. There are literally an uncountable number of inherent "facts" in any empirical situation. Further, every potential course of action starts a chain of cause, effect, and interaction that logically is without end. Consider the simple problem of entering a building with only one entryway, a door with a standard knob. An endless amount of time could be devoted to gathering factual material about this situation: for example, the precise location and physical characteristics of all external parts of the building; a detailed record of the climatic conditions of the neighborhood; a biography of the potential door opener, down to the variation in the length of the fingers of the hand that is designated to grasp the knob. If our decision maker adopts a strategy of collecting *all* the facts before he acts, it follows that he will never act. The human mind cannot consider every aspect of an empirical problem. Some attributes of the problem must be ignored if a decision is to be made. The decision maker must abstract from the empirical situation those factors which he considers to be most relevant to the problem he faces. Abstraction is the first and necessary step in the solution of any human problem.

MODEL BUILDING

After the decision maker has selected the critical factors, or variables, from the empirical situation, he combines them in some logical manner so that they form a counterpart or model of the empirical problem. Our man on the outside may select the door, its knob, and its hinges as the pertinent variables in his problem. A model is a simplified representation of an empirical situation. Ideally, it strips a natural phenomenon of its bewildering complexity and duplicates the essential behavior of the natural phenomenon with a few variables, simply related. The simpler the model, the better for the decision maker, provided it serves as a reasonably reliable counterpart of the empirical problem. The advantages of a simple model are:

1. It is economical of time and thought.
2. It can be understood more readily by the decision maker.
3. If necessary, the model can be modified quickly and effectively.

The object of the decision maker is not to construct a model that is as close as possible to reality in every respect. Such a model would require an infinite length of time to construct, and then it might be beyond human comprehension. Rather, the decision maker wants the simplest model that predicts outcomes reasonably well and is consistent with effective action on his part.

SOLUTIONS

After the model has been constructed, certain conclusions may be derived about its behavior by means of logic. The decision maker then bases his action or solution on these conclusions. If the logic in deriving the conclusions from the abstracted variables is correct, and if the relevant variables have been abstracted, then the solution to the model problem will also serve as an effective solution for the empirical problem. From our example, the decision maker may infer the existence of a latch which can be moved by turning the doorknob; then he may deduce that the door can be opened by applying force in a certain direction, determined by the location of the hinges. He has created a model and derived conclusions in the classic manner: "If A, B, and C are true, then X, Y, and Z follow." His solution may be to walk up to the door, turn the knob, and push. The door may open, testifying once more to the remarkable co-operation between nature and man's intellectual processes. Or the door may not open.

ERRORS

There are two general sources of error in decision making. The first is a mistake in logic in the process of reasoning from premises to conclusions to solutions. The hinges may be located in such a fashion that the door can be opened only by turning the knob and pulling, rather than pushing. Instead of "if A, B, and C, then X, Y, and Z," the theory should be in the form of "if A, B, and C, then X, Y, and M." It is conceivable that errors of this type could be eliminated. Secondly, the decision maker may select the wrong variables, or not enough variables, for constructing his model. The door may be locked, and the proper form of the model would start "if A, B, C, and D—." Or the door may be booby-trapped, so that the proper model should be "if T, then E," where E is an explosion and the solution would be to open the door with a howitzer or, alternatively, to spend the night in a foxhole. The possibility of errors of this type cannot be avoided, for to do so would require that all conceivably pertinent variables be included in the model, and this would preclude decisive action. Abstraction always does some violence to reality, but it is a necessary condition for problem solving. Thus, decision making carries with it the unavoidable possibility of error.

MODEL-BUILDING TECHNIQUES

Models may be represented in a variety of ways. For simple, repetitive problems the entire decision-making process may take place in the mind of the decision maker, perhaps in a quite informal, intuitive manner. We walk, eat, and open doors every day without the aid of a formal model of the related problems our actions are resolving. If the problem is somewhat more unusual or complex, we spend more time thinking about it. We may be explicit to the extent of selecting the important elements of the problem and proceeding to examine and experiment with them.

The appropriate technique for describing and relating selected variables depends to a large extent on the nature of the variables. If the variables are subject to measurement of some form, and particularly if they can be given a quantitative representation, then there are strong reasons for selecting a mathematical representation of the model. First, there is a rigorous inherent discipline in mathematics which insures a certain orderly procedure on the part of the investigator: You must be specific about what variables you have abstracted and what relationships you are assuming to exist among them. For example, it is more difficult to make implicit assumptions in a mathematical model than in a literary model. Secondly, mathematics is a powerful technique for relating variables and for deriving logical conclusions from given premises. Mathematics makes it possible to handle problems which require models of great complexity. Mathematics greatly facilitates the decision-making process where quantitative analysis is applicable.

In the relatively recent past (since World War II) a large number of business problems have been given a quantitative representation with some degree of success, leading to a general approach which has been designated as operations research. Of course, the quantitative representation and resolution of business problems is much older than the term "operations research"—witness the practice of accounting. However, quantitative analysis has been extended to many other areas of the business firm's operations and in some cases has become established as the most effective way of approaching certain business decision problems. It is quite likely that the future businessman will have to be as knowledgeable about these techniques and models as he currently is about accounting techniques and models.

A further word of caution may be in order. The business executive should never become the captive of a quantitative model and automatically adopt its conclusions as his business decision. We know the conclusion derived from the model contains some degree of error because of the abstraction process. The question of when the error becomes so large that the conclusion must be modified before it can be adopted as a solution is one of judgment. Operations research is an aid to business judgment and not a substitute for it. A certain amount of constructive skepticism is as desirable in considering quantitative analysis of business problems as it is in any other decision-making process. Further, there are many significant business problems which simply cannot be given an appropriate quantitative representation, and the decision maker must rely upon qualitative models and solutions.

Within the constraints of these qualifications, quantitative analysis can become an extremely productive technique for managerial decision making. Problems which would confound the intuition of the most experienced executive may, on occasion, be resolved with relative ease.

DECISIONS AND PROBABILITY

Business decisions are made in one of two essentially different contexts: under conditions approaching certainty and, more generally, under conditions of uncertainty. The quantitative analysis which supports decision making under certainty usually takes the form of maximizing some objective (say, profit or production) subject to constraints (say, costs).

In a previous example, we compared the alternatives "accept the order" and "refuse the order" on a 1,000-unit government contract. This was a decision under certainty. We compared the two alternatives; and since the profit was $15,000 greater for accepting the order, we chose that alternative.

Suppose, however, that we change slightly the above situation. We shall market our product at a price of $50 per unit. And as before, our expenses for producing X units are:

$$E = a + bX$$
$$= 5,000 + 30X.$$

But now, we are uncertain about the actual level of sales. Sales may be 100 units, 250 units, or 1,000 units, and we are not sure which level will actually materialize. Our alternatives are (1) to market the product and accept whatever profit or loss materializes, or (2) to reject the whole project and obtain zero profit. Assume the $5,000 of fixed costs are incurred before we know the actual demand, but that the units can be produced after the demand is known (thus there is no inventory problem).

Let us compute the profit for each level of sales if we market the product (see Table 1–1).

Even though we have clearly enumerated the alternatives and their consequences, the decision is not obvious. The best alternative depends upon how "likely" each sales level may be. If we were cer-

TABLE 1–1

States of Nature: Sales Levels (Units)	Profit
100	−$ 3,000
250	0
1,000	15,000

tain that sales would be 1,000 units, we should market the product. If sales were to be only 100 units for sure, we should reject the whole project and avoid a loss of $3,000. If sales were 250 units, we would be indifferent as to which alternative is selected.

When the true state of nature is unknown, the decision maker has to act with imperfect information. There are several possible decision-making procedures, and we shall investigate some of the more interesting techniques later in this book. However, at this point, we shall introduce the Bayes decision rule. This is an orderly and consistent technique which can be extremely useful for business decision making. The decision maker performs the following calculations for each possible act (or decision) which is feasible:

1. Lists the set of possible values the state of nature may take on for the period (or periods) in question.
2. Assigns a probability weight to each of the possible states of nature (the probabilities may be subjective weights, though objective information should be incorporated if it is available).
3. Computes for each state of nature the consequences of the given act. The consequences in certain cases may be in terms of dollars, but are more generally in terms of a measure which is called utility, and which incorporates psychological reactions to the monetary gains or losses.

4. Multiplies for a specific act the probability of each state of nature by the consequences of that act and state, and sums these products for all the possible states. This is the expected value of the act.

These computations should be made for each possible act. That decision with the highest expected value is the Bayes solution, and following this criterion, it would be the decision which would be taken.

Steps 1 and 3 in the above process have already been done—we have listed the states of nature (possible sales levels) and the profits associated with each.

Let us suppose that our decision maker feels that there are two chances out of five that the sales level will be 100 units (i.e., a probability of 0.40 is assigned to this state of nature); two chances out of

TABLE 1-2

Sales (Units)	Probability (Weight)	Profit	Weight × Profit
100..................	0.40	−$ 3,000	−$1,200
250..................	0.40	0	0
1,000.................	0.20	15,000	3,000
	1.00		$1,800

five that sales will be 250 units (again a probability of 0.40); and one chance out of five that sales will be 1,000 units (a probability of 0.20).

With these probabilities, we can compute a weighted average or expected profit for marketing the product (see Table 1–2).

The expected profit or expected monetary value for marketing the product is $1,800, compared to zero for rejecting the project. Hence, using the Bayes decision rule, we would proceed to market the product (this conclusion assumes that the consequences measured in dollars also measure utility).

Note that if sales actually amount to 100 units, the decision maker, after the fact, has incurred a loss of $3,000 that he might have avoided had he had more precise information about future sales.

In some situations, one possible course of action would be for the decision maker to gather additional information rather than make the basic decision now. The original probabilities (called prior probabilities) would then be revised in the light of that information, and the decision process would be repeated, with the next step being a final decision or the gathering of additional information.

It should be noted that personal feelings and judgment come into the decision process at three levels. First, they affect the choice of the probabilities which are assigned to the possible states of nature. These may be subjective estimates. Second, personal feelings affect the measures of the consequences which will result from a certain state of nature occurring with a given act. Last, they affect the choice of the objective or the decision criterion. The Bayes decision criterion is preferred by the authors of this book, but there is by no means unanimous opinion in the academic or business communities relative to its superiority. Its prime advantage is that it helps the decision maker to act consistently with his feelings about the likelihood of the states, and the consequences associated with each state and act.

CONCLUSION

Decision making under uncertainty requires that the decision maker use his judgment and experience about future events. He must ascertain which outcomes are more "likely" than others and combine this knowledge with the consequences associated with the various decisions. Such a process lies behind the familiar willingness to "take a calculated risk."

The Bayes decision process that we have described is merely a logical way of bringing both the decision maker's judgment and the economic consequences of a given action to bear upon the decision. Implicit in any reasonable intuitive strategy that one may devise for action under uncertainty is a probability distribution about possible outcomes.

Some mathematicians do not think that "probabilities" should be based upon subjective intuition. They argue that only objective probabilities for repetitive events have any true meaning. However, in the real world, such objective probabilities are frequently not available—and decisions must be made upon the best available information. Thus the authors feel that the Bayes decision process is a logical procedure to apply to business decision making.

BIBLIOGRAPHY

BAUMOL, W. J. *Economic Theory and Operations Analysis.* Englewood Cliffs, N.J.: Prentice-Hall, Inc., 1961.

BROSS, I. D. J. *Design for Decision.* New York: Macmillan Co., 1953.

DORFMAN, R. "Operations Research," *American Economic Review*, September, 1960.

MILLER, D. W., and STARR, M. K. *Executive Decisions and Operations Research*. Englewood Cliffs, N.J.: Prentice-Hall, Inc., 1960.

PRATT, J. W.; RAIFFA, H.; and SCHLAIFER, R. "The Foundations of Decision under Uncertainty: An Elementary Exposition," *Journal of the American Statistical Association*, June, 1964, pp. 353–75.

SAVAGE, L. J. *The Foundations of Statistics*. New York: John Wiley & Sons, Inc., 1954.

SCHLAIFER, R. *Probability and Statistics for Business Decisions*. New York: McGraw-Hill Book Co., Inc., 1959.

SIMON, H. A. "Theories of Decision-Making in Economics and Behavioral Science," *American Economic Review*, June, 1959.

QUESTIONS AND PROBLEMS

1–1. Setting the price of a product is a very important business decision. What are elements of uncertainty in the decision to change the price of a product?

1–2. In what sense are there "opponents" when a price is set for a product?

1–3. A family is planning a picnic. In what sense is nature the opponent? Is it reasonable to use probabilities to describe the likelihood of the different states of nature?

1–4. Profit maximization has sometimes been described as the prime criterion to be applied in business decision making. If you were a business manager, what additional criteria would you employ in your decision making?

1–5. A possible model of total expenses is:

$$T = a + bX$$

where

T = Total costs
a = Fixed costs
b = Variable costs
X = Number of units

Discuss the adequacy of this model as a predictor of the total costs associated with a given output.

1–6. Assume we know the fixed costs to be $10,000 but there is a probability distribution associated with variable costs. Because of a pending labor contract the variable costs for one unit may be $0.90, $1.00, or $1.10, with probabilities 0.4, 0.5, and 0.1. Compute the expected cost for five thousand units.

1–7. Mr. Jones presently owns a common stock which is selling on the market for $100 a share. Describe how the subjective feelings of Mr. Jones would enter into the decision to hold the stock or to sell.

1–8. You have an opportunity to engage in an "investment" which costs $1.00 and which has the following cash pay-offs for the possible states of nature:

State of Nature	Probability of State	Cash Pay-offs
Rain.........................	0.2	−$0.50
Cloudy.......................	0.5	1.00
Clear........................	0.3	2.50

Is the investment desirable? Following your recommendation, are you certain of the outcome?

1–9. The Crude Oil Company is considering drilling for oil on property it leases. Is it reasonable to specify a probability of finding oil?

1–10. You are a poultry exporter. The federal government has offered you a contract to supply American military establishments abroad at a price of 31 cents per pound. The contract would absorb your total annual production. Your alternative market is Europe, where the price you can receive is 50 cents per pound, less tariff. Representatives of France and the United States are now negotiating the European tariff level for poultry. In your judgment, there are four possible levels, with the following subjective probabilities:

Possible Tariff	Probability
$0.10.......................................	0.1
0.15.......................................	0.2
0.20.......................................	0.3
0.25.......................................	0.4

What decision would you make?

Chapter 2

A SURVEY OF PROBABILITY CONCEPTS

IF ALL business decisions could be made under conditions of certainty, the only valid justification for a poor decision would be failure to consider all the pertinent facts. In this context, "conditions of certainty" means an ability to make a *perfect* forecast of the future. Unfortunately, however, the businessman rarely, if ever, operates in such a world. Usually, the businessman is forced to make decisions when he is very uncertain as to what will happen after he makes the decision. In this latter situation the mathematical theory of probability furnishes a tool which can be of great help to the decision maker.

The mathematical theory of probability is rigorous and well defined, and the reader is referred to books on mathematics treating the subject (see the end of the chapter for several references). In this chapter, we shall present some of the notation and basic relationships which the reader will have to apply in later chapters.

OBJECTIVE AND SUBJECTIVE PROBABILITIES

Most of us are familiar with the laws of chance regarding coin flipping. If someone asks about the probability of a head on one toss of a coin, the answer will be one half, or 0.50. This answer assumes that the coin is a *fair* coin and that it is "fairly" tossed. If the coin is bent or weighted, or is two-tailed, the answer to this question will be quite different. Assume there is a large amount of common experience regarding the tossing of a specific coin and everyone agrees the coin is fair; that is, the head or tail has proven to be "equally likely" in a large number of trials. The relative frequency interpretation of probabilities indicates that when historical experience is available and if many trials are performed, i.e., if someone flips a coin one million times, the expected number of heads (i.e., the average number) is 500,000, or 0.50 × 1,000,000.

12

In this example, a 0.50 probability of heads is assumed to be an objective probability. Where did we obtain the 0.50 objective probability used in the above example? The relative frequency interpretation of probabilities makes use of available historical experience.

For example, assume a coin is tossed fairly 10,000 times and 5,000 heads appear. From this evidence, we may conclude that the probability of heads is 0.50, and we could use this information in forecasting what will happen with additional tosses. Assuming the coin is tossed twice more, we would expect the results of the additional two tosses to be as shown in Table 2–1.

TABLE 2–1

Number of Heads	Probability
0	$\frac{1}{4}$
1	$\frac{1}{2}$
2	$\frac{1}{4}$
3 or more	0

Table 2–1 was prepared using the objective probability of 0.50 for the probability of a head. While there is a 0.50 probability of one and only one head appearing in two tosses, and one head is our best guess, there is also a 0.50 probability that some other number of heads will appear. If we toss the coin in the same manner for an additional one million tosses, the probability of 500,000 heads will be very small (since the number of heads could well be 500,001, or 499,999 or 499,-998, etc.), but 500,000 heads will still be the expected or average number of heads.

In contrast to the above, a subjective interpretation of probabilities is often more useful for business decision making. In the case of objective probability, definitive historical information, common experience (objective evidence), or rigorous analysis lie behind the probability assignment. In the case of the subjective interpretation, historical information may not be available and instead of objective evidence personal experience becomes the basis of the probability assignment. For business decision-making purposes the subjective interpretation is frequently required, since reliable objective evidence is not available.

Let us illustrate the contrast by an example. Suppose we have a box containing three red and seven black balls. If the balls are mixed thoroughly, and if they all have the same "feel," we would assign an objective probability of 0.30 of drawing a red ball and 0.70 of drawing a black ball. As in the coin example, we could get general agreement on these probabilities, since they are based on reliable objective evidence.

In contrast to the above situation, assume a businessman is trying to decide whether or not to buy a new factory and the success of the factory depends largely on whether or not there is a depression in the next five years. If a probability is assigned to the occurrence of a depression, it would be a subjective weight. A long history and common experience, which can be projected into the future with confidence, are not directly available, as in the coin or ball problems. However, it may be appropriate, and indeed necessary, to consider the event "occurrence of a depression"; and after gathering evidence and using his business judgment, the businessman may be able to assign a probability to that event that is reasonable for his decision-making purposes. There would certainly be less agreement on this probability than there would be on the probabilities of drawing a red ball, or a fair coin coming up heads, in the previous examples. Since we are primarily concerned in this book with business decisions, we shall often assign subjective probabilities to events which have a critical bearing on the business decision; this device aims to assure consistency between a decision maker's judgment about the likelihood of the possible states of nature and his actions.

BASIC DEFINITIONS OF PROBABILITY

Two of the fundamental definitions of the mathematical theory of probability are:

1. Probabilities of the various possible mutually exclusive and exhaustive states of a trial must sum to one.
2. Probabilities are always greater than or equal to zero (i.e., probabilities are never negative) and are equal to or less than one. The "equal to or less than one" requirement follows from the first property. The smaller the probability the less likely the event.

The first definition of probability theory indicates that if A and B are the only candidates for an office, the probability that A will win plus the probability that B will win must sum to one (assuming a tie is not possible).

The second definition described above results in the following interpretations. If an event has a positive probability, it may possibly occur; the event may be impossible, in which case it has a zero probability; or the event may be certain to occur, in which case the probability is equal to one. Regardless of whether probabilities are interpreted as objective probabilities or as subjective weights, it is useful to think in terms of a weight scale running from zero to one. If someone tosses a coin 500 times to obtain an estimate of objective probabilities and the results are 225 heads and 275 tails, the range of possible results may be converted to a zero-to-one scale by dividing by 500, i.e., $\frac{0}{500} = 0$ and $\frac{500}{500} = 1$. The actual results are $\frac{225}{500} = 0.45$ heads and $\frac{275}{500} = 0.55$ tails. Hence, if we wish to derive probabilities, we shall manipulate the data so as to adhere to the zero-to-one scale. The 0.45 and the 0.55 may be used as estimators of the true probabilities of heads and tails.

MUTUALLY EXCLUSIVE EVENTS

If we have a set of mutually exclusive events (only one of the events can occur on any one trial), the probabilities of these events can be added to obtain the probability that at least one of a given collection of the events will occur.

Example

The probabilities shown in Table 2–2 (p. 16) reflect the subjective estimate of an editor regarding the relative chances of four candidates for a public office (assume a tie is not possible).

These events are mutually exclusive, since in one election (or in one trial) only one event may occur; therefore the probabilities are additive. The probability of a Democratic victory is 0.30; of a Republican victory, 0.70; or of either B or C winning, 0.68. The probability of both B and C winning is zero.

INDEPENDENT EVENTS

Events may be either independent or dependent. If two events are (statistically) independent, the occurrence of the one event will not affect the probability of the occurrence of the second event.[1]

When two (or more) events are independent, the probability of

---

[1] Statistical independence or dependence is to be distinguished from causal independence or dependence. Simply because two events are statistically dependent upon each other does not imply that one is caused by the other. Whenever we use the terms "dependence" or "independence," statistical dependence or independence will be meant.

TABLE 2–2

Event: Elect	Probability
Democratic candidate A	0.18
Democratic candidate B	0.12
Republican candidate C	0.56
Republican candidate D	0.14
	1.00

both events (or more than two events) occurring is equal to the product of the probabilities of the individual events. That is:

$$(2\text{–}1) \qquad P(AB) = P(A) \cdot P(B)$$

where

$$P(A) = \text{Probability of event } A$$
$$P(B) = \text{Probability of event } B$$
$$P(AB) = \text{Probability of events } A \text{ and } B \text{ both occurring.}$$

Equation 2–1 indicates that the probability of A and B occurring is equal to the probability of A times the probability of B, if A and B are independent. If A is the probability of a head on the first toss of the coin and B is the probability of a head on the second toss of the coin, then:

$$P(A) = \tfrac{1}{2}$$
$$P(B) = \tfrac{1}{2}$$
$$P(AB) = \tfrac{1}{2} \cdot \tfrac{1}{2} = \tfrac{1}{4}.$$

The probability of A and then B occurring (two heads) is one fourth. $P(AB)$ is the *joint probability* of events A and B.

Further, to define independence mathematically, we need another symbol:

$P(B|A)$—This symbol is read "the probability of event B, given that event A has occurred." $P(B|A)$ is the *conditional* probability of event B, given that event A has taken place. Note that $P(B|A)$ does not mean the probability of event B divided by A—the vertical line followed by A means "given that event A has occurred."

With independent events:

$$(2\text{–}2) \qquad P(B|A) = P(B).$$

That is, the probability of event B, given that event A has occurred, is equal to the probability of event B if the two events are independent. With two independent events, the occurrence of the one event does not affect the probability of the occurrence of the second [in like manner, $P(A|B) = P(A)$]. Equations 2–1 and 2–2 are the basic definitions of independence between two events.

DEPENDENT EVENTS

Two events are dependent if the occurrence of one of the events will affect the probability of the occurrence of the second event.

Example—Dependent Events

Flip a fair coin and determine whether heads or tails results. If heads results, flip the coin again. If tails, flip an unfair coin which has a three-fourths probability of heads and a one-fourth probability of tails. Is the probability of heads on the second toss in any way affected by the results of the first toss? The answer here is yes, since the results of the first toss affect which coin (fair or unfair) is to be tossed the second time.

CONDITIONAL, MARGINAL AND JOINT PROBABILITIES

We now introduce a very important probability relationship:

$$(2\text{-}3) \qquad P(B|A) = \frac{P(AB)}{P(A)}, \quad P(A) \neq 0$$

The conditional probability of event B, given that event A has occurred, is equal to the joint probability of A and B, divided by the probability of event A.

Instead of writing $P(B|A) = \dfrac{P(AB)}{P(A)}$, we can multiply both sides of the equation by $P(A)$ and rewrite equation 2-3 as:

$$(2\text{-}4) \qquad P(AB) = P(B|A) \cdot P(A).$$

That is, the joint probability of A and B is equal to the conditional probability of B given A times the probability of A.

Let us look at these formulas assuming independent events. By equation 2-3:

$$P(B|A) = \frac{P(AB)}{P(A)}.$$

But by equation 2-1:

$$P(AB) = P(A) \cdot P(B)$$

for independent events. Substituting $P(A) \cdot P(B)$ for $P(AB)$ in equation 2-3 gives:

$$(2\text{-}2) \qquad P(B|A) = \frac{P(A) \cdot P(B)}{P(A)} = P(B).$$

This is the mathematical definition of independence given earlier. We shall next make use of two examples to illustrate:

1. Unconditional (marginal) probabilities. The term "marginal" refers to the fact that the probabilities are found in the margins of a joint probability table (see Table 2–4) and they sum to one. A marginal probability refers to the probability of the occurrence of an event not conditional on the occurrence of another event. $P(A)$ and $P(B)$ are examples of marginal probabilities.
2. Conditional probabilities such as $P(A|B)$ and $P(B|A)$.
3. Joint probabilities such as $P(AB)$.

Example 1

Assume we have three boxes which contain red and black balls as follows:

Box 1........................3 red and 7 black
Box 2........................6 red and 4 black
Box 3........................8 red and 2 black.

Suppose we draw a ball from box 1; if it is red, we draw a ball from box 2. If the ball drawn from box 1 is black, we draw a ball from box 3. The diagram in Table 2–3 illustrates the game.

TABLE 2–3

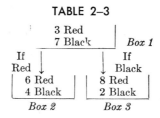

Let us raise the following probability questions about this game:

1. What is the probability of drawing a red ball from box 1? This probability is an *unconditional* or *marginal* probability; it is 0.30 (the marginal probability of getting a black is 0.70).
2. Suppose we draw a ball from box 1 and it is red; then what is the probability of getting another red ball when we draw from box 2? The answer is 0.60. This is an example of a conditional probability. That is, the probability of a red ball on the second draw if the draw from box 1 is red is a conditional probability.
3. Suppose our first draw from box 1 was black; then the *conditional* probability of our second draw (from box 3 this time) being red is 0.80. It is clear that the draw from box 1 (the conditioning event) is very important in determining the probabilities of red (or black) on the second draw.
4. Suppose, before we draw any balls, we ask the question: What is the probability of drawing two red balls? This would be a *joint* probabil-

FIGURE 2–1

Tree Diagram

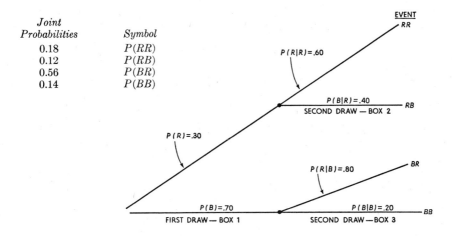

ity; the event would be a red ball on both draws. This question is a little more complicated than the above three, and some analysis will be of value. Computations are as follows:

(2–4) $$P(AB) = P(B|A) \cdot P(A)$$

	Marginal	·	Conditional	=	Joint
Event	$P(A)$	·	$P(B|A)$	=	$P(AB)$
RR	$P(R) = 0.30$		$P(R|R) = 0.60$		$P(RR) = 0.18$
RB	$P(R) = 0.30$		$P(B|R) = 0.40$		$P(RB) = 0.12$
BR	$P(B) = 0.70$		$P(R|B) = 0.80$		$P(BR) = 0.56$
BB	$P(B) = 0.70$		$P(B|B) = 0.20$		$P(BB) = 0.14$

Figure 2–1 shows the joint probability of two red balls as 0.18 [i.e., $P(RR)$, the top branch of the tree]. The joint probabilities may be read as follows:

Two red balls. . . . . $P(RR) = 0.18$
A red ball on first draw and a black ball on second draw. . . . . . $P(RB) = 0.12$
A black ball on first draw and a red ball on second draw. . . . . . $P(BR) = 0.56$
Two black balls. . . . . $P(BB) = \underline{0.14}$
                                                                                                    $\overline{1.00}$

In Table 2–4 the intersections of the rows and columns are *joint* probabilities: The column on the right gives the unconditional probabilities (*marginals*) of the outcome of the first draw; the bottom row gives the *unconditional* or *marginal* probabilities of the outcomes

TABLE 2–4
Joint Probability Table

First Draw \ Second Draw	R	B	Marginal Probability of Outcome on First Draw
R	$P(RR)$ 0.18	$P(RB)$ 0.12	0.30
B	$P(BR)$ 0.56	$P(BB)$ 0.14	0.70
Marginal probability of outcome on second draw....................	0.74	0.26	1.00

of the second draw. Table 2–4 effectively summarizes the tree diagram. Now, let us compute some additional probabilities:

1. Probability of a red and a black ball,
   regardless of order   = 0.56 + 0.12 = 0.68
2. Probability of a black ball on
   draw 2   = 0.26
   Explanatory calculation:
   Probability of red-black   = 0.12
   Probability of black-black   = 0.14
   Probability of black on
      draw 2   = 0.26
3. Probability of second draw being
   red *if* first draw is red   = 0.60
   If first draw is red, we are in the R row,
      which totals 0.30. The question
      is what proportion is 0.18 of
      0.30, and the answer is 0.60;
      or in terms of the appropriate
      formula:

$$P(R_2|R_1) = \frac{P(R_2R_1)}{P(R_1)} = \frac{0.18}{0.30} = 0.60.$$

Example 2

Suppose a fair coin is flipped twice and we ask for the following probabilities:

1. Probability of two heads.
2. Probability of one head and one tail in two flips.
3. Probability of the second toss being a head.

TABLE 2–5

Outcome (Event)	Probability	Formula
HH	$P(HH) = \frac{1}{2} \cdot \frac{1}{2} = \frac{1}{4}$	$P(H) \cdot P(H)$
HT	$P(HT) = \frac{1}{2} \cdot \frac{1}{2} = \frac{1}{4}$	$P(H) \cdot P(T)$
TH	$P(TH) = \frac{1}{2} \cdot \frac{1}{2} = \frac{1}{4}$	$P(T) \cdot P(H)$
TT	$P(TT) = \frac{1}{2} \cdot \frac{1}{2} = \frac{1}{4}$	$P(T) \cdot P(T)$

4. Probability of the second toss being a head, *given* that the first toss is a tail.

Table 2–5 gives all possible outcomes for two tosses and their probabilities.

Now, let us answer questions 1 to 4:

1. $P(HH) = \frac{1}{4}$
2. $P(HT + TH) = \frac{1}{2}$
3. $P(HH + TH) = \frac{1}{2}$

4. $P(H|T) = \dfrac{P(HT)}{P(T)} = \dfrac{\frac{1}{4}}{\frac{1}{2}} = \frac{1}{2}.$

The important feature of the above example is that it illustrates *independence*. Note that the last two probabilities computed are the same; the probability of a head on the second toss is one half regardless of the outcome of the first toss. The two events are said to be *independent*, since the outcome of the second toss is not affected by the outcome of the first toss. That was not the case in Example 1, where the outcome of the second draw was affected by the outcome of the first draw. To summarize this result:

Dependence (Example 1):

$$\text{Conditional Probability of Red on Second Draw, Given Red on First Draw} = \frac{\text{Joint Probability of } RR\ (0.18)}{\text{Marginal Probability of Red on First Draw } (0.30)} = 0.60.$$

General formula:

(2–3)　　　　　　　$P(A|B) = \dfrac{P(AB)}{P(B)}.$

Independence (Example 2):

$$\text{Conditional Probability of a Head on Second Toss, Given a Tail on First Toss} = \frac{\text{Joint Probability of } TH\ (\frac{1}{4})}{\text{Marginal Probability of Tail on First Toss } (\frac{1}{2})} = 0.50, \text{ Marginal Probability of Tossing a Head}$$

General formula:

(2–2)　　　　　　　$P(A|B) = P(A).$

REVISION OF PROBABILITIES

Having discussed joint and conditional probabilities, let us investigate how probabilities are revised to take account of new information.

Assume we are interested in tossing a coin and we do not know whether the coin is fair or unfair. If the coin is fair, the probability of a tail is 0.50; but if the coin is unfair, the probability of a tail is 0.10.

FIGURE 2–2

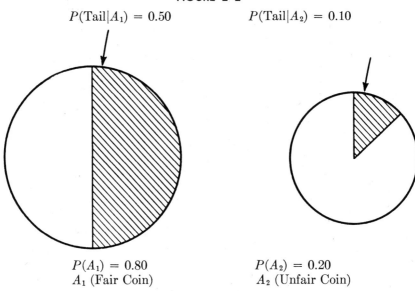

$P(\text{Tail}|A_1) = 0.50$ $P(\text{Tail}|A_2) = 0.10$

$P(A_1) = 0.80$
A_1 (Fair Coin)

$P(A_2) = 0.20$
A_2 (Unfair Coin)

Assume we assign a prior probability to the coin being fair of 0.80 and a probability of 0.20 to the coin being unfair. The event "fair coin" will be designated A_1, and the event "unfair coin" will be designated A_2. Assume we toss the coin once; say a tail is the result.

Figure 2–2 shows that the conditional probability of a tail, given that the coin is fair, is 0.50, i.e., $P(\text{Tail}|A_1) = 0.50$. If the coin is unfair, the probability of a tail is 0.10, i.e., $P(\text{Tail}|A_2) = 0.10$.

By equation 2–4, the joint probability of a tail *and* A_1 is equal to:

$$P(\text{Tail and } A_1) = P(A_1) \cdot P(\text{Tail}|A_1) = 0.80 \cdot 0.50 = 0.40.$$

The joint probability of a tail *and* A_2 is equal to:

$$P(\text{Tail and } A_2) = P(A_2) \cdot P(\text{Tail}|A_2) = 0.20 \cdot 0.10 = 0.02.$$

If we are computing $P(\text{Tail and } A_1)$, there is a 0.80 probability that A_1 is the true state; and if A_1 is the true state, there is a 0.50

FIGURE 2–3

P(Tails and A_2) $= 0.02$
P(Tails and A_1) $= 0.40$

P(Tails) $= 0.42$

probability that a tail will result. The probability of state A_1 being true and then flipping a tail is $(0.80 \cdot 0.50)$, or 0.40.

A tail can occur in combination with the state "fair coin" or in combination with the state "unfair coin." The probability of the former combination is 0.40; of the latter, 0.02. The sum of the probabilities gives the unconditional probability of a tail on the first toss, i.e., P(Tail) $= 0.40 + 0.02 = 0.42$.

Figure 2–3 shows that if a tail occurs, and if we do not know the true state, the probability of state A_1 being the true state is P(Tails and A_1) divided by P(Tails), or $\dfrac{0.40}{0.42}$; this is the posterior probability of A_1. Thus, $\dfrac{0.40}{0.42}$ is the probability of A_1, given that a tail has occurred on the first toss. Using equation 2–3:

$$P(A_1|\text{Tails}) = \frac{P(A_1 \text{ Tails})}{P(\text{Tails})} = \frac{0.40}{0.42} = 0.95.$$

In like manner:

$$P(A_2|\text{Tails}) = \frac{P(A_2 \text{ Tails})}{P(\text{Tails})} = \frac{0.02}{0.42} = 0.05.$$

In more general symbols:

$$P(A_i|B) = \frac{P(A_i B)}{P(B)}.$$

In this example the *revised prior probabilities* for the next toss of the coin are 0.95 that it is fair and 0.05 that it is unfair (they were 0.80 and 0.20). These probabilities exist after one toss when the toss results in a tail. It is reasonable that the probability that the coin is unfair has decreased, since a tail appeared on the first toss and the unfair coin has only a 0.10 probability of a tail.

RANDOM VARIABLE

A probability function is a rule which assigns probabilities to each element of a set of events that may occur. If, in turn, we can assign a

TABLE 2–6

Random Variable (Denoted by a Capital Letter)	Values of the Random Variable	Description of the Values of the Random Variable
U . . . . 2, 3, . . . , 12		The possible outcomes from throwing a pair of dice
X 0, 1, 2, 3, 4, 5		The possible number of heads, tossing a coin five times
Y . . . . 0, 1, 2, . . . , S		The possible daily sales of newspapers by a newsboy, where S represents his stock
Z . . . . 0, 0.01, 0.02, . . .		The possible values of the cost of capital for a corporation

specific numerical value to each element of the set of events, a function which assigns these numerical values is termed a random variable. The value of a random variable is the general outcome of a random (or probability) experiment. It is useful to distinguish between the random variable itself and the values that it can take on. The value of a random variable is unknown until the event occurs (i.e., until the random experiment has been performed). However, the probability that the random variable will be any specific value is known in advance. The probability of each value of the random variable is equal to the sum of the probabilities of the events which are assigned that value of the random variable. Some examples of random variables are shown in Table 2–6.

THE MEAN OF A RANDOM VARIABLE

The mean of a random variable is the sum of the values of the random variable weighted by the probability that the random variable will take on that value. Consider the example of Table 2–7.

TABLE 2–7

Computation of the Mean

Values of the Random Variable, X (Tomorrow's Demand)	Probability of X_i, $P(X_i)$	Weighted Demand, $X_i P(X_i)$
$X_1 = 25$ units	$P(X_1) = 0.05$	1.25
$X_2 = 26$ units	$P(X_2) = 0.10$	2.60
$X_3 = 27$ units	$P(X_3) = 0.15$	4.05
$X_4 = 28$ units	$P(X_4) = 0.30$	8.40
$X_5 = 29$ units	$P(X_5) = 0.20$	5.80
$X_6 = 30$ units	$P(X_6) = 0.20$	6.00
	1.00	$E(X) = 28.10$

In this case, 28.10 is the *mean* or *expected* demand. This is written as $E(X) = 28.10$, or as $\bar{X} = 28.10$.[2] The mean of the random variable is often referred to as the expected value or the expectation of the random variable.

The mean is calculated, as in the above example, by weighting each value of the random variable by its probability, and summing. The mathematical definition of the mean, in symbols, is:

$$(2\text{-}5) \qquad E(X) = \sum_{i=1}^{n} X_i P(X_i) = \bar{X}.$$

X_i is the ith value of the random variable; $P(X_i)$ is the probability of the ith value; and $\sum_{i=1}^{n}$ is a symbol meaning summation of all items for $i = 1$ to $i = n$, inclusive. The symbol Σ is read as "sigma." In our example, $n = 6$, since there are six possible values of the random variable. Hence:

$$E(X) = \bar{X} = \sum_{i=1}^{n} X_i P(X_i) = X_1 P(X_1) + X_2 P(X_2) + \ldots + X_6 P(X_6)$$

$$E(X) = \bar{X} = \sum_{i=1}^{n} X_i P(X_i) = 25(0.05) + 26(0.10) + 27(0.15) + 28(0.30)$$

$$+ 29(0.20) + 30(0.20) = 28.10.$$

SUMS OF RANDOM VARIABLES

The expectation of a sum of random variables is the sum of the expectations of those random variables. Thus the mean of the random variable $(X + Y + Z)$ is:

$$(2\text{-}6) \quad E(X + Y + Z) = E(X) + E(Y) + E(Z) = \bar{X} + \bar{Y} + \bar{Z}.$$

The expectation of a constant times a random variable is the constant times the expectation of the random variable:

$$(2\text{-}7) \qquad E(cX) = cE(X) = c\bar{X}.$$

THE VARIANCE AND STANDARD DEVIATION OF A RANDOM VARIABLE

We might like to know something about how the values of the random variable are dispersed about the mean. The variance and the standard deviation provide measures of this dispersion.

---

[2] Many statisticians only use $\bar{X}$ to represent the mean of a sample. In this section, we use $\bar{X}$ to be the mean of a probability distribution because it simplifies the notation.

The variance is defined as the sum of the *squared* deviations of the values of the random variable from its mean, weighted by the probability of the deviation. The sum of the weighted (unsquared) deviations is zero. The mathematical statement is as follows:

$$(2\text{-}8) \qquad \mathrm{Var}(X) = \sum_{i=1}^{n} (X_i - \bar{X})^2 P(X_i).$$

$\bar{X}$ is the mean; X_i, the ith value of the random variable; and $P(X_i)$, its probability. Note that the larger the dispersion of all X_i's for $i = 1$ to $i = n$, inclusive, the larger the $(X_i - \bar{X})^2$, and the larger the variance. The variance is the expectation of the function $(X_i - \bar{X})^2$. We can also compute the variance of the random variable from equation 2–9.

$$(2\text{-}9) \qquad \mathrm{Var}(X) = E(X^2) - \bar{X}^2.$$

where $E(X^2)$ is the expected value (i.e., mean) of the variable (X^2). This is a convenient form for calculating the variance. For example, the variance of $X_1 = 1$, $X_2 = 4$, $X_3 = 7$, each with equal probability, is:

$$\mathrm{Var}(X) = \tfrac{1}{3}[(1)^2 + (4)^2 + (7)^2] - (4)^2$$
$$= 22 - 16 = 6.$$

In the above computations,

$$\bar{X} = 4$$

and

$$E(X^2) = \tfrac{1}{3}(1^2) + \tfrac{1}{3}(4^2) + \tfrac{1}{3}(7^2) = \tfrac{1}{3}(1^2 + 4^2 + 7^2).$$

The variance of a constant times a random variable is the constant squared times the variance of the random variable. That is:

$$(2\text{-}10) \qquad \mathrm{Var}(cX) = c^2\,\mathrm{Var}(X).$$

The variance of a sum of independent random variables equals the sum of the variances. Thus:

$$(2\text{-}11) \qquad \mathrm{Var}(X + Y + Z) = \mathrm{Var}(X) + \mathrm{Var}(Y) + \mathrm{Var}(Z)$$

if X, Y, and Z are independent of each other.

If the value of the random variable X is a constant, the mean is the constant value. Therefore, $(X_i - \bar{X})$ would be zero for all X_i, and the variance would be zero, indicating there is no dispersion around the mean.

In Table 2–8, we calculate the variance of the random variable, demand, of our earlier example using equation 2–8.

TABLE 2–8
Computation of the Variance

Value of the Random Variable, X_i	Probability, $P(X_i)$	Squared Deviation from the Mean of 28.1—$(X_i - \overline{X})^2$	Squared Deviation Weighted by the Probability— $(X_i - \overline{X})^2 P(X_i)$
$X_1 = 25$	0.05	$(25 - 28.1)^2 = 9.61$	0.4805
$X_2 = 25$	0.10	$(26 - 28.1)^2 = 4.41$	0.4410
$X_3 = 27$	0.15	$(27 - 28.1)^2 = 1.21$	0.1815
$X_4 = 28$	0.30	$(28 - 28.1)^2 = 0.01$	0.0030
$X_5 = 29$	0.20	$(29 - 28.1)^2 = 0.81$	0.1620
$X_6 = 30$	0.20	$(30 - 28.1)^2 = 3.61$	0.7220
	1.00		1.9900

$$\text{Var}(X) = \left[\sum_{i=1}^{6} (X_i - 28.1)^2 P(X_i) \right] = 1.9900$$

The *standard deviation* is the square root of the variance, and in the basic example the standard deviation is $\sqrt{1.99}$, or about 1.4. The standard deviation is usually designated by σ (a small sigma).

THE BERNOULLI PROCESS AND THE BINOMIAL DISTRIBUTION

A Bernoulli process may be described as follows:

1. The outcomes or results of each trial in the process are characterized as one of two types of possible outcomes, such as:
   a) Success, failure.
   b) Yes, no.
   c) Heads, tails.
   d) Zero, one.
2. The probability of the outcome of any trial is "stable" and does not change throughout the process. For example, the probability of heads, given a fair coin, is 0.50 and does not change, regardless of the number of times the coin is tossed.
3. The outcome of any trial is *independent* of the outcome of any previous trial. In other words, the past history of the process would not change the probability assigned to the next trial. In our coin example, we would assign a probability of 0.50 to the next toss coming up heads, even if we had recorded heads on the last ten trials (we assume the coin is fair).
4. The number of trials is discrete and can be represented by an integer such as 1, 2, 3, etc.

Given a certain process, we may know that it is Bernoulli, but we may or may not know the stable probability characteristic of the process. With a fair coin, we may know the process is Bernoulli with probability 0.50 of a success (say, heads) and probability 0.50 of a failure (tails). However, if we are given a coin and told it is not fair, the process (flipping the coin) may still be Bernoulli, but we do not know the probability characteristic. Hence, we may have a Bernoulli process with a known or unknown probability characteristic.

Many business processes can be characterized as Bernoulli for analytical purposes, even though they are not true Bernoulli in every respect. If the "fit" is close enough, we may assume that the Bernoulli process is a reasonable characterization. Let us discuss some examples.

Example 1

Suppose we are concerned with a production process where a certain part (or product) is being turned out on a machine. We may be interested in classifying the parts as "good" or "defective," in which case the process may be Bernoulli. If the machine is not subject to fast wear, i.e., if a setting will last for a long run of parts, the probability of good parts may be sufficiently stable for the process to qualify as Bernoulli. If, on the other hand, more defectives occur as the end of the run approaches, the process is not Bernoulli. In many such processes the occurrence of goods and defectives is sufficiently randomized (no pattern is observable) to call the process Bernoulli. The probability of goods and defectives may remain stable through a production run, but it may vary from run to run (because of machine setting, for example). In such a situation the process could still be considered Bernoulli, but the probability of a success (or failure) will change from run to run.

Example 2

A different example of a Bernoulli process is a survey to determine whether or not consumers prefer liquid to powdered soaps. The outcome of a survey interview could be characterized as "yes" (success) or "no" (failure) answers to the question. If the sample of consumers was sufficiently randomized (no pattern to the way in which the yes or no answers occur), Bernoulli (with an unknown probability) may be a useful description of the process.

Note that *if* the probability of a success in a Bernoulli process is 0.50, the probability of a failure is also 0.50 (since the probabilities of the event happening and the event not happening add to one). If the probability of a success is p, the probability of a failure is $(1 - p)$.

THE BINOMIAL PROBABILITY DISTRIBUTION

In order to answer probability questions about a Bernoulli process, we need to know what the probability parameter of the process is, such as the 0.50 in the coin example. In addition, we need to know the number of trials we are going to use. Hence, to analyze a Bernoulli process, we need to know (1) the process probability characteristic, p; and (2) the number of trials, n.

The following probability equality and inequality symbols and relationships are useful:

Relationship or Symbol	Interpretation
$P(R = r\|p, n)$	The probability that the unknown number of successes, R (the random variable), is equal to some specific number, r (say, 10), given a specific number of trials, n (say, 20), and some specific probability (p) of a success.
$P(R \geq r\|p, n)$	The probability that the number of successes is *greater than or equal to* a specific number, r.
$P(R > r\|p, n)$	The probability that the number of successes is *greater* than a specific number. This inequality is exclusive, that is, $P(R > 10)$ excludes 10, and includes 11 and up.
$P(R \leq r\|p, n)$	The probability that the number of successes is less than or equal to a specific number (say, 10).
$P(R < r\|p, n)$	The probability that the number of successes is less than a specific number.
$P(R = 10) = P(R \geq 10)$ $- P(R \geq 11)$	The probability of exactly 10 successes can be read from Table E (in the Appendix at the end of the text) by subtracting two cumulative probabilities. If

$$P(R \geq 11)$$

is subtracted from $P(R \geq 10)$, the result is the probability of *exactly* 10.

| $P(R < 10) = 1 - P(R \geq 10)$ | Since the probabilities add to one, if the probability of 10 or more successes is subtracted from one, the result is the probability of less than 10 successes. |

Relationship or Symbol	*Interpretation*
$P(R \leq 10) = 1 - P(R \geq 11)$	Since *less than or equal to* 10 includes 10, subtract the probability of 11 or more successes from one.
$P(R > 10) = P(R \geq 11)$	To read a strict inequality from Table E (in the Appendix at the end of the text), add one to the number desired. The

$$P(R > 10)$$

excludes 10, so this probability is the same as $P(R \geq 11)$, which includes 11 but excludes 10.

Example 1

Suppose we are to toss a fair coin three times and would like to compute the following probabilities:

   a) The probability of three heads in three tosses
   b) The probability of two or more heads in three tosses
   c) The probability of less than two heads in three tosses

In this example the Bernoulli process p is 0.50, and a head constitutes a success. The number of trials (n) is three.

The first probability is the probability of three heads (successes) in three tosses (three trials), given that the probability of a head on any one toss is 0.50. This probability can be abbreviated as follows:

$$P(R = 3 | p = 0.50, n = 3) = ?$$

where P = probability, R = number of successes, n = number of trials, and p = probability of a success on any one trial. The left side of the equation should be read "the probability of three successes, given a process probability of 0.50 and three trials."

TABLE 2–9

Possible Outcomes	Probabilities of Each Outcome
HHH	$\frac{1}{8}$
HHT	$\frac{1}{8}$
HTH	$\frac{1}{8}$
THH	$\frac{1}{8}$
TTH	$\frac{1}{8}$
THT	$\frac{1}{8}$
HTT	$\frac{1}{8}$
TTT	$\frac{1}{8}$
	1

In answering the probability questions, let us list all the possible outcomes of the three trials and compute the probabilities (see Table 2–9).

Questions and Probabilities	Interpretation
a) $P(R = 3 \mid p = 0.50, n = 3) = \frac{1}{8}$	The probability of three heads in three trials is one eighth. This is the probability of HHH.
b) $P(R \geq 2 \mid p = 0.50, n = 3) = \frac{4}{8}$	The probability of two or more heads is four eighths. This is the probability of two heads plus the probability of three heads and is calculated by summing the probabilities of the following combinations: HHH, HHT, HTH, THH.
c) $P(R < 2 \mid p = 0.50, n = 3) = \frac{4}{8}$	The probability of less than two successes is the probability of either zero or one head and is calculated by summing the probabilities of the following combinations: TTH, THT, HTT, TTT.

Calculations	Explanation
a) $P(R = 3 \mid p = 0.50, n = 3) = 0.1250$	Look in Table E (in the Appendix at the end of the text), under $n = 3$, $p = 0.50$; read down the column to $$P(R \geq 3) = 0.1250,$$ and subtract from this $$p(R \geq 4) = 0$$ (four successes in three trials is impossible). The answer is 0.1250, or one eighth.
b) $P(R \geq 2 \mid p = 0.50, n = 3) = 0.5000$	Look in Table E under $n = 3$, $$p = 0.50$$ and read $R \geq 2$; the answer is 0.50. If we wanted $P(R = 2)$, we would compute this as follows:

$$
\begin{aligned}
P(R \geq 2 \mid 0.50, 10) &= 0.5000 \\
-P(R \geq 3 \mid 0.50, 10) &= -0.1250 \\
\hline
P(R = 2 \mid 0.50, 10) &= 0.3750
\end{aligned}
$$

c) $P(R < 2|p = 0.50, n = 3) = 0.5000$ This probability is equal to

$$1 - P(R \geq 2) =$$
$$1 - 0.50 = 0.50.$$

Example 2

A large lot of manufactured goods is to be sampled as a check on its quality.[3] Suppose that 10 per cent of the items are defective and that a sample of twenty items is drawn from the lot. What are the following probabilities?

a) Probability of exactly zero defectives in the sample
b) Probability of more than one defective in the sample
c) Probability of less than two defectives in the sample

We can answer as follows. Let $p = 0.10$ and $n = 20$. Then:

a) $P(R = 0|p = 0.10, n = 20) = P(R \geq 0) - P(R \geq 1)$
$$= 1.0 - 0.8784 = 0.1216.$$
   The probability of zero or more defectives is 1.0, and $P(R \geq 1)$ is read directly from Table E.
b) $P(R > 1) = P(R \geq 2) = 0.6083$ from Table E.
c) $P(R < 2) = 1.0 - P(R \geq 2) = 1.0 - 0.6083 = 0.3917.$

BIBLIOGRAPHY

FELLER, W. *An Introduction to Probability Theory and Its Applications.* 2d ed. New York: John Wiley & Sons, Inc., 1957.

FRASER, D. A. S. *Statistics: An Introduction.* New York: John Wiley & Sons, Inc., 1958.

GOLDBERG, SAMUEL. *Probability: An Introduction.* Englewood Cliffs, N. J.: Prentice-Hall, Inc., 1960.

KEMENY, J. G.; SNELL, J. L.; and THOMPSON, G. L. *Introduction to Finite Mathematics.* New York: Prentice-Hall, Inc., 1957.

NATIONAL BUREAU OF STANDARDS. *The Tables of the Binomial Probability Distribution.* Applied Mathematics Series 6. New York, 1950.

PARZEN, E. *Modern Probability and Its Applications.* New York: John Wiley & Sons, Inc., 1960.

ROMIG, H. G. *Binomial Tables.* New York: John Wiley & Sons, Inc., 1953.

SAVAGE, L. J. *The Foundations of Statistics.* New York: John Wiley & Sons, Inc., 1954.

---

[3] Strictly speaking, if the lot is of finite size, the Bernoulli assumptions are not exactly satisfied, and the hypergeometric distribution should be employed. However, if the lot is large relative to the sample, the use of the Bernoulli assumption introduces little error.

SCHLAIFER, R. *Probability and Statistics for Business Decisions.* New York: McGraw-Hill Book Co., Inc., 1959.

Tables of the Cumulative Binomial Probability Distribution. Cambridge: Harvard University Press, 1955.

PROBLEMS

2-1. Which of the following frequency distributions would be "objective" and which "subjective"?
  a) Number of heads in 100,000 tosses of a fair coin
  b) Number of heads in the next 100,000 tosses of an untested coin
  c) Number of "prosperous" years in the next ten years
  d) The earnings of the Ford Motor Company in the next five years (number of "profitable" and number of "loss" years)
  e) The probability of drawing the name of a male randomly from the student directory of Cornell University

2-2. Discuss the following statements:
  a) "There is a 1.5 probability that the next president will be _____."
  b) "The probability of the sun not rising tomorrow is −1.0."
  c) "There is a 0.40 probability that I'll pass and a 0.70 probability that I'll flunk the examination."

2-3. Discuss whether the following events are dependent or independent:
  a) 1) The Giants winning the World Series
     2) The Giants winning the pennant of the National League
  b) 1) The savings from using a machine in year 2
     2) The savings from using the same machine in year 1
  c) 1) The successful marketing of a high-priced car following
     2) The successful marketing of a low-priced clothing line

2-4. Consider the following two urns:

	Urn 1	Urn 2
Red balls....................	7	4
Black balls....................	3	6

$P(R_1) = P$ of red on first draw
$P(R_2) = P$ of red on second draw
$P(B_1) = P$ of black on first draw
$P(B_2) = P$ of black on second draw

  a) Take a ball from urn 1, replace it, and take a second ball. What is the probability of:
  1) Two reds being drawn?
  2) A red on the second draw if a red is drawn on the first draw?
  3) A red on the second draw if a black is drawn on the first draw?
  b) Take a ball from urn 1; replace it. Take a ball from urn 2 if the first ball was black; otherwise, draw a ball from urn 1. What is the probability of:

    1) Two reds being drawn?

    2) A red on the second draw if a red is drawn on the first draw?

    3) A red on the second draw if a black is drawn on the first draw?

2-5. Draw a tree diagram for Problem 2–4a.

2-6. Draw a tree diagram for Problem 2–4b.

2-7. Prepare a joint probability table for Problem 2–4a.

2-8. Prepare a joint probability table for Problem 2–4b.

2-9. Compute the following probabilities which pertain to flipping a fair coin three times:

    a) P (three heads)

    b) P (two or more heads in three tosses)

    c) P (one or more tails in three tosses)

    d) P (the last toss being a head)

2-10. a) What is the probability of eight heads in eight tosses of a fair coin?

    b) Suppose a fair coin is flipped seven times and all the tosses are heads. What is the probability of the eighth toss being a head? Explain.

2-11. Assume three urns:

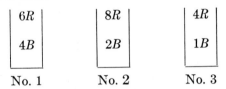

6R	8R	4R
4B	2B	1B
No. 1	No. 2	No. 3

Draw a ball from No. 1; if red, go to No. 2; if black, go to No. 3.

    a) What is P (red on second draw, given red on draw 1)?

    b) What is P (black on second draw, given red on draw 1)?

    c) What is $P($ red on second draw, given black on draw 1)?

    d) What is P (black on second draw, given black on draw 1)?

    e) How would the answers to (a)–(d) change if urn No. 3 was as follows:

| 7R |
| 3B |
| No. 3 |

    Explain why there is a difference in the probabilities of (e) compared to (c) and (d).

2-12. The following probabilities are assigned to the possible values of the fraction defective, in a manufacturing process. Compute the mean, the variance, and the standard deviation of the random variable, fraction defective.

Event	Probability of Event
0.01 defective	0.10
0.02 defective	0.15
0.03 defective	0.20
0.04 defective	0.30
0.05 defective	0.20
0.10 defective	0.03
0.15 defective	0.02
	1.00

2–13. Assume that we have a box containing six red balls and four black balls. We draw two balls, one at a time, without replacing the first ball. For this experiment:

a) Draw a tree diagram showing the process.

b) Prepare a joint probability table.

c) Compute the following probabilities:

$$P(B_2|B_1)$$
$$P(R_2|B_1)$$
$$P(R_2|R_1)$$

2–14. Assume there are two urns:

6R		8R
4B		2B
No. 1		No. 2

There is equal probability of choosing each urn. You take an urn, draw one ball, and find it is red. You want to know which urn you have.

a) What is the probability that you drew the ball from urn 1? From urn 2?

b) If the ball is black, what is the probability that the ball is from urn 1?

2–15. Specify which of the following are Bernoulli processes:

a) A house-to-house salesman making a sales call

b) Placing coins in a slot machine which has two pay-offs—zero or jackpot

c) Purchase of shares of common stock

d) Inspection of a wire coil for defects as it is being manufactured

e) Inspection of castings as they come off the production line

Give brief explanations for your answers.

2–16. Assume an unfair coin has a 0.60 probability of a tail and a 0.40 probability of a head. Determine the following:

a) In two tosses the probability of:

1) Two heads

2) Two tails

3) One head

    4) One or more heads
    5) One or more tails
    6) One tail or less
  b) In three tosses, the probability of:
    1) Three heads
    2) Two heads
    3) One head
    4) One or more heads

2–17. Using the binomial tables, look up the following probabilities:

$$a)\ P(R = 4 | 0.50, 10)$$
$$b)\ P(R > 4 | 0.50, 10)$$
$$c)\ P(R \geq 4 | 0.40,\ 8)$$
$$d)\ P(R < 4 | 0.20, 10)$$
$$e)\ P(R = 0 | 0.30, 10)$$

2–18. A sales manager lists the following probabilities for various sales levels for a new product:

Probability	Sales (in Units)
0.10	50
0.30	100
0.30	150
0.15	200
0.10	250
0.05	300

    Calculate the mean, the variance, and the standard deviation for the random variable sales. (Hint: One way to make the computations easier is to treat blocks of 50 as one unit. Thus, 200 is four, 250 is five, etc.)

2–19. Assume that the probability of a salesman making a sale at a randomly selected house is 0.1. If a salesman makes twenty calls a day, determine the following:

  a) The probability of no sales
  b) The probability of one sale
  c) The probability of four or more sales
  d) The probability of more than four sales
  e) The probability of four sales

2–20. A corporate president, in response to a question at lunch, said there was about one chance in a million that his firm would fail as a result of a depression in the next 10 years. Later, you read that the same man informed the stockholders of the firm that "even if there is a depression, the probability is 999/1,000 that we shall survive." The firm's monthly newsletter contains a signed article by this man in which he says the chances of a depression in the next 10 years are one in a hundred. Is he consistent in his probability assessments?

2–21. You are in charge of the long-range planning department for a large English construction company. There is a possibility of two major construction projects during the period under consideration: a tunnel under the Channel to France, and an expanded English missile base system for the United States Air Force. The two projects will, to some extent, require different engineering skills and equipment. The company that has acquired part of such specialized factors will have a decided advantage in contract negotiation. It is beyond your firm's resources to staff for both projects, and the president has instructed you to choose between them. Upon inquiry among members of Parliament, you conclude that the most critical circumstance affecting the tunnel project is the fate of England's application for admission to the Common Market. If England is admitted to the Common Market, most experts seem to think that the probability is 0.8 that the tunnel will be built. If England is not admitted, the probability is reduced to 0.1, in their view. It is your estimate that the probability is about 0.3 for England to be admitted to the Common Market during the period under consideration.

You proceed to Washington to make a comparable analysis of the chances of the missile base system. To your surprise, you find that the American military planners are disturbed by the news stories regarding the tunnel. Should the tunnel be built, there is only one chance in ten that the Air Force would authorize the missile system. The chances are about 50–50 if the tunnel is not constructed. If you accept the subjective probability assessments of your informants, what course of action would you suggest to your firm to maximize the probability of success?

Chapter 3

CONDITIONAL AND EXPECTED VALUE

In THIS chapter, we continue our consideration of the application of probability concepts to business decisions which must be made under conditions of uncertainty. We shall attempt to develop a means for making consistent decisions under uncertainty and for estimating the cost of uncertainty. We shall assume that expected monetary value is the appropriate criterion for decision making, unless a different assumption is stated.

Example

Suppose a grocer is faced with a problem of how many cases of milk to stock to meet tomorrow's demand. Assume that any milk that remains unsold at the end of the day will represent a complete loss to the grocer. Also, any unsatisfied demand bears no cost except the cost of the loss sale; the customer will come back the following day. This example is highly simplified but illustrates the basic principles of conditional and expected value.

In our analysis of the grocer's problem, it would be helpful if we knew something about past sales, on the assumption that this experience may serve as a guide to what may be expected in the future. Suppose the grocer has maintained records such as those shown in Table 3–1.

With a purchase price (variable cost) of $8.00 per case and a selling price of $10 per case, the table of conditional values (Table 3–2) is a description of the problem facing the grocer.

The possible actions (number to buy) facing the grocer are listed across the top of the table. It is, of course, possible to buy 24 or 29 cases, etc.; but if in the last 200 days, sales were in the range of 25–28 cases, the grocer might view a stock of greater than 28 or less than 25 as not worthy of consideration. We shall make this assumption. The possible (conceivable) events—in this example the possible sales

38

—are listed in the far left column. If the grocer is willing to assign probabilities in accordance with the historical data, then events (sales) other than those listed will carry zero probabilities; they are considered impossible events and are not listed.

TABLE 3–1

Historical Demand

Total Demand per Day	Number of Days Each Sales Level Was Recorded	Probability of Each Event
25 cases.......	20	0.10
26 cases.......	60	0.30
27 cases.......	100	0.50
28 cases.......	20	0.10
	200	1.00

TABLE 3–2

Conditional Values

Possible Demand (Event)	Possible Actions			
	Stock 25	Stock 26	Stock 27	Stock 28
25 cases............	$50	$42	$34	$26
26 cases............	50	52	44	36
27 cases............	50	52	54	46
28 cases............	50	52	54	56

CONDITIONAL VALUE

Table 3–2 can be thought of as a "conditional value" or "conditional profit" table. Corresponding to each action the grocer takes, and each event that happens, there is a certain "conditional" positive or negative profit. These profits are conditional in the sense that a certain profit results from following a specific course of action (act) and having a specific sale (event) occur. All the possible combinations are shown in Table 3–2.

Looking at the act column, "Stock 27," let us trace through the calculation of each dollar amount. This is done in Table 3–3. Similar computations have to be made for acts "Stock 25," "Stock 26," and "Stock 28."

The calculations of Table 3–3 show that if 27 cases are stocked,

TABLE 3–3
Conditional Profits of Act "Stock 27"

Assumed Event: Demand	Selling Price	Total Revenue	Cost of 27 Units (27 · $8.00)	Conditional Profit of Act "Stock 27"
25.................	$10	$250	$216	$34
26.................	10	260	216	44
27.................	10	270	216	54
28.................	10	270	216	54

only 27 can be sold, even if the demand turns out to be 28 cases or more. Hence the profit reaches a maximum of $54 for the sale of 27 units, and levels off at that figure despite the demand for 28 or more units.

THE LOSS TABLE

In addition to making a table showing conditional profits (Table 3–2), it is possible to construct a table showing conditional *opportunity losses* (Table 3–4). Consider the act "Stock 28." If the demand turns out to be 28, the grocer will make a profit of $56. This is the best he can do with a demand of 28. With a demand of 28, and if he had stocked only 27, he would have made $54; this act would entail

TABLE 3–4
Conditional Opportunity Losses

Assumed Event: Demand	Act			
	Stock 25	Stock 26	Stock 27	Stock 28
25...............	0	8	16	24
26...............	2	0	8	16
27...............	4	2	0	8
28...............	6	4	2	0

Computations of Conditional Opportunity Losses for Table 3–4

Event (De- mand)	Optimum Act for Each Event	Profit of Optimum Act	Difference between Profit of Optimum Act and the Act of Stocking:			
			25	26	27	28
25......	25	$50	50 − 50 = 0	50 − 42 = 8	50 − 34 = 16	50 − 26 = 24
26......	26	52	52 − 50 = 2	52 − 52 = 0	52 − 44 = 8	52 − 36 = 16
27......	27	54	54 − 50 = 4	54 − 52 = 2	54 − 54 = 0	54 − 46 = 8
28......	28	56	56 − 50 = 6	56 − 52 = 4	56 − 54 = 2	56 − 56 = 0

a $2.00 *opportunity loss* over the *best* action with a demand of 28. If the demand was 28 and the grocer stocked 25, he would have suffered a $6.00 conditional opportunity loss ($56 − $50). Opportunity loss can be defined as the *amount of profit forgone by not stocking the number of units which will give the highest profit for each demand level*. With this definition, the loss table shown in Table 3–4 can be constructed.

It should be emphasized that a conditional profit (or loss) relates to a profit conditional on:

1. An event happening, and
2. A given action

We do not know which event is going to occur: There is uncertainty. Therefore the conditional profit for a decision is not one number but a table of profits (or losses) associated with possible states. Profit is $44 only on condition of both stocking 27 units and an actual demand of 26 units. If the demand is different than 26 units, the actual profit will be different than $44.

EXPECTED MONETARY VALUE

Even though the conditional value and loss tables help characterize the problem facing the grocer, it is not yet possible to offer an optimum solution. The grocer could choose the best act if he knew the event (if he had advance knowledge of tomorrow's demand), but this information is not available in our example. The problem facing the grocer is to make some forecast of the event and then choose an act that is consistent with the forecast. Suppose he makes this forecast by assigning probabilities to the possible events and then analyzes his action alternatives. If he assigns probabilities based on historical information (see Table 3–1), they would be as shown in Table 3–5. If the grocer believes that for some reason, tomorrow's demand will vary somewhat from the observed pattern, he should modify his probability assignment. The next step is to bring

TABLE 3–5

Event: Demand	Probability of Event
25	0.10
26	0.30
27	0.50
28	0.10
	1.00

TABLE 3–6

Calculations of Expected Monetary Values

| Event | Proba-bility of Event | Act: Stock 26 | | | Act: Stock 27 | |
		Condi-tional Value	Expected Value: CV Weighted by Probability of Event	Condi-tional Value	Expected Value: CV Weighted by Probability of Event
25........	0.10	$42	$ 4.20	$34	$ 3.40
26........	0.30	52	15.60	44	13.20
27........	0.50	52	26.00	54	27.00
28........	0.10	52	5.20	54	5.40
	1.00				
Expected Monetary Value............$51.00					$49.00

the assigned probabilities into the analysis. We accomplish this by *weighting the conditional values of each event in the conditional value table by the probability of the event occurring, and adding the products.* The resulting number is the expected *monetary value* for the act; the optimum act is the one with the highest expected monetary value. The calculations are given in Table 3–6 for the acts of stocking 26 and 27 units. The calculations for 25 and 28 units would be similar.

In Table 3–6 the expected monetary value (EMV) is calculated by multiplying each conditional value by its probability and then adding the weighted conditional values. Table 3–7 shows the ex-

TABLE 3–7

Summary of Expected Monetary Values

Act	Expected Monetary Value
Stock 25.........$50.00	
Stock 26......... 51.00 (optimum act)	
Stock 27......... 49.00	
Stock 28......... 42.00	

pected monetary values for all acts. The grocer expects act "stock 26" to have a value of $51, the highest EMV. Therefore, he should stock 26 cases. To summarize, our plan for solving the grocer's problem is as follows:

1. Construct a pay-off (conditional value) table listing the acts and events that are considered to be possibilities. In listing the events, be sure that each event is mutually exclusive (i.e., make sure that no two or more events can occur simultaneously) and that all events considered together are exhaustive (i.e., that the events listed cover all the possibilities). This table considers the economics of the prob-

lem (costs and revenues) by calculating a conditional value (or loss) for each act and event combination.

2. Assign probabilities to the events.
3. Calculate an *EMV* for each act by weighting (multiplying) the conditional values by the assigned probabilities and adding the weighted conditional values to obtain the *EMV* of the act.
4. Choose the act with the largest *EMV*.

EXPECTED OPPORTUNITY LOSS

An alternative analysis is for the grocer to choose the best act by minimizing expected opportunity loss (*EOL*). The procedure is the same as just outlined except that instead of using the pay-off table (conditional value table, Table 3–2) and conditional profits, we shall use the conditional opportunity loss table (Table 3–4) and conditional opportunity losses. The calculations for act "Stock 26" and act "Stock 27" are as given in Table 3–8.

From Table 3–9, we find that the grocer should choose act "Stock 26," which has an expected loss of $2.20, the lowest of the four expected opportunity losses.

Let us summarize the various measures of profitability which have been introduced:

Conditional Value. The absolute profit which would result following a given action, and also conditional upon a given event occurring.

Conditional Opportunity Loss. The relative loss (that is, the profit not earned) following a given action, and also conditional upon a given event occurring.

Expected Monetary Value. The conditional values weighted by the probability of the events occurring, and summed for each act.

TABLE 3–8
Calculation of Expected Opportunity Losses

Event	Proba-bility of Event	Act: Stock 26		Act: Stock 27	
		Condi-tional Losses	Expected Opportunity Loss: *CL* Weighted by Probability of Event	Condi-tional Losses	Expected Opportunity Loss: *CL* Weighted by Probability of Event
25......	0.10	$8.00	$0.80	$16.00	$1.60
26......	0.30	0.00	0.00	8.00	2.40
27......	0.50	2.00	1.00	0.00	0.00
28......	0.10	4.00	0.40	2.00	0.20
	1.00				
Expected Opportunity Loss..........$2.20					$4.20

TABLE 3–9

Summary of Expected Opportunity Losses

Act	Expected Opportunity Losses	Comparison of Expected Opportunity Losses with Optimum
Stock 25.......$ 3.20		$1.00
Stock 26....... 2.20 (optimum act)		0.00
Stock 27....... 4.20		2.00
Stock 28....... 11.20		9.00

Expected Opportunity Loss. The conditional opportunity losses weighted by the probability of the events occurring, and summed for each act.

The optimum act is the act with the greatest expected monetary value, and thus the smallest expected opportunity loss.

EXPECTED UTILITY

Although expected monetary value may be a good guide to action in many cases, it may not be in others. This does not destroy our model; it means we must modify the analysis when the situation warrants it. Let us consider a major difficulty with expected monetary value.

Suppose a businessman has a chance to invest a large sum of money in a very speculative new product. Assume that if the product is successful, he will earn (in present value terms) profits of $1 million. However, he must risk a loss of $500,000 to develop, produce, and sell the new product. Our businessman's conditional value table is given in Table 3–10.

If, after gathering evidence, the businessman assigns a subjective probability of 0.90 of success, the *EMV* of the act "Invest" would be $850,000, i.e. ($1,000,000 · 0.90 − $500,000 · 0.10 = $850,-000), as compared with an *EMV* of zero for the act "Do not invest."

TABLE 3–10

Conditional Value

(*Brackets Indicate Loss*)

Event	Act	
	Invest	Do Not Invest
Product successful............$1,000,000		0
Product not successful......... (500,000)		0

Suppose, however, that the businessman is in a very difficult financial position and a $500,000 loss would result in certain bankruptcy. In such a case, *EMV* may be a poor guide to action. The businessman may be unwilling to take the chance of losing $500,000, regardless of the size of the conditional profits or the *EMV*, because of the undesirable consequences of the loss. If so, the businessman has a large disutility for such a loss, and this should be brought into the analysis.

If utility considerations are to be ignored, or in problems where utility for money is approximately linear (see Chapter 14), *EMV* is a reasonable guide to action. For example, when the potential losses are not too great and the prospective profit range is narrow, utility considerations usually are not significant. Such is the case in our grocer's problem, and *EMV* is adequate.

However, where actions are contemplated that involve large potential losses, it may be desirable to make the analysis more appropriate by bringing in utility considerations. This can be done by calculating the *expected utility value* of possible actions rather than the *expected monetary value*. This modification of the analysis will be discussed in Chapter 14. For purposes of the initial chapters, we shall assume that the situation is such that utility considerations are unimportant (i.e., the expected monetary value is a reasonable measure of the expected utility).

EXPECTED PROFIT UNDER CERTAINTY

Returning to our example of the grocer, let us raise the following question: "What profit could the grocer *expect* to make in the future if each day's demand could be predicted *with certainty* the day before the particular demand occurred?" To answer this question, let us construct a conditional value table which will show the condi-

TABLE 3–11
Conditional Value Table

Event: Demand	Act			
	Stock 25	Stock 26	Stock 27	Stock 28
25..................	$50			
26..................		$52		
27..................			$54	
28..................				$56

tional profit for the *best* act, given each event. Table 3–11 is constructed by choosing the best act and recording the highest profit figures for each event (this information can be obtained from Table 3–2). For example, if we knew tomorrow's demand would be 27, we would stock 27 cases, for a profit of $54. If we stocked 26, we would forgo the $2.00 profit on one unit; and if we stocked 28, we would have to scrap one unit at a loss of $8.00. Table 3–11 shows the grocer what the best action is for each possible event.

Let us convert these conditional optimal profit figures to an expectation. This can be done by weighting each profit item by its

TABLE 3–12

Expected Profit under Certainty

Event	Probability of Event	Conditional Profit under Certainty	Expected Profit under Certainty
25................	0.10	$50	$ 5.00
26................	0.30	52	15.60
27................	0.50	54	27.00
28................	0.10	56	5.60
			$53.20

probability of occurring. The resulting amount, $53.20, is called the *expected profit under certainty*. The calculation is shown in Table 3–12, where the expected profit under certainty ($53.20) is the profit the grocer could *expect* if he had available a *perfect* predictor whereby each day's demand could be predicted in advance. Thus the optimum amount would be ordered each day.

Before the perfect predictor is used, the grocer is still uncertain as to what the prediction will be, since any one of the four events may occur. Before the prediction, the profit under certainty is an *expectation*, since we do not know which event will occur. To decide whether or not to use the predictor, our grocer must assign a value to the perfect prediction and compare this value with the cost of the predictor. Remember that we do not know what the prediction will be.

EXPECTED VALUE OF PERFECT INFORMATION

In many decision problems the businessman faces the question of whether to act now or delay action and seek more information. The important thing to the businessman is to balance the *cost* of additional information against the *value* (additional profit) of the

information. The cost part of this decision (cost of obtaining information) is usually easier to calculate than the value of the information. However, using the expected value model, we have a
way of quantifying the value of additional information.

Referring again to our grocer example, we showed in Table 3–12
that the expected profit under certainty is $53.20. This amount, an
expectation, is a measure of the best the grocer could do with a *perfect* predictor. Previously, in Table 3–7, we showed that the *EMV* of
the best act under uncertainty, "Stock 26," is $51.00. The difference,

TABLE 3–13

	Act			
	Stock 25	Stock 26	Stock 27	Stock 28
EMV (uncertainty)	$50.00	$51.00	$49.00	$42.00
EOL	3.20	2.20	4.20	11.20
Expected Profit (Certainty)	$53.20	$53.20	$53.20	$53.20

$53.20 − $51.00 = $2.20, is the maximum amount by which the
grocer could increase his expected profit if he had available a free,
perfect predictive device. Hence, $2.20 is the *expected value of perfect information (EVPI)*. Note from Table 3–9 that $2.20 is also the
expected opportunity loss of the optimum act. We might expect this
result, since the perfect predictor should reduce the opportunity loss
that exists under uncertainty to zero. Hence the expected opportunity loss of the optimum act measures the *EVPI*. A useful check on
computations is provided by the identity: *EMV* + *EOL* of any act
equals the expected profit under certainty. This calculation is shown
in Table 3–13.

It is important to note that it is the *EOL* of the *optimal* act which
is equal to the *EVPI*. If the grocer chooses the act "Stock 28," he
will have an *EMV* of $42.00 and an *EOL* of $11.20. The *EVPI* is *not*
$11.20, because the grocer can increase his *EMV* to $51.00 by choosing a different act ("Stock 26"), and this requires *no* additional information. The value of additional information is measured starting
from the assumption that the optimal action would be chosen, given
the information already available.

CONCLUSION

We have developed a method for using probabilities in making
business decisions under conditions of uncertainty; the procedure

may also be used for establishing the value of additional information. Future chapters will use many of the concepts introduced in this chapter. In this chapter the events were few and discontinuous (discrete events). Later, we shall discuss continuous probability distributions. Instead of a few possible events, the number of possible events will become very large.

APPENDIX

Symbolic Presentation

In this Appendix, we introduce symbols which are useful in expressing the decision process in mathematical terms.[1]

Let D be the set of all possible decisions, and d a specific decision.

d_1 = The decision to order 25
d_2 = The decision to order 26, etc.

Let Q be the set of all possible events or states of nature, and q a specific event.

q_1 = The state that demand is 25
q_2 = The state that demand is 26, etc.

Let $R(q, d)$ be the profit if q is the true state and d is the decision. $R(q, d)$ is positive if there is a profit and negative if there is a loss. Later, we shall find it useful to introduce L, an opportunity loss function, and use it instead of R, the profit function.

From Table 3–2, we find different values of $R(q, d)$. For example:

$R(q_1, d_1)$ = 50 (the profit for demand of 25 and order 25)
$R(q_2, d_2)$ = 52 (the profit for demand of 26 and order 26)
$R(q_3, d_3)$ = 54 (the profit for demand of 27 and order of 27)
$R(q_4, d_3)$ = 54 (the profit for demand of 28 and order 27)

We can speak of the entries in Table 3–2 as conditional values or, equivalently, as profits for given q and d.

We can also express the opportunity loss symbolically. Let $L(q_i, d_j)$ be the opportunity loss for the q_i state of nature and the d_j decision, and $\underset{d}{\text{Max}}\, R(q_i, d)$ be the maximum profit for the q_i state of nature resulting from the best decision, d. Then:

$$L(q_i, d_j) = \underset{d}{\text{Max}}\, R(q_i, d) - R(q_i, d_j).$$

---

[1] The reader may choose to by-pass this Appendix. However, the symbols are used in later chapters, and this Appendix is useful as a means of introducing them.

The opportunity loss is equal to the profit resulting from the best decision for state q_i less the profit resulting from the jth decision. Let demand be q_4, or 28. The values of the opportunity losses are:

$$L(q_4, d_j) = \underset{d}{\text{Max}}\; R(q_4, d) - R(q_4, d_j)$$
$$L(q_4, d_1) = 56 - 50 = 6$$
$$L(q_4, d_2) = 56 - 52 = 4$$
$$L(q_4, d_3) = 56 - 54 = 2$$
$$L(q_4, d_4) = 56 - 56 = 0$$

These are the values shown in Table 3–4 for the event "Demand is 28."

TABLE 3–14

q_i	$p(q_i)$	$R(q_i, d_4)$	$p(q_i)\,R(q_i, d_4)$
$q_1 = 25$	0.10	26	$ 2.60
$q_2 = 26$	0.30	36	10.80
$q_3 = 27$	0.50	46	23.00
$q_4 = 28$	0.10	56	5.60
	1.00	$\bar{R}(d_4) =$	$42.00

Symbolically, the expected monetary value of a decision d_j is the average of $R(q_i, d_j)$ over all values of q_i:

$$EMV(d_j) = E[R(q_i, d_j)].$$

Using the symbol $\bar{R}(d_j)$ to represent the expected monetary value or average profit of decision d_j, and $p(q_i)$ to measure the probability of state q_i, we have:

$$\bar{R}(d_j) = \sum_i p(q_i)R(q_i d_j).$$

For the decision "Stock 28" the computations are as shown in Table 3–14. We follow the rule of choosing that decision which results in the largest $\bar{R}(d_j)$ or, equivalently, the largest EMV.

The expected opportunity loss for decision d_j may be represented by $\bar{L}(d_j)$:

$$\bar{L}(d_j) = E[L(q_i, d_j)]$$
$$= \sum_i p(q_i)\, L(q_i, d_j).$$

For act "Stock 28" the expected opportunity loss is as shown in Table 3–15.

TABLE 3–15

q_i	$p(q_i)$	$L(q_i, d_4)$	$p(q_i) L(q_i, d_4)$
$q_1 = 25$	0.10	24	$ 2.40
$q_2 = 26$	0.30	16	4.80
$q_3 = 27$	0.50	8	4.00
$q_4 = 28$	0.10	0	0.00
	1.00	$\bar{L}(d_4) =$	$11.20

We may rewrite the equation for $\bar{L}(d_j)$ by substituting for $L(q_i, d_j)$:

$$\bar{L}(d_j) = \sum_i p(q_i) \left[\underset{d}{\text{Max}} \; R(q_i, d) - R(q_i, d_j) \right]$$

$$= \sum_i p(q_i) \, \underset{d}{\text{Max}} \, R(q_i, d) - \sum_i p(q_i) \, R(q_i, d_j).$$

The first term is a constant which we shall replace by the symbol $C;$ the second term is $\bar{R}(d_j)$; thus:

$$\bar{L}(d_j) = C - \bar{R}(d_j).$$

The expected opportunity loss is minimized by the decision d_j, which has the largest $\bar{R}(d_j)$. Hence the decision may be made using the maximum value of $\bar{R}(d_j)$ or the minimum value of $\bar{L}(d_j)$.

Above, we derived the following equation for the expected opportunity loss of decision d_j:

$$\bar{L}(d_j) = C - \bar{R}(d_j).$$

The C in the equation is the expected profit under certainty and is equal to:

$$C = \sum_i p(q_i) \, \underset{d}{\text{Max}} \, R(q_i, d).$$

Rearranging terms:

$$C = \bar{R}(d_j) + \bar{L}(d_j)$$

where $\bar{R}(d_j)$ is the expected monetary value and $\bar{L}(d_j)$ is the expected opportunity loss of the jth decision.

We have defined C as the expected profit under certainty, and obtained:

$$\bar{L}(d_j) = C - \bar{R}(d_j).$$

If d_j is the best act, then $\bar{L}(d_j)$ is the expected value of perfect information.

BIBLIOGRAPHY

Bross, I. D. J. *Design for Decision.* New York: Macmillan Co., 1953.
Chernoff, H., and Moses, L. E. *Elementary Decision Theory.* New York: John Wiley & Sons, Inc., 1959.

SCHLAIFER, R. *Probability and Statistics for Business Decisions.* New York: McGraw-Hill Book Co., Inc., 1959.

THRALL, R. M.; COOMBS, C. H.; and DAVIS, R. L. (eds.). *Decision Processes.* New York: John Wiley & Sons, Inc., 1954.

PROBLEMS

3-1. An analysis and forecast of next month's sales results in the following probability distribution:

Total Demand	Probability
10 units	0.10
11 units	0.70
12 units	0.20
	1.00

The profit per unit is $5.00. The cost of the product sold is $6.00. If the product is not sold during the month, it is worthless (leftover units are of no value).

a) Compute the expected (mean) sales for the month.

b) Prepare a table of conditional values for the different possible acts.

c) Prepare a table of expected monetary values, and indicate the optimum act.

3-2. Continuation of Problem 3-1.

a) Prepare a table of conditional opportunity losses.

b) Prepare a table of expected opportunity losses.

c) Indicate the optimum act.

d) Rank the acts. Show the differences between the expected opportunity losses of each act and the *EOL* of the optimum act.

e) Refer to Problem 3-1. Rank the acts, using expected values. Show the differences between the *EMV* of each act and the *EMV* of the optimum act. Compare these results with those of part (*d*).

3-3. Refer to Problem 3-1.

a) Present the conditional value table, assuming certainty (i.e., a perfect predicting device).

b) Present the expected value table, assuming certainty.

c) Compute the expected value of perfect information.

3-4.

Event	Probability of Event	Conditional Monetary Value of:		
		Act 1	Act 2	Act 3
A	0.35	4	3	2
B	0.45	4	6	5
C	0.20	4	6	8

a) Present a table of expected monetary values, and determine the optimum act.
b) Present a table of expected opportunity losses.
c) Compute the conditional value table, assuming certainty.
d) Compute the expected value table, assuming certainty.
e) Compute the expected value of perfect information.

3-5. A newsstand operator assigns probabilities to the demand for *Fine* magazine as follows:

Demand	Probability of Event
10 copies	0.10
11 copies	0.15
12 copies	0.20
13 copies	0.25
14 copies	0.30
	1.00

An issue sells for 50 cents and costs 30 cents.

a) If the operator *can* return free of charge any unsold copies, how many should he order?
b) If the operator *cannot* return unsold copies, how many copies should he order?
c) Explain why the number of copies ordered increases as the salvage value of unsold copies increases.

3-6. A manufacturer of sporting goods has the following demand and probability schedule for a yearly fishing guide magazine:

Demand	Probability of Event
100,000	0.20
200,000	0.20
300,000	0.20
400,000	0.20
500,000	0.20
	1.00

The incremental costs of production are $4.00 per thousand, the selling price is $5.00 per thousand, and the salvage value of unsold magazines is zero.

a) The manufacturer reasons as follows: "Since there is equal chance of demand being less or greater than 300,000, I shall produce the most likely amount, 300,000." Do you agree? If not, why not?
b) What is the expected value of a perfect prediction?
c) Show that the *EMV* of each act plus the *EOL* of each act equals the expected profit under certainty.

3-7. A real estate investor owns a gasoline station which he has leased to a major oil company for a rental fee based on a share of profits. If the station is successful, the present value of future rentals is estimated at $1 million. If the station is not successful, the present value of the rentals will be $200,000. The oil company has offered the investor $600,000 to buy the property outright. On an expected monetary value basis, what probability would need be assigned to "success" for the investor to be indifferent between selling and not selling?

3–8. A wholesaler of sporting goods has an opportunity to buy 5,000 pairs of skis that have been declared surplus by the government. The wholesaler will pay $5.00 a pair, and he can obtain $10 a pair by selling the skis to retailers. The price is well established, but the wholesaler is in doubt as to just how many pairs he will be able to sell. Any skis left over he can sell to discount outlets at $2.00 a pair. After a careful consideration of the historical data, the wholesaler assigns probabilities to demand as follows:

Retailer's Demand	Probability
1,000 pairs	0.60
3,000 pairs	0.30
5,000 pairs	0.10
	1.00

a) Compute the conditional monetary value of the different possible levels of demand.
b) Compute the expected monetary values.
c) Compute the expected profit under certainty.
d) Compute the expected value of perfect information.

3–9. A bookstore owner can purchase 20,000 of a publisher's leftovers for 50 cents a copy. By making use of advertising in a nationally distributed newspaper, he hopes to be able to sell the books for $2.00 a copy. Leftover books can be sold at 20 cents a copy to other retailers. His estimate of demand is:

Estimated Demand	Probability of Demand
5,000	0.10
10,000	0.50
20,000	0.40
	1.00

The cost of advertising is $12,000, and incremental costs of shipping the books which are sold are 25 cents per copy.
a) Should the bookstore owner purchase the books?
b) What is the expected profit under certainty?
c) What is the expected cost of uncertainty?
d) What is the maximum amount the owner should pay for perfect information?

3–10. A manufacturer of hair tonic is considering production of a new hair dressing which he hopes will increase sales. The incremental profit is $10 per unit (on a present value basis), and the necessary investment in equipment is $500,000. The estimate of yearly demand is as follows:

Units of Demand	Probability
30,000	0.05
40,000	0.10
50,000	0.20
60,000	0.30
70,000	0.35
	1.00

a) Should the new product be produced?

b) What is the expected value of perfect information?

c) How would the expected value of perfect information change if the probability of 30,000 units was 0.10 and the probability of 70,000 units was 0.30? What causes this change?

3–11. When a new shopping center is built, the electric company must assign a transformer to the location. Since this is done before the occupants of the shopping center are known, there is uncertainty about the amount of electricity to be used (for example, beauty salons use much more electricity than toy stores) and hence uncertainty about the size of transformer needed. A too small transformer would have to be replaced, and one too large would result in more expense than necessary. A table giving these costs is shown below:

Cost Table

Amount of Electricity Ultimately Needed	Size of Transformer Originally Installed:		
	Small	Medium	Large
Little	50	100	150
Medium	140	100	150
Much	190	190	150

Suppose, for a given shopping center, the following probabilities are assigned to the amount of electricity ultimately needed:

Need	Probability
Little	0.2
Medium	0.7
Much	0.1
	1.0

a) Draw up an opportunity loss table.

b) What decision should be made? Why?

c) What is the expected value of perfect information?

Chapter 4

DECISION THEORY

WE SHALL define decision theory as being primarily concerned with how to assist people (or organizations) in making decisions, and improving the decision process under conditions of uncertainty. Decision theory enables the decision maker to analyze a certain set of complex situations with many alternatives and many different possible consequences. The major objective is to identify a course of action which is consistent with the basic psychological desires of the decision maker.

Business managers frequently deal with complicated decisions by assuming certainty. That is, the data which go into the computations are assumed to be known without question; or at most, a disclaiming statement is made, such as "Of course, the facts are not known with certainty." This approach is reasonable for many decisions. Decision making, even under certainty, can be complex. It may be desirable to start with the situation where the facts are assumed to be known. Many conventional solutions offered to such problems as inventory control, "make or buy," capital budgeting, and pricing assume certainty.

In this chapter, we shall discuss the art of decision making under uncertainty. The inventory decision is used as an illustration. It will become obvious that absolutely correct answers are difficult to find when the future is uncertain, but that there are some reasonable approaches to a class of decision problems that should be understood by the businessman.

THE DECISION PROBLEM

We shall consider in this chapter a relatively common type of decision. There will be several possible acts and several possible states of nature. For example, the possible acts may be:

55

1. To decide the number of units of inventory to order
2. To buy or not to buy fire insurance
3. To make or to buy a product
4. To invest or not to invest in a piece of equipment
5. To add or not to add a new product line
6. To change the price or not to change the price of a product (and if so, the amount of the change)

By states of nature, we mean the actual possible events which may occur. One of the states of nature is the true state, but we do not know which one. Possible states of nature or events for each of the above acts are:

1. Demand for the product may be 0, 1, 2, 3, . . . , 50.
2. A fire may occur, or a fire may not occur.
3. If we make the product, the cost of making it may be 10 cents, 11 cents, . . . , 50 cents.
4. If we invest in the equipment, its cost saving per hour may be $1.00, $1.01, $1.02, . . . , $2.50.
5. If we add a new product line, the sales may be one million, two million, etc.
6. If we change the price, the unit sales may be 1,000–2,000, 2,001–3,000, . . . , 9,001–10,000.

Not knowing which of the states of nature is the true state, we place a probability distribution on the possible occurrence of each event (we can have as fine a breakdown as we wish of the possible states). The probability distribution could be based on objective evidence of the past if the decision maker feels the same forces will continue to operate in the future. However, we are not restricted to objective probabilities. It may be reasonable to assign the probabilities that the decision maker thinks appropriate to the possible states of nature, so that he may act consistently with his beliefs about the possible events and the economic consequences of those events. To the extent possible, objective evidence should be supplied to help the decision maker improve his assignment of probabilities.

An Example

To illustrate the discussion, we shall develop an example. This is a simple inventory decision problem, similar to the type already introduced in Chapter 3. The problem is to determine how many units to order. The price of the product is $5.00, the cost is $3.00, and profit per unit is $2.00. Unsold units have no salvage value. The possible states of nature (possible demands) and their probabilities are as shown in Table 4–1.

The possible acts are to buy zero, one, or two units (it would be unreasonable to buy three if the probability of selling three units is zero). The possible states of nature are that demand will be zero, one, or two units requested. The first step in obtaining a solution is to prepare a table (see Table 4–2) showing the profits which will result

TABLE 4–1*

Q: Demand	$p(q_i)$
$q_1 = 0$	0.05
$q_2 = 1$	0.60
$q_3 = 2$	0.35
	1.00

from each combination of act and state of nature. We have called this a conditional profit or pay-off table. The profits are conditional on choosing a certain act and having a given state of nature come true; the symbolic representation of an entry is $R(q_i, d_j)$.

TABLE 4–2*
Conditional Profit Table

State of Nature—Demand Is:	Acts		
	d_1 Buy 0	d_2 Buy 1	d_3 Buy 2
$q_i = 0$	0	(3)	(6)
$q_2 = 1$	0	2	(1)
$q_3 = 2$	0	2	4

*Losses (negative profits) are shown in parentheses.

The decision to be made is to decide on whether zero, one, or two units should be ordered. It is not obvious how many units should be ordered. The solution to even this relatively simple problem is complex; in fact, it is not clear what the answer "should" be. We shall consider several possible decision criteria.

DECISION CRITERIA

In considering some of the possible decision criteria, we shall list them in reverse order of our preference. Thus, we shall start out with the least desirable criterion and work our way toward those which the authors prefer. The possible criteria include:

1. Maximizing the maximum possible profit (maximax criterion);[1] i.e., choose the d_j with the maximum $R(q_i, d_j)$.

---

[1] A weighted average of minimum and maximum pay-offs of each procedure has been suggested but will not be discussed here.

2. Assuming equally likely events. Choose the d_j which maximizes $\sum_i R(q_i, d_j)$.

3. Maximizing the minimum possible profit, the maximin procedure (or minimizing the maximum possible cost, the minimax procedure).
4. Basing the decision on the profits of the event with the maximum likelihood of occurring.
5. Using the Bayes decision rule: Multiply the consequences of each act by the probabilities of the several occurrences, and sum the products. The act with the largest expected value is the most desirable decision [maximize $\bar{R}(d_j)$, where $\bar{R}(d_j) = \sum_i p(q_i)R(q_i, d_j)$].

The type of decision being studied here may be described as a game against nature. It has been suggested that decision theory is a branch of game theory; however, it should be remembered that nature does not think and plot against its opponent. Criteria which may be completely reasonable in game theory (such as minimax) are less reasonable in a game against nature. This distinction is important, since the criticism which follows applies only in decisions involving nature, not decisions involving a thinking opponent.

There will be one major assumption in the discussion which follows. We shall assume that the decision maker has a utility function which is linear with respect to money. That is, $2.00 is twice as desirable as $1.00, $4.00 twice as desirable as $2.00, $8.00 twice as desirable as $4.00, and so on. Most people act in a manner which indicates that this assumption is not valid. Thus, it would be appropriate to introduce a new measure (call it utility) instead of dollars. This would be useful, but it would distract one from the primary discussion. Therefore the assumption is made here that it is appropriate to use the dollar measure of rewards. A more detailed discussion of this assumption is given in Chapter 14.

MAXIMAX

Maximax chooses the act which maximizes the maximum possible profit. It is not a procedure which is generally followed, and for good reason. It ignores possible losses and the probabilities of making or not making a profit. It might appeal to a highly adventurous person, but he would probably not prosper for long, since he would be attempting projects with very little chance of being successful. It would seem desirable systematically to incorporate into the decision the probabilities of success and failure.

In the example of this chapter the maximax criterion would result in an order of two units, since that act results in a profit of $4.00 if the demand is two units. $R(q = 2, d = 2)$ is the maximum $R(q_i, d_j)$. In the present problem, this decision may not seem unreasonable, but suppose the probability of demand being two was 0.0001. Would an order size of two still be reasonable?

EQUALLY LIKELY

This procedure suggests that we add the possible consequences of each act and divide by the number of possible events. The act with the highest $\frac{1}{n} \sum_i R(q_i, d_j)$ is the most desirable act. If we know little about the probability of the possible events, some would argue that we should then assume that each event is equally likely. It is rare that we do not have some idea about the probability of possible events. These probabilities, which may or may not be based on objective evidence, should be used in the analysis if our action is to be consistent with our judgment. Automatically assuming the events are equally likely will not insure such consistency if we feel one event is more likely to occur than another. For example, in the present problem a specific probability distribution is given. There is no reason to assume that there is equal probability that each event will occur.

As long as it is thought appropriate to use probabilities, and where there is no reason to assume the probabilities of the states of nature are equally likely, then the best estimate of the probabilities should be used, rather than the "equally likely" assumption.

MINIMAX

Minimax suggests that we choose the act with the minimum maximum loss or, alternatively, with the maximum minimum profit. That is, we should make sure that we can earn at least R dollars, and search for the act which gives the largest R (or the smallest loss, if we are discussing losses).

In the example the minimax act would be to order zero units. The maximum possible loss with zero units is zero dollars; with the other two acts the maximum losses are $3.00 and $6.00.

Unless there is zero probability of loss, minimax tends to lead to a decision to do nothing. It is a very conservative decision criterion.

Ultimately, a minimaxer would be faced with the threat of starving to death (by doing nothing) and would be forced into action. Or, in terms of business activity, the corporation would become stagnant and would be overcome by competition willing to innovate and to take reasonable chances of suffering losses.

In some situations, minimax may not even lead to a conservative decision. For example, assume Table 4–3 shows the conditional costs associated with the only two possible acts. "Buy insurance" is the

TABLE 4–3

	Acts	
States of Nature	Buy Insurance	Do Not Buy
q_1............................	$100	$101
q_2............................	100	1

best act according to minimax, since the maximum cost is $100 (the maximum cost of "Do not buy insurance" is $101). However, if the two given states of nature are equally likely, or if state q_2 is more likely than state q_i, then most individuals would label "Do not buy" as being more conservative and more desirable.

MAXIMUM LIKELIHOOD

Using the maximum-likelihood decision criterion procedure, we only consider the consequences of the state of nature which is most likely to occur and choose the best act for that state of nature. In the example being considered, this is state "Demand is one," leading to a decision to order one unit. This is a reasonable decision in the present context, but it might not always be so. For example, assume the probability of demand being one is 0.51 and demand being two is 0.49. Now, it is not clear that to order one is the best decision. To add further evidence that the maximum-likelihood decision may be faulty, reduce the loss on a leftover unit (increase the salvage value) until there is practically no penalty connected with leftovers. With the 0.49 probability of selling the second unit, it is reasonably likely that to order two is a better decision.

Since the maximum-likelihood criterion ignores the consequences of all states except the state with the highest probability, it fails to make use of much of the information which is available to the decision maker. By failing to make use of this information, it can arrive at decisions which may not be reasonable.

BAYES DECISION RULE

The Bayes decision rule says to compute the expected value of each act (multiply the conditional profit by the probability of the state of nature, and sum the products for each state) and take the act with the largest expected value, i.e., maximize $\bar{R}(d_j)$.

The expected values of the three acts are computed as shown in Table 4–4. The act with the highest expected value is "buy one"; thus, we should buy one unit. If the probabilities were changed, or if the conditional profits were different because of changes in price,

TABLE 4–4*

Buy 0	Buy 1	Buy 2
$0 \times 0.05 = 0$	$(3) \times 0.05 = (0.15)$	$(6) \times 0.05 = (0.30)$
$0 \times 0.60 = 0$	$2 \times 0.60 = 1.20$	$(1) \times 0.60 = (0.60)$
$0 \times 0.35 = 0$	$2 \times 0.35 = 0.70$	$4 \times 0.35 = 1.40$
$\bar{R}(d_1) = \overline{0}$	$\bar{R}(d_2) = \overline{1.75}$	$\bar{R}(d_3) = \overline{0.50}$

*The parentheses indicate a loss.

costs, or salvage value, the expected value would be recomputed, with a possible change in decision.

In practice, the inventory problem is not solved using the pay-off table and computing the expected value of each possible act. However, the procedures which are used are based on the above analysis. That is, conventional inventory procedure assumes it is appropriate to use the Bayes decision rule, with money measures representing the utilities.

In the chapters of this book, not all the problems are approached from the point of view of decision making under uncertainty. However, when uncertainty is present, it is assumed that it is reasonable to use the expected value of the act and to choose the act with the highest expected value. To be generally valid, the value should be measured in terms of utility, though there will be many situations where it is appropriate to use expected monetary value.

LINEAR FUNCTIONS

If the cost or profit function is linear, i.e., of the form $P = \sum_i a_i X_i$, then the Bayes decision computations may be simplified. Instead of computing the conditional profit for each act and each state of nature, we can compute the average state of nature and insert it in the profit or cost equation.

Example

Assume profit P is equal to an unknown constant b times the number of units sold, Q, but we are not sure of the value of b (i.e., there are several possible states of nature). However, we do have the information shown in Table 4–5.

TABLE 4–5

Values of b	Probability
$1.50	0.20
1.60	0.70
1.70	0.10

The basic profit equation is:

$$P = bQ$$

Assume the number of units to be sold the next period is known to be ten. The average or expected profit is:

$$E(P) = E(bQ) = QE(b).$$

The above equation results because Q is a constant, and the expectation of a constant times a random variable is equal to the constant times the mean of the variable. Thus the expected profit is equal to Q times the expectation of b:

$$E(b) = 1.50(0.20) + 1.60(0.70) + 1.70(0.10) = 1.59.$$

The expected profit is:

$$E(P) = 10 \times 1.59 = \$15.90.$$

Assume that instead of knowing Q with certainty, we know that b is $1.50 per unit, and we have the probability distribution for Q (the values of Q are now the states of nature) shown in Table 4–6.

TABLE 4–6

Value of Q	Probability
9	0.4
10	0.5
11	0.1

The basic profit equation remains:

$$P = bQ.$$

Since b is now a constant:

$$E(P) = E(bQ) = bE(Q).$$

The value of $E(Q)$ is:

$$E(Q) = 9(0.4) + 10(0.5) + 11(0.1) = 9.7.$$

The expected profit is:

$$E(P) = 1.50 \times 9.7 = \$14.55.$$

Now, let us assume that neither b nor Q is known with certainty (both are random variables with the probability distributions given above). We shall make the important assumption that b and Q are independent. If any two random variables, X and Y, are independent, then the expectation of their product is equal to the product of their expectations:

$$E(XY) = E(X)\ E(Y).$$

In our example:

$$P = bQ$$

and

$$E(P) = E(bQ) = E(b)\ E(Q).$$

Substituting the values for the expectations of b and Q:

$$E(P) = 1.59 \times 9.7 = \$15.42.$$

Thus, if we assume uncertainty for both b and Q, we have an expected profit of \$15.42 and can make our plans accordingly. However, it should be noted that \$15.42 is an expectation. The profit may be as low as \$13.50 (if $Q = 9$ and $b = \$1.50$) or as high as \$18.70 (if $Q = 11$ and $b = \$1.70$).

The use of the relatively simple mathematical techniques presented here greatly simplifies the computations of the expected profit, with no loss of information (if we accept the Bayes decision rule as our decision criterion).

COMPARING DECISION RULES

Assume there are three different decision rules—t_1, t_2, and t_3—associated with a decision problem. For each decision rule a curve can be drawn showing the profit for each state of nature. See Figure 4–1.

FIGURE 4–1

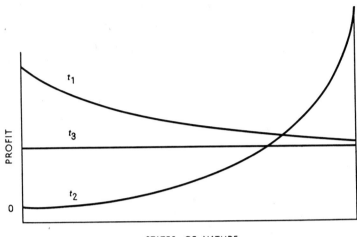

STATES OF NATURE

The following conclusions can be reached concerning the decision being discussed:

1. Rule t_1 is the minimax decision (t_1 has the maximum minimum profit).
2. Rule t_2 is the maximax decision (t_2 has the maximum possible profit).
3. Rule t_3 is an inadmissible decision rule, since t_3 is dominated by t_1 (all values of t_1 are above all values of t_3).
4. Rule t_1 is most desirable if all the states of nature are equally likely (the area under t_1 is the greatest).

The equally likely assumption of the states of nature has some intuitive appeal, but this appeal is not well founded. Assume the

FIGURE 4–2

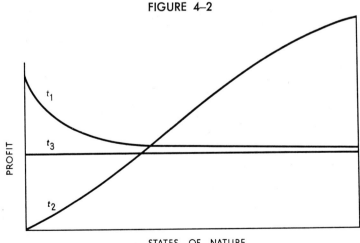

STATES OF NATURE

states of nature are redescribed by a different function that expands the right side of the graph (for example, square the present measure). Figure 4–2 shows t_2 may be best.

The Bayes decision procedure is to sum the product of the profit function and the probability density function associated with the states of nature. The decision rule with the maximum expected profit is the optimum decision (it can only be t_1 or t_2, since t_3 is dominated by t_1).

CONCLUSION

Decision theory concerns itself with choosing the best act from a set of possible acts, given uncertainty as to the state of nature which exists. By the use of the Bayes decision rule, this can be accomplished in a manner which is consistent with the decision maker's beliefs, even if there are no objective probabilities which can be applied to the states of nature.

A prime contribution of this procedure is that it focuses attention on all possible events and requires a calculation of the consequences of each act and each possible state of nature. Even if the analysis stopped with the conditional value table, this would be a contribution to the art of decision making. But by the use of the Bayes decision rule, it is possible to go further. For a decision maker to stop with the one computation using the most likely event is not justified in view of the techniques which are available for incorporating uncertainty into the analysis.

BIBLIOGRAPHY

BAUMOL, W. J. *Economic Theory and Operations Analysis.* Englewood Cliffs, N.J.: Prentice-Hall, Inc., 1961.

BROSS, I. D. J. *Design for Decision.* New York: Macmillan Co., 1953.

CHERNOFF, H., and MOSES, L. E. *Elementary Decision Theory.* New York: John Wiley & Sons, Inc., 1959.

LUCE, R. D., and RAIFFA, H. *Games and Decisions.* New York: John Wiley & Sons, Inc., 1957.

QUESTIONS AND PROBLEMS

4–1. A businessman is presented with a conditional profit table. What criterion should he use in making his decision as to which act is most desirable? Discuss the relative merits of maximax, assuming equally likely events, minimax, and the Bayes decision rule in the context of a business decision.

4-2. It has been stated in the text that decisions cannot always be based on computations involving only the monetary expressions of the consequences. Describe some business situations where factors other than money are important.

4-3. In the presence of decision making under uncertainty, can the expert evolve a procedure which will guarantee the correct decision? Explain.

4-4. Is it correct to say that $E(XY)$ is equal to $E(X)E(Y)$? Is it correct to say that $E(X + Y)$ is equal to $E(X) + E(Y)$?

4-5. Total cost of a product is equal to:

$$T = 10,000 + bX.$$

The total revenue is $R = 20X$. The variable cost per unit for the next period is a random variable with the following probability distribution:

b	$p(b)$
$5.00	0.10
6.00	0.50
7.00	0.40

Required:

a) Compute the expected profit for the coming period, assuming that 1,000 units are expected to be sold.

b) Compute the expected profit for the coming period, assuming that there is a 0.5 probability of selling 1,000 units and a 0.5 probability of zero units.

4-6. The following probabilities are assigned to the possible values of fraction defective, in a manufacturing process.

Event	Probability of Event
0.01 defective	0.10
0.02 defective	0.15
0.03 defective	0.20
0.04 defective	0.30
0.05 defective	0.20
0.10 defective	0.03
0.15 defective	0.02
	1.00

Suppose we have a lot of 50,000 parts and each defective costs 25 cents in rework costs. What is the expected rework cost? Would it be cheaper to inspect 100 per cent of the lot if it costs 3 cents per item to inspect (assuming that all defectives are removed by inspection)?

4-7. A sales manager lists the following probabilities for various demand levels for a new product:

| | *Demand* |
Probability	*(in Units)*
0.10..............................	50
0.30..............................	100
0.30..............................	150
0.15..............................	200
0.10..............................	250
0.05..............................	300

Suppose that the cost of introducing the product is \$500 and profit per unit sold is \$5.00. What is the expected profit from the new product?

4–8. You are president of an American corporation which manufactures aircraft. There has been some talk in Washington about (*a*) going to the moon, (*b*) not going to the moon, and (*c*) going to the moon with the Russians. In your judgment the probability of these states is 0.5, 0.4, and 0.1, respectively. You must make plans in the light of these possible states. Your alternatives are (*a*) to continue to make airplanes only, which would provide you with an expected \$10-million profit regardless of the moon decision; or (*b*) to design a pay-load system for the moon shot (if the program falls through, you would lose \$30 million; if it does not fall through, you will make a profit of \$40 million, regardless of Russian participation or not); or (*c*) to design a pay-load and booster system. If the program falls through, you will lose \$100 million. If we go, but with Russian participation, it is likely that we shall use Russia's booster system, and your profits will be \$20 million. If we go alone, your profits would be \$80 million.

Assume you base your decision on dollar profits.

a) What is the maximax act?

b) What is the act on the assumption of equally likely states?

c) What is the minimax act?

d) What is the maximum-likelihood act?

e) What is the Bayesian act?

f) Which decision do you prefer?

Chapter 5

DECISION THEORY
WITH EXPERIMENTS

IN THIS chapter, we introduce the opportunity to experiment, i.e., to gather additional information, before making the decision. The decision process will include the following components:

1. An objective, or a decision criterion, for the firm (for example, maximize expected profit, or maximize expected utility, or minimax).
2. A set of the possible acts or decisions which are available.
3. A set of possible outcomes of the process.
4. A set of possible probability distribution functions which may apply to the process.
5. A loss function, which measures the utility of a decision and an outcome.
6. An opportunity to experiment (this may not be available for all decisions).
7. A rule which tells us what decision to make.

We shall use the following symbols for the analysis:

D—All possible decisions
Q—All possible outcomes of the process
F—All possible probability distribution functions
S—All results of an experiment
T—All possible rules

d—A specific decision
q—A specific outcome of the process
p—A specific function
s—A specific result
t—A rule which tells what d to make if we find s is the result of an experiment

$W(q, d)$—The loss if q is the true state and d is the decision
$R(p, d)$—The risk or expected loss for a given decision and a given p
$\bar{R}(d)$—The average or expected risk over all values of p

It is possible for the loss to be negative; a negative loss is positive profit.

68

THE DECISION PROCESS

There are two alternative procedures we can follow in implementing statistical decision theory:

1. Experiment and then make the necessary computations to determine which decision is optimum.
2. Before the experiment, determine what decision is optimum for each possible outcome of the experiment. When the results of the experiment are obtained, it is merely necessary to read off the optimum decision for that outcome of the experiment. Since the two procedures are the same except for the sequence of computations (in one, the experimental results are actually observed; in the other, they are anticipated), the following outline of the first procedure applies to both procedures except for details of order of events. We shall assume in this chapter that the value of experimenting has already been determined to exceed the cost.

The decision process may be outlined as follows:

1. Choose the decision criterion; we shall use the Bayes decision rule.
2. Describe the set of possible outcomes of the process and possible decisions.
3. Decide what type of probability distribution applies to the process, and assign probabilities to the possible values of the process parameter. Probabilities will be assigned to different values of p in the following example on the assumption that the binomial probability distribution is appropriate for this case.
4. Determine a loss function, $W(q, d)$, which describes the consequences of each decision (d) and each possible outcome of the process (q).
5. Conduct an experiment.
6. Revise the assigned probabilities (see item 3).
7. For each decision, compute the risk for each value of the process parameter, p (this is the expected loss for the decision and the given value of p).
8. Using the revised probabilities (see item 6), compute the expected risk of each decision.
9. The optimum decision is the act with the lowest expected risk.

The following example illustrates an application of decision theory to a problem.

Example

We must bet on a toss of a coin of unknown physical characteristics. The coin is tossed mechanically by a machine. The decision we have to make is whether to bet heads or tails.

We are given the opportunity of experimenting. The coin may be tossed twice before we have to bet.

There are two possible outcomes of the process (flipping a coin); thus, Q consists of the set:

q_1—The outcome is a head.
q_2—The outcome is a tail.

Both Q and F may be said to refer to states of nature. Q refers to the set of possible outcomes of the process. F refers to the set of distribution functions which are possible. The process being described is a Bernoulli process, and the binomial probability distribution applies. The F in this situation refers to all possible values of p for the binomial probability distribution.

Assume there are three possible states of nature for the values of p:

p_1—The probability of a head is equal to 0.5.
p_2—The probability of a head is equal to 1.0.
p_3—The probability of a head is equal to zero.

There are two possible decisions:

d_1—Bet heads.
d_2—Bet tails.

Assume the loss function is as follows:

1. If we bet heads and are correct, the loss is -100 (that is, we gain 100). For example, $W(q_1, d_1) = -100$; since the state q_1 is "The outcome is a head" and d_1 is the decision to bet heads, we would be correct.
2. If we bet heads and we are wrong, the loss is 400. For example, $W(q_2, d_1) = 400$; since the state q_2 is "The outcome is a tail" and d_1 is to bet heads, we would lose.
3. If we bet tails and we are correct, we lose -100; i.e., $W(q_2, d_2) = -100$.
4. If we bet tails and are wrong, we lose 100; i.e., $W(q_1, d_2) = 100$.

The computation of risk or expected losses associated with each state of nature and each decision is shown in Tables 5–1 and 5–2. Table 5–3 and Figure 5–1 show the conditional risks.

TABLE 5–1
For Betting Heads

		Proba-bility of Heads		Loss if Correct		Proba-bility of Tails		Loss if Wrong		Expected Loss or Risk for Each p_i
$R(p_1, d_1)$	=	0.5	×	-100	+	0.5	×	400	=	150
$R(p_2, d_1)$	=	1.0	×	-100	+	0.0	×	400	=	-100
$R(p_3, d_1)$	=	0.0	×	-100	+	1.0	×	400	=	400

TABLE 5–2

For Betting Tails

	Proba-bility of Heads		Loss if Wrong		Proba-bility of Tails		Loss if Correct		Expected Loss or Risk for Each p_i
$R(p_1, d_2)$ =	0.5	×	100	+	0.5	×	−100	=	0
$R(p_2, d_2)$ =	1.0	×	100	+	0.0	×	−100	=	100
$R(p_3, d_2)$ =	0.0	×	100	+	1.0	×	−100	=	−100

TABLE 5–3

Conditional Risks

States of Nature ╲ Acts	d_1 Bet Heads	d_2 Bet Tails
p_1........................	150	0
p_2........................	−100	100
p_3........................	400	−100

We could conduct the experiment (toss the coin twice) and act intuitively as follows:

Results of Ex-periment		*Assume p_i Is True*	*If p_i Is True, Then We Might Act as Follows*
s_1	HT	p_1 (i.e., $P(H) = 0.5$)	Choose d_1 or d_2 randomly[1]
s_2	HH	p_2 (i.e., $P(H) = 1.0$)	d_1
s_3	TT	p_3 (i.e., $P(H) = 0.0$)	d_2
s_4	TH	p_1 (i.e., $P(H) = 0.5$)	Choose d_1 or d_2 randomly[1]

If s_1 or s_4 occurs, then we know p_1 is the true state of nature, but we do not know whether to bet heads or tails. We can select randomly (i.e., toss a fair coin and bet the outcome will be the same as the coin just tossed), but we shall be wrong 0.5 of the time. The decisions to bet heads if s_2 and to bet tails if s_3 seem reasonable, but they may not be correct. The true state may be p_1. The procedure would ignore the loss function and the prior feelings we may have about the probabilities of the various states of nature being true.

We shall illustrate an alternative procedure. Assume the experiment is conducted and two heads occur (i.e., s_2 is the result of the experiment). Also, assume that before the experiment, we had a set of prior subjective probabilities relative to the three states of nature,

---

[1] We still do not know for certain which q_i will be the outcome.

FIGURE 5–1

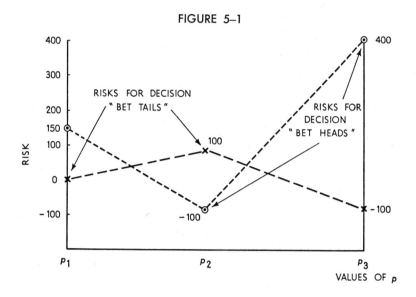

p_1, p_2, and p_3, as follows: 0.50, 0.25, and 0.25. It is necessary to adjust these probabilities in the light of the experiment. Table 5–4 accomplishes this adjustment of prior probabilities to compute the posterior probabilities.

There is zero probability that p_3 is the true state of nature (with two heads appearing in the experiment, there is no chance that the probability of a head is zero). The probability of p_2 being true is 0.67, and the probability of p_1 is 0.33. If p_2 is true, we would bet heads, i.e., make decision d_1, but we do not know for certain that p_2 is true. If p_1 is true, then we would prefer d_2. This can be shown by an abbreviated version of Table 5–3:

States	Acts	d_1	d_2
p_1..........................		150	0
p_2..........................		−100	100

Using the Bayes decision rule we compute the expected loss for each decision and choose the act with the lowest expected loss. If we define the entries of the above table as being the "risk" of the decision and state, then we want to compute the expected risk of each decision. Let $R(p_j, d_i)$ be the risk of decision d_i, assuming the true state of nature to be p_j. The expected risk is then $\bar{R}(d_i)$.

$$\bar{R}(d_1) = 0.33 \times 150 + 0.67 \times (-100) = -17$$
$$\bar{R}(d_2) = 0.33 \times 0 + 0.67 \ (100) = 67$$

The expected risk of d_1 is less than that of d_2; thus, we would bet heads assuming the result of the experiment was s_2, two heads. This is our first decision rule, t_1: If the experiment gives a result s_2 (i.e., two heads), then bet heads. We could establish this rule before the experiment or wait until the results of the experiment are known.

TABLE 5–4

Computation of Posterior Probabilities*

State of Nature	1 Priors $P(p_i)$	2 $P(s_2\|p_i)$	3 $P(s_2, p_i)$ (1×2)	4 Posterior Probability $P(p_i\|s_2) = \dfrac{P(s_2, p_i)}{P(s_2)}$
p_1.............	0.50	0.25	0.125	0.33
p_2.............	0.25	1.00	0.250	0.67
p_3.............	0.25	0.00	0.000	0.00
	1.00		$P(s_2) = 0.375$	1.00

* The revision of the probabilities is an application of the Bayes theorem, i.e.,

$$P(A|B) = \frac{P(AB)}{P(B)}. \text{ See Chapter 2.}$$

It should not be assumed that if we use t_1 when s_2 occurs, we shall always be correct. We shall be wrong 0.165 of the time (the probability is based on our current knowledge).[2] Also, if the loss function changes (for example, if there is a loss of 1,000 if we bet heads and tails appears), we might choose d_2 if s_2 occurs.

We have evolved one decision rule for one experiment. We also want rules to go with results s_1, s_3, and s_4. Computations similar to those just made would indicate that we should choose d_2 (bet tails) if any experimental result other than s_2 occurs.

Instead of using a Bayes decision rule and minimizing expected risk, we could use a minimax or some other decision rule. Looking at the conditioned risk (Table 5–3) after p_3 has been eliminated by the results of the experiment leads to a minimax decision of d_2. The maximum loss is 100 if we choose d_2, and it is 150 if we choose d_1 (d_2 minimizes the maximum possible loss). As explained previously, the minimax criterion does not take into consideration the probabilities of the possible events.

---

[2] The probability of p_1 is 0.33; and if p_1 occurs, there is a 0.50 probability of a tail. The joint probability is $0.33 \times 0.50 = 0.165$.

DECISION THEORY AND BUSINESS DECISIONS

The above model is valid for many decisions, but there are some situations where a somewhat simpler procedure may be used. In the above example, there are two levels of stochastic processes. At one hand, the parameter p is a random variable. At the second level, the final outcome is the result of a stochastic process, with the parameter p controlling the process.

For some types of situations, there will only be one unknown. For example, the decision may hinge on the demand for the product in the next year. The only unknown, subject to a probability distribution, is demand. In this situation (which could be an inventory problem) the decision process is as follows:

1. Choose the decision criterion; we suggest the Bayes decision rule.
2. Describe the set of possible outcomes and possible decisions.
3. Assign probabilities to the possible outcomes (states of nature).
4. Determine a loss function.
5. Conduct an experiment.
6. Revise the assigned probabilities.
7. Compute the expected loss or expected risk for each decision.
8. The optimum decision is the act with the lowest expected loss.

The above process assumes that it has previously been determined that experimentation is desirable. Later chapters will investigate that question.

SUMMARY

Statistical decision theory involves the choice of a decision criterion (i.e., a goal)—say, minimize expected risk. If possible and feasible, an experiment is conducted which leads to a result s. The prior probabilities of the states of nature are revised, based on s. The expected risk of each possible decision is computed, and the act with the lowest expected risk is chosen as the optimum act. A rule t may be established which states that if statistical result s occurs, we shall make decision d.

Chapters 8 and 13 will expand upon the material presented in this chapter and put the subject in a realistic business decision-making context. The purpose of this chapter is to introduce the concepts of experimenting in a decision framework.

BIBLIOGRAPHY

See the Bibliography at the end of Chapter 4.

QUESTIONS AND PROBLEMS

5-1. Using the example of the chapter, determine decision rules for outcomes s_1, s_3, and s_4.

5-2. The example of the chapter used a situation which is not typical of those encountered by businessmen. What difficulties are encountered in applying the model described in a normal business situation?

5-3. Distinguish between a loss function, $W(q, d)$; a risk function, $R(p, d)$; and the expected risk, $\bar{R}(d)$.

5-4. You are charged with the inventory control job in the Volant Manufacturing Company. You think there is about a 0.4 chance of a recession next year. If there is a recession next year, you should sell the AE4 model now for the last-offer price of $1 million, because you could get only $800,000 for it in a recession year. These amounts would be received in one year. However, you have a promise from the purchasing agent of a leading company to buy AE4 for $1.3 million if there is no recession (amount payable one year hence). After some preliminary calculations, you are still undecided about selling, and determine to gather evidence about the chances of a recession next year. You discover that bad debts have been rising recently. A little investigation indicates that for the last ten recessions, bad debts started to increase approximately a year early in eight instances. You are willing to accept 0.8 as an estimate of the probability of bad debts rising, given that a recession will occur a year later. In the same sense, you find that for ten randomly selected normal years, the economy experienced rising bad debts the previous year in three instances. Thus, you take 0.3 as an estimate of $P(\text{Rising bad debts}|\text{No recession next year})$. If you revise your prior probabilities according to the Bayes theorem, what would you do about the AE4?

5-5. The probability of two dice, if they are fair dice, giving either a seven or an 11, is $2/9$. If the dice are loaded in a certain fashion, the probability of a seven or an 11 is $4/9$. An acquaintance asks you to play a game with him. If he throws a seven or an 11, he will collect $3.00 from you; and if not, he will pay you $1.00. Since the game would give you an advantage if the dice were fair, you have suspicions about your acquaintance. In particular, you feel that there is a 0.7 chance that he is using loaded dice with probability $4/9$ for seven or 11. To allay your fears, your opponent offers to let you roll the dice twice. You do, and roll a four and a six. Should you play the game with your acquaintance? Show your calculations.

Chapter 6

DECISION THEORY AND
CLASSICAL STATISTICS

MODERN statistical decision theory aims at choosing the optimum course of action. Classical statistics has the same objective, but a somewhat different approach, and frequently arrives at a less useful answer for purposes of business decision making.

CLASSICAL STATISTICS

The following explanation somewhat simplifies the scope of classical statistics; but hopefully, it conveys the main stream of the concepts. We shall illustrate classical statistics using a decision problem.

To determine whether or not to market a new product, we are interested in estimating the extent of the demand for the product. A statistician using the classical approach might do any or all of the following:

1. Make a point estimate of demand. He could estimate p, the proportion of people who, when approached, will buy the product.
2. Make an interval estimation; e.g., p, the proportion who will buy the product, will be larger than 0.04 and less than 0.16, with 0.95 certainty.
3. Test two hypotheses. The hypotheses may be:
   a) That p is equal to or less than 0.09.
   b) That p is greater than 0.09.

The statistician has various tests he applies in performing the above operations. If he is making a point estimate, he will want the estimator to be unbiased, i.e., the average of a large number of estimates would be equal to the true value of the parameter being estimated, as well as satisfying other requirements.

76

Assume a random sample of 100 persons are contacted out of a population of 10 million, and 10 persons purchase the product. The unbiased estimate of the proportion of people who will buy the product is:

$$p = \frac{10}{100} = 0.10.$$

An unbiased estimate of the number who will buy is 10,000,000 × 0.10, or one million. This is a point estimate of demand. This estimate is made without reference to the economic considerations of cost or revenues, and a decision made using just the

FIGURE 6-1

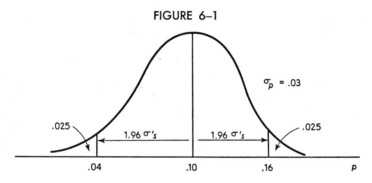

estimate of one million customers would be an intuitive decision. It should also be noted that because of the small size of the sample the one million would not necessarily be a reliable predictor of demand.

Instead of making a point estimate, we can make an interval estimate. Let us assume the standard deviation of the proportion of success, σ_p, is 0.03.[1] We can estimate with 0.95 probability that the true proportion who will buy will fall within ±1.96 standard deviations of the estimate of the mean, assuming the distribution of sample proportions is normal. (See Figure 6-1.)

Why were the 1.96 σ's and the 0.95 probability chosen, rather than 0.90 or 0.99? It is a matter of arbitrary convention, and any other choice of the number of standard deviations and the probabilities would have been just as reasonable. The advantage of an interval estimate is that it takes some pressure off the statistician. He no longer has to be exactly correct. It also removes the implication that the statistician knows the exact, correct answer.

Neither of the two procedures described were concerned with the basic decision that is being made. They merely estimated values of

---

[1] The source of σ_p could be past experience or an estimate from the sample.

the parameter of a process. The third procedure, hypothesis testing, is concerned with comparing two decisions and arriving at a decision rule for choosing one of the decisions, based on sample evidence. The analysis is assumed to take place prior to the taking of a sample.

We shall assume that an analysis of the economic considerations indicates that with a 0.09 fraction of persons in the market purchasing the product, the firm will break even, and the firm would be indifferent as to whether or not the product is sold if 0.09 of those contacted purchase the product. The hypotheses are:

1. The proportion of persons who will buy is equal to or less than 0.09; thus the product should not be sold.
2. The proportion of persons who will buy is greater than 0.09; thus the product should be sold.

Which hypothesis is valid? If we knew with certainty that the true proportion (i.e., the proportion of persons who would buy) is equal to 0.10, the decision would be easy—we would market the product. However, the actual proportion buying could easily be less than the break-even proportion of 0.09. In like manner, if we knew the true proportion was less than 0.09, we could make a "reject" decision, but there is a probability that the true proportion is larger than 0.09. The classical approach is to investigate the probabilities of success and error of a decision rule with the true proportion being given different values.

We can define hypothesis 1 as the null hypothesis (if this hypothesis is true, we want to avoid making an error) and hypothesis 2 as the alternative hypothesis.[2] There are two types of errors which may be made:

Type 1:   When the null hypothesis is true, arrive at the conclusion that the proportion who will buy is greater than 0.09.
Type 2:   When the alternative hypothesis is true, arrive at the conclusion that the proportion who will buy is less than 0.09.

What is the probability of making the first type of error, assuming the mean of the population takes on different values? We shall use the following decision rule in our computations: Accept the null hypothesis if the sample indicates 0.11 or less will buy, i.e., if $\frac{r}{n} \leq 0.11$, where r is the number buying and n is the sample size.

Table 6–1 (column 3) shows the probability of accepting the null

_____

[2] The labeling of one hypothesis as being the null hypothesis is conventional procedure; but this may be an arbitrary process, and too much importance should not be placed on the labeling.

TABLE 6–1

1 Assumed True Value of p	2 $P(r \geq 12 \mid p, n = 100)$	3 $P(r \leq 11) = 1 - P(r \geq 12)$
0.00...............	0.0000	1.0000
0.07...............	0.0469	0.9531
0.09...............	0.1876	0.8124
0.11...............	0.4206	0.5794
0.13...............	0.6611	0.3389

hypothesis, which, in the context of this example, means rejecting the product for selected values of p. We are limiting the number of values of p in order to simplify the computations.

Explanation of Table 6–1

Column 1 gives the assumed true value of p.

Column 2 gives the probability of the sample of 100 having 12 or more than 12 purchasers, given different values of p. These probabilities may be obtained from binomial probability tables.

Column 3 is equal to one minus column 2 and gives the probability of the sample having 11 or less than 11 purchasers. These are the values of the operating characteristic curve based on a decision rule "Choose the null hypothesis if $\frac{r}{n} \leq 0.11$." With a sample size of 100, this rule is equivalent to requiring that $r \leq 11$.

Column 3 gives the probability of being correct for true values of $p \leq 0.09$; i.e., if the true p is less than the break-even proportion, then the probabilities shown in column 3 are the probabilities of be-

FIGURE 6–2

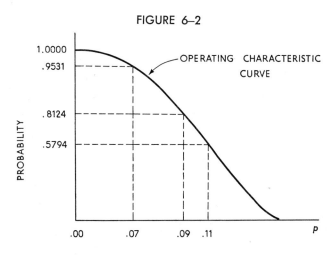

ing correct. Column 3 gives the probabilities of being in error for the values of $p > 0.09$. The graph of column 3 of Table 6–1 (see Figure 6–2) is called the operating characteristic curve.

PROBABILITY

If the true p is less than 0.09 (the break-even proportion), then the null hypothesis is correct, and the operating characteristic curve shows the conditional probability of making the correct decision (using the decision rule that if $\frac{r}{n}$ is less than 0.11, reject the product). If $p > 0.09$, then the operating characteristic curve shows the probability of making an error (the error arises because $\frac{r}{n}$ is less

FIGURE 6–3

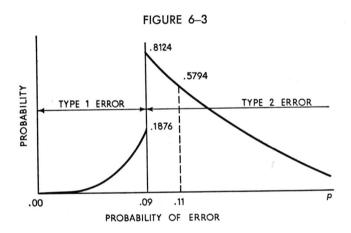

PROBABILITY OF ERROR

than 0.11, despite the fact that the true p is greater than the break-even proportion of 0.09).

If the true p is 0.07, there is a 0.9531 probability of making the correct decision (i.e., rejecting the product and assuming the null hypothesis is correct). It follows that there is a 0.0469 probability of error. For values of p less than 0.09, we find the probability of error by subtracting the operating characteristic curve from one. For values of p greater than 0.09 the operating characteristic curve measures the probability of error. Figure 6–3 shows the probabilities of error for all values of p, assuming the decision rule "Accept the null hypothesis if $\frac{r}{n} \leq 0.11$" is used.

One important question has been deferred to this point. How did we arrive at the decision rule "Reject the product unless the sample proportion is greater than 0.11"? We wanted to avoid the type 1 error; thus, we made it less probable to declare the null hypothesis true if it was actually not true. Economically, we wanted to be reasonably certain to reject the product if the true p was less than 0.09. One way of accomplishing this objective is to make the barrier to acceptance relatively high.

In practice, the statistician sets the "level of significance." This is the maximum probability of a type 1 error. In the example the maximum probability of a type 1 error is equal to 0.1876, and this arises when the true p is equal to 0.09. In addition, the probability of a type 2 error is set for some value of p—say, p equal to 0.11. Assume that this probability is set at 0.58. With these two probabilities established, we would find that the decision rule as described in this example satisfies the probabilities of error which are required.[3]

The so-called "level of significance" can be decreased below 0.1876 by changing the decision rule; but in doing so, we would increase the probabilities of type 2 errors. We could also decide to decrease the type 2 errors, but this would increase the level of significance, unless the reduction was accomplished by an increase in sample size.

The question may be asked as to how we arrived at a desired level of significance of 0.1876 and a desired probability of error of 0.58 for p equal to 0.11. There is no completely satisfactory answer to this question, and this is one of the weaknesses of the classical hypothesis-testing procedure. We want to bring into the analysis the economic consequences arising from the two types of errors, but it is not clear how to accomplish this systematically within the classical framework, and the classical statistical model generally stops at this point.

In theory, one could set the type 1 and type 2 errors so as to minimize the economic consequences of these errors times the probability of the errors occurring. First, it is usually unrealistic to attach all economic consequences to two values (those points at which the type 1 and type 2 errors are measured, $p = 0.09$ and $p = 0.11$ in the above example). Secondly, no account is taken of the likelihood of different states of nature (in the example, different values of p). Implicit in this omission is the assumption that all states are equally likely to occur (that is, $p = 0.09$ is as likely as $p = 0.11$). This may be a very unrealistic assumption.

---

[3] With a given n, we can solve for the critical value of r. Also, by changing $\frac{r}{n}$, we can change the probabilities of error.

INCORPORATING CONSEQUENCES

In the example being discussed, we can make two types of errors, with the following consequences:

1. We can accept the product when marketing the product is not desirable. The loss will be a function of the true p (the lower the true p, the larger is the loss arising from leftover units). Assume this type of loss is equal to:
$$W = 100(0.09 - p) \text{ if } p \leq 0.09.$$

2. We can reject the product when marketing the product is desirable. The profits lost will be a function of the true p. Assume this loss is equal to:
$$W = 60(p - 0.09) \text{ if } p > 0.09.$$

We can plot these two loss functions for different values of p.

Figure 6–4 shows the losses which are associated with the different possible states of nature, i.e., the different values of p, the proportion of people who will buy. The Bayes decision rule says we should compute the expected loss or risk function of this decision rule and choose the rule with the lowest expected risk. Figure 6–3 gives the probability of the error for the different values of p and a specific decision rule. If we multiply the probabilities from Figure 6–3 by the losses of Figure 6–4, we obtain the risk or expected loss curves of Figure 6–5. These are called butterfly curves. Since the loss with p equal to 0.09 is zero, the curves take on the zero value at p equal to 0.09. This is interesting because the level of significance (the probability of a type 1 error at $p = 0.09$) generally receives considerable attention. Since the loss at the break-even p is zero, and

FIGURE 6–4

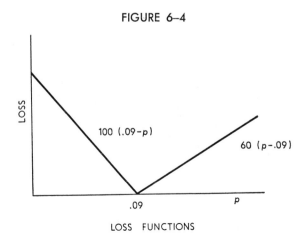

LOSS FUNCTIONS

FIGURE 6–5

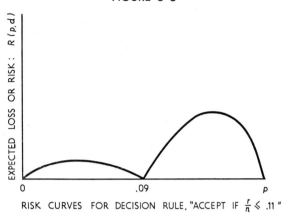

RISK CURVES FOR DECISION RULE, "ACCEPT IF $\frac{r}{n} \leqslant .11$"

near to zero for values of p close to the break-even point, the probability of making an error at that point, or close to that point, is not of significant interest.

The computation of the values shown in Figure 6–5 is illustrated by Table 6–2.

The next step in the Bayes procedure is to assign probabilities to the possible states of nature, the values of p, and compute the expected risk (we are taking an expectation of the expected loss). Assume the probabilities shown in Table 6–3 are assigned (only selected values of p are allowed, to simplify the computations). Table 6–3 shows the computations of the expected risk.

The expected risk of the 0.11 decision rule is 0.239. This computation of expected risk would be repeated for other possible decision rules; the rule with the lowest expected risk is the Bayes decision rule.

The classical statistician might stop with the computation of the operating characteristic curve (or one minus this amount), or with

TABLE 6–2

| 1 | 2 | 3 | | 4 |
| | | Loss | | Risk or |
Possible Values of p	Probability of Error	$100(0.09 - p)$	$60(p - 0.09)$	Expected Loss (Col. 2 × Col. 3)
0.00..........	0.0000	9		0.0000
0.07..........	0.0469	2		0.0938
0.09..........	0.1876	0	0.0	0.0000
0.11..........	0.5794		1.2	0.6953
0.13..........	0.3389		2.4	0.8134

TABLE 6–3

1 Possible Values of p	2 Proba- bilities of p	3 Risk (from Table 6–2)	4 Product of Prob- ability and Risk (Col. 2 × Col. 3)
0.00.	0.1	0.0000	0.00000
0.07.	0.2	0.0938	0.01876
0.09.	0.4	0.0000	0.00000
0.11.	0.2	0.6953	0.13906
0.13.	0.1	0.8134	0.08134
	1.0	Expected risk $= \bar{R}(d) =$	0.23916

the resulting probability-of-error curves. He might add the loss functions and even multiply the error curves by the loss functions to
obtain the butterfly or risk curves, though this step is frequently
omitted. He is not likely to be sympathetic to the computation of the
expected risk using subjective probabilities assigned to the different
possible values of p. If objective evidence is available, then he might
incorporate this into the analysis, though not necessarily systematically by computing the expected risk.

The differences between statistical decision theory using the
Bayes decision rule and classical statistics are not exactly defined,
but one important difference is the explicit computation of expected
risk by the Bayes decision maker. The failure of some statisticians to
include some loss function in the decision process would be another
difference, though a large number of modern statisticians would
agree to the necessity of including a loss function in the analysis.

It is not uncommon for statisticians to speak of hypothesis testing
or interval estimation without reference to the losses resulting from
incorrect decisions. This is an undesirable omission. The consequences of incorrect decisions are a necessary part of the decision
process.

Of course, there is a large class of decision problems where
economic consequences cannot be accurately measured or are of
meaningless importance compared to noneconomic consequences.
Such, for example, would be the decision problem of the scientist in-
vestigating a new drug. He must decide if the new drug is effective or
not. The consequences of an incorrect decision may possibly affect
the sufferings of many people and the reputation of the scientist.
One would like to be very sure about the correct decision in such
situations. The classical statistics decision framework is designed for
such problems as this. It tells the scientist how confident he can be

about his results (with, for example, only a $\frac{1}{100}$ chance of being wrong) and when he must find more evidence before making his decision.

Thus, classical statistics was designed, and is useful, for scientific or experimental work where the probability of error is more accurately measured than the consequences of a decision. The business decision maker frequently has a situation where objective probabilities are lacking, but the consequences are subject to measurement.

BIBLIOGRAPHY

See the Bibliography at the end of Chapter 4.

QUESTIONS AND PROBLEMS

6–1. Discuss the following statement: "Statistics is a science and an objective discipline. As such, it has no place for subjective probabilities. The use of subjective probabilities may be psychology—but not statistics."

6–2. Using the example in the chapter, compute the expected risk, $\bar{R}(d)$, of the decision rule "Accept the null hypothesis if $\frac{r}{n} \leq 0.10$" for $n = 20$.

6–3. Using the example in the chapter, compute the expected risk, $\bar{R}(d)$, of the decision rule "Accept the null hypothesis if $\frac{r}{n} \leq 0.05$" for $n = 20$.

6–4. Using the example in the chapter, compute the expected risk, $\bar{R}(d)$, of the decision rule "Accept the null hypothesis if $\frac{r}{n} \leq 0$" for $n = 20$.

6–5. Compare the values of $\bar{R}(d)$ in Problems 6–2 through 6–4. Explain why one has less expected risk than the others.

Chapter 7

THE NORMAL PROBABILITY
DISTRIBUTION AND THE VALUE
OF INFORMATION

THERE ARE two types of probability distributions—the discrete distribution and the continuous distribution. The discrete distribution is called a probability mass function (p.m.f.), and the continuous probability function is called a probability density function (p.d.f.). In a p.m.f. (discrete distribution) the random variable is allowed to take on only selected values (for example, 0.1, 0.2, or 0.3, but perhaps not 0.11, 0.21, or 0.31).

We could indicate the proportion of families which have X members. A family may have four members, but it cannot have 4.2 members; thus, X must be an integer. Sometimes, we classify the data so that we may use a discrete probability distribution, where we could use a continuous distribution. For example, it is possible that any amount of product may be demanded, but we may classify the demand for a day as falling into classifications of tenths of a ton, i.e., 0.1, 0.2, etc.

The binomial distribution, which is described in Chapter 2, is another example of a discrete probability distribution. The random variable, number of successes, can only take on zero and positive integer values from one to n (the number of trials).

A continuous probability density function is a distribution where the value of the random variable may be any number within some given range of values—say, between zero and infinity. For example, assuming a p.d.f. of the height of a population, there would be a value of the density function for 5.3 feet, 5.324 feet, 5.32431 feet, etc., but the height cannot be negative. The density function has a value for all possible values of the random variable. The density

86

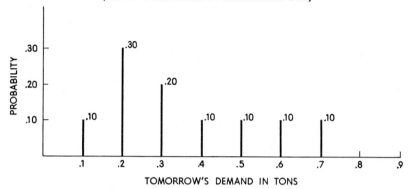

FIGURE 7-1

Probability Mass Function (p.m.f.)
(*Note the Sum of the Probabilities Is One*)

function measures the height of the graph for the value of the random variable; it is not the probability of the event.

Graphs of the two types of distributions are shown in Figures 7-1 and 7-2.

CUMULATIVE MASS FUNCTION

Associated with probability mass functions are cumulative mass functions. A cumulative mass function shows cumulative probability. Let us assume a random variable with the simple discrete probability mass function shown in Table 7-1.

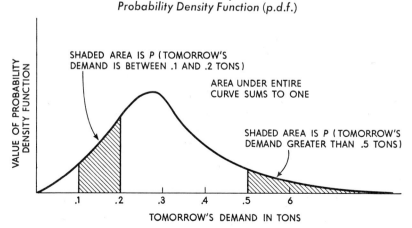

FIGURE 7-2

Continuous Probability Distribution
Probability Density Function (p.d.f.)

TABLE 7–1

S	$P(S)$
0	0.00
1	0.20
2	0.40
3	0.30
4	0.10
	1.00

TABLE 7–2

S	$P(S = s)$	$P(S \leq s)$
0	0.00	0.00
1	0.20	0.20
2	0.40	0.60
3	0.30	0.90
4	0.10	1.00

In addition to being interested in the probability of S being equal to two, i.e., $[P(S = 2) = 0.40]$, we may wish to know the probability of S being equal to or less than two, i.e., $[P(S \leq 2) = 0.60]$. The function giving values of this nature is called the cumulative mass function. The probability mass function and cumulative mass function of a "less than or equal to" type for the example in Table 7–1 is shown in Table 7–2 and Figure 7–3.

FIGURE 7–3

Example of Probability Mass Function and Cumulative Mass Function

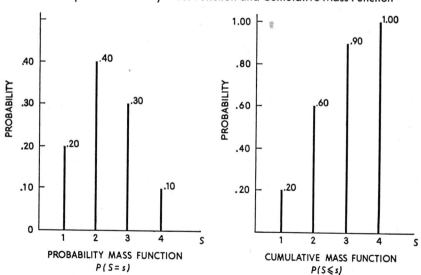

We may also wish to know the probability of S being greater than two $[P(S > 2) = 1 - P(S \leq 2) = 1 - 0.60 = 0.40]$.

Given the probability mass function, we can obtain the cumulative mass function and such variations as $P(S \geq 2)$ or $P(2 < S < 4)$.

CUMULATIVE DISTRIBUTION FUNCTIONS

Cumulative distribution functions are associated with probability density functions just as cumulative mass functions are associated with probability mass functions.

FIGURE 7–4

Probability Density Function $f(S) = \dfrac{1}{b-a}, a \leq S \leq b;$
$$= 0, \text{ Otherwise.}$$

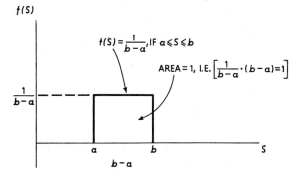

We shall illustrate the cumulative distribution function using a rectangular probability distribution (see Figure 7–4). If S is between

FIGURE 7–5

$F(S)$, Cumulative Distribution Function for $f(S) = \dfrac{1}{b-a}$

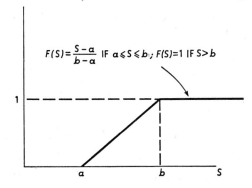

a and b ($a \leq S \leq b$), then the value of the probability density function is $\dfrac{1}{b - a}$, and zero otherwise.

If we sum the area under the probability density function

$$f(S) = \frac{1}{b - a}$$

for each value of S, we obtain the cumulative distribution, $F(S)$. We use $f(\cdot)$ to represent the probability density function and $F(\cdot)$ to represent the cumulative distribution function of the "less than or equal to" type (see Figure 7–5).

THE NORMAL PROBABILITY DISTRIBUTION

The normal distribution is an extremely important one. It is easier to manipulate mathematically than many other distributions,

FIGURE 7–6

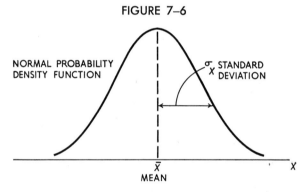

and is a good approximation for several of the others. In many cases the normal distribution is a reasonable approximation for a prior probability distribution for business decision purposes; and in the following chapters, we shall use the normal distribution in many of

FIGURE 7–7

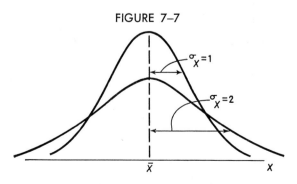

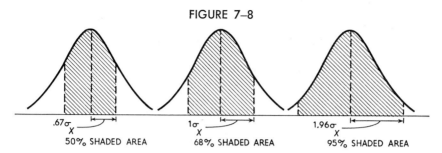

FIGURE 7–8

.67σ
X
50% SHADED AREA

1σ
X
68% SHADED AREA

1.96σ
X
95% SHADED AREA

the applications. Despite its general application, it should not be assumed that every process can be described as having a normal distribution.

The normal distribution has a probability density function which is a smooth, symmetric, continuous, bell-shaped curve, as pictured in Figure 7–6. The area under the curve over any interval on the horizontal axis represents the probability of the random variable, X, taking on a value in that interval. The area under the curve sums to one.

This curve reaches a maximum at the mean of the distribution. One half of the area lies on either side of the mean. The greater the value of σ_X, the standard deviation, the more spread-out the curve. This is illustrated in Figure 7–7.

With any normal distribution, approximately 0.50 of the area lies within ±0.67 standard deviations from the mean; about 0.68 of the area lies within ±1.0 standard deviations; and 0.95 of the area lies within ±1.96 standard deviations. See Figure 7–8.

Since the normal probability function is continuous (a probability density function), probability cannot be read directly from the graphs. We must consider the probability of the value of a random variable being in an interval (see Figure 7–9).

FIGURE 7–9

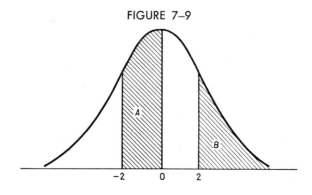

−2   0   2

In Figure 7–9:

$$P(-2 \leq X \leq 0) = \text{Shaded area } A$$
$$P(X \geq 2) = \text{Shaded area } B$$
$$P(0 \leq X \leq 2) = \text{Area between } A \text{ and } B \text{ (also equal to the shaded area}$$
$$A \text{ because of the symmetry of the normal curve).}$$

RIGHT AND LEFT TAILS

We are now ready to discuss the right and left tails of normal probability distributions.

FIGURE 7–10

Normal Curve

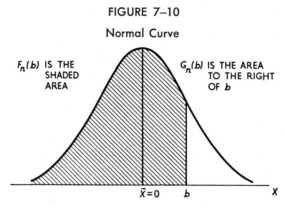

The symbol F_n is used to represent a cumulative distribution function of a normal probability distribution. It is the area under the *left* tail of a normal probability density function. In Figure 7–10 the shaded area is the left tail of a normal curve, i.e., $F_n(b)$.

$F_n(b)$ is the probability of X being equal to or less than b, i.e., $F_n(b) = P(X \leq b)$.

We now introduce a new symbol, G, which we define as the area under the *right* tail of a probability density function. In Figure 7–10 the unshaded area is the right tail of a normal curve, i.e., $G_n(b)$.

$G_n(b)$ is the probability of X being greater than b, i.e.,

$$G_n(b) = P(X > b).$$

From Figure 7–10, it can be seen that $F_n(b)$ and $G_n(b)$ are related:[1]

(7–1) $$G_n(b) = 1 - F_n(b).$$

---

[1] The basic mathematical relationships are also important:

$$F_n(b) = \int_{-\infty}^{b} f_n(X)\,dX$$

and

$$G_n(b) = \int_{b}^{\infty} f_n(X)\,dX.$$

NORMAL PROBABILITY TABLES

A normal distribution with $\bar{X} = 0$ (mean of zero) and $\sigma_X = 1$ (standard deviation of one) is said to be a *standard* normal distribution. If a normal distribution has a mean other than zero or a standard deviation other than one, we may standardize the distribution. The ability to standardize normal distributions is one of the useful features of the distribution, and allows us to look up normal probabilities in a relatively short table.

To standardize a normal random variable, we shall define a new *standardized normal variable U* as follows:

$$(7\text{-}2) \qquad U = \frac{X - \bar{X}}{\sigma_X}$$

where X is the nonstandardized normal random variable we are concerned with, $\bar{X}$ is the mean of this random variable, and σ_X is the standard deviation. In the above expression, U is the distance of X from its mean, $\bar{X}$, measured in units of standard deviations. For example, if $U = 4$, then:

$$4 = \frac{X - \bar{X}}{\sigma_X}$$
$$4\sigma_X = X - \bar{X}$$

Thus, $U = 4$ corresponds to a value of X which is four standard deviations from its mean. As a result of this operation, U is a standardized, normally distributed random variable, and has a mean of zero and a standard deviation of one. Since we look up the probabilities in terms of U, and all U's have a mean of zero and a standard deviation of one, we need only one table of probabilities. Table B (in the Appendix at the end of the text) is a table of cumulative normal probabilities.

Assume we are concerned with a normally distributed random variable, X, with mean $\bar{X} = 8$ and standard deviation $\sigma_X = 3$. Let us find the following probabilities:

1. $P(X > 10)$
2. $P(X \leq 10)$
3. $P(10 < X \leq 15)$

Example 1

We first standardize the random variable X:

$$U = \frac{X - \bar{X}}{\sigma_X} = \frac{10 - 8}{3} = \frac{2}{3} = 0.67$$

We then look up the probability $P(U < 0.67)$ and find it to be about 0.7486. The probability of X being larger than 10 is 0.2514 (note that Table B gives 0.7486 and $1-0.7486 = 0.2514$).

Example 2

$$P(X \leq 10) = P(U < 0.67) = 0.7486$$

If the probability of X being greater than 10 is 0.25, the probability of its being less than 10 is 0.75. In terms of areas, if the area to the right of 10 is 0.25, and the total area under the density function is one, then the area to the left of 10 is $(1 - 0.25)$, or 0.75.

Example 3

We know $P(X > 10) = 0.2514$ from Example 1. To calculate $P(X \leq 15)$, we must compute U for a value of 15:

$$U = \frac{15 - 8}{3} = \frac{7}{3} = 2.33.$$

In Table B (in the Appendix at the end of the text), we find

$$P(U > 2.33) = 0.00990.$$

Note that

$$P(U \leq 2.33) = 1 - P(U > 2.33) = 1 - 0.00990 = 0.9901.$$

The probability of X being larger than 10 and less than 15 (or, equivalently, U being larger than 0.67 and less than 2.33) is:

$$P(10 < X \leq 15) = P(0.67 < U \leq 2.33) = P(U > 0.67) - P(U > 2.33)$$
$$= 0.2514 - 0.0099 = 0.2415.$$

An alternative computation is:

$$P(10 < X \leq 15) = P(U \leq 2.33) - P(U \leq 0.67)$$
$$= 0.9901 - 0.7486 = 0.2415.$$

NORMAL DENSITY FUNCTIONS

For some type of calculations, we might want to know the value of a normal density function for a given number of standard deviations from the mean. While this value would be different for each normal density function, depending on the size of its standard deviation, there is a relationship between all normal density functions and the standard normal density function:

$$f(U) = \frac{f^*(U)}{\sigma_X},$$

where $f^*(U)$ is the standard normal density function. The larger the σ_X, the smaller is the value of the density function (the more spread-out is the curve).

Example

Assume $f^*(2) = 0.05399$, that is, the height of the standard normal density function two σ's from the mean is 0.05399. What is $f(2)$ for a normal density function with $\sigma_X = 5$?

$$f(2) = \frac{f^*(2)}{\sigma_X} = \frac{0.05399}{5} = 0.0108.$$

NORMAL PRIOR PROBABILITIES AND THE VALUE OF INFORMATION

In the preceding sections, we described the general characteristics of the normal probability distribution. We shall now show the use of the normal distribution as a prior probability distribution. Our discussion here will follow closely the explanation of expected value contained in Chapter 3. The difference will be the use of continuous, rather than discrete, prior probabilities.

Suppose a company has an opportunity to buy for $8,600 a machine which, if successful, will save labor hours in a certain production process which now uses a large amount of hand labor. The physical life of this machine is one year. Assume the incremental cost of a labor hour to the company is $4.00; thus, if the machine will save more than 2,150 labor hours $\left(\dfrac{\$8,600}{\$4.00} = 2,150\right)$, the company would benefit from owning the machine.

Let us assume that the production engineer feels that the mean number of hours saved will be 2,300. He also feels that there is a 50–50 chance that the mean hours of savings could be less than 2,100 or more than 2,500 hours for the year.

With this description of the engineer's feelings, it is possible to assume that a specific normal distribution will fit his prior expectations. The mean of the distribution is 2,300. If we can determine the standard deviation, we have described the normal prior probability distribution.

In the normal distribution, roughly one half the area (hence, one half the probability) lies within ± 0.67 standard deviations of the mean. Figure 7–11 approximates the fit of a normal distribution to the engineer's estimates. The engineer has estimated a mean of 2,300

FIGURE 7–11

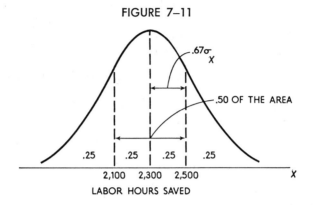

LABOR HOURS SAVED

hours, and he has judged that the true mean lies between 2,100 and 2,500 hours, with probability 0.50. Hence, one half the area must lie outside these limits, 0.25 on the left side and 0.25 on the right side. We can see that if we move in a positive direction of 200 units, we move out $0.67\sigma_X$; that is:

$$0.67\sigma_X = 200 \text{ hours}$$
$$\sigma_X = \frac{200}{0.67} = 300 \text{ hours.}$$

The normal prior distribution has a standard deviation of approximately 300 hours.

Note also that the normal distribution assigns probabilities to both large positive and negative hour savings. This will be in accordance with the engineer's judgment if he feels the probabilities are symmetrically distributed around the mean.

To summarize, we have taken the engineer's narrative description and converted it to a normal prior distribution with mean $\bar{X} = 2,300$ hours and standard deviation $\sigma_X = 300$ hours. We also know that in order to break even, the machine must save at least 2,150 hours; and for every hour that actual savings differ from 2,150, the profit changes at a rate of $4.00 per hour.

Profits can be represented as a linear function of hours saved, with zero profit at 2,150 hours. Thus:

$$\text{Profits} = \pi = -8,600 + 4X$$

where X is the number of hours saved. And since this is a linear function, expected profits can be determined by replacing X by its expected value $E(X) = \bar{X}$:[2]

$$E(\pi) = -8,600 + 4\bar{X}$$
$$= -8,600 + 4(2,300) = 600.$$

---

[2] See Chapter 4.

Whenever the estimate of mean savings $(\bar{X})$ is above the break-even point, expected profits are positive, and we should buy the machine (assume we are willing to buy the machine on a break-even basis; that is, in this chapter, we shall ignore utility considerations and the interest return required for acceptable investments). Even though the engineer's prior probability distribution is fairly tight (the standard deviation, $\sigma_X = 300$, is relatively small compared to the size of the mean, so that the engineer is fairly certain of his estimate of the mean), perhaps it would pay us to gather more information before we act. Hence, we are interested in the expected value of perfect information $(EVPI)$.

Let us first define the conditional value of perfect information. Suppose we buy the machine and it turns out that the actual savings are less than 2,150 hours. In such a case, how much do we lose? If we use X_b to stand for the break-even amount of 2,150 hours, the conditional profit of the machine may be defined as follows:

(Marginal Profit per Hour) · (Difference from X_b) = Conditional Profit
$4.00(X - X_b)$ = Conditional Profit from Buying Machine (conditional upon the value of X, the actual hours saved)

The above definition makes use of the fact that our profit changes at a rate of $4.00 for every hour we differ from the break-even point. If we save more than 2,150 hours, the profit increases; likewise, our loss will increase by $4.00 for every hour we fall short of the break-even point. Thus the conditional opportunity loss (assuming we buy the equipment) will be:

$$\begin{cases} \$4.00(X_b - X) \text{ if } X \leq X_b \\ 0 \text{ if } X > X_b \end{cases}$$

where X = hours that are saved and $X_b = 2{,}150$, the hours required to break even. The conditional opportunity loss is the profit which is lost (or loss incurred) by making the incorrect decision.

The reader will recall that the $EVPI$ is a measure of the value of a perfect predictor or perfect information. It is the expectation of the conditional value of perfect information.

We have decided that our best act, based on present information and using the mean savings, is to buy the machine. If a perfect prediction device were to tell us the actual hour savings would be 2,852, or any number greater than 2,150, we would choose the same act as we would have chosen without this information, and the predictor would be of no value. However, if our predictor were to tell us the true hour savings would actually be 2,029, or any number less than 2,150, then we would not buy the machine, and we would avoid

FIGURE 7–12

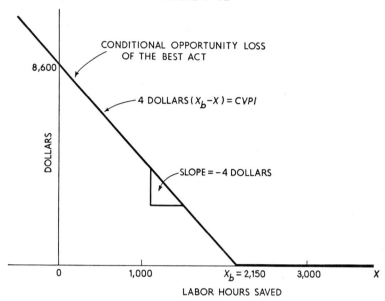

LABOR HOURS SAVED

a loss. Hence the predictor has value *only* if we change our decision when given the new information. The computation of conditional value of perfect information ($CVPI$) may be summarized as follows:

$$CVPI = \begin{cases} 0 \text{ if } X > 2{,}150 \\ \$4.00(X_b - X) \text{ if } X \le 2{,}150. \end{cases}$$

This functional relationship is graphed in Figure 7–12, which shows that perfect information is worth nothing if the forecast of hours

FIGURE 7–13

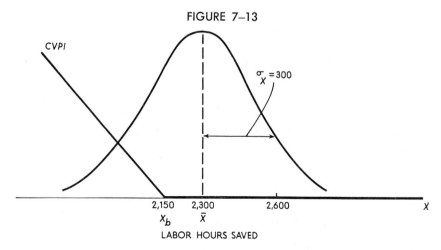

LABOR HOURS SAVED

saved is greater than X_b and increases linearly to the left of the break-even point (the hours saved are less than 2,150 and are decreasing).

The expected value of perfect information is calculated by weighting the conditional value of perfect information by the probability distribution. It is equal to the expected opportunity loss of the best act.

Figure 7–13 shows the prior normal probability distribution superimposed on the conditional value graph. The $EVPI$ is the sum of the product of the normal curve and the $CVPI$ line to the left of the break-even point. This results because $CVPI = 0$ for values of X greater than X_b (2,150 hours).

FIGURE 7–14

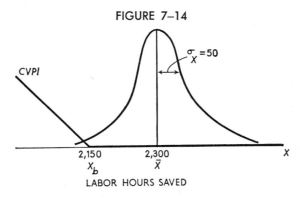

LABOR HOURS SAVED

It can also be seen that the larger the standard deviation, σ_X, the higher the $EVPI$. This is because the larger the σ_X, the more spread-out the normal curve, and the greater the probability weight given the larger losses (i.e., the higher values of the $CVPI$ line). If the engineer was very close to being certain that the value of the mean was 2,300, there would be little or no expected value of perfect information. Figure 7–14 shows a situation where the value of information is very low. A σ_X of 50 hours would result in a situation of this nature.

The reason for perfect information being almost valueless in this latter situation is because σ_X of the prior distribution is quite small compared to the mean and to the distance from the mean to the break-even point. Note that the closer X_b is to $\bar{X}$ (with a given σ_X), the higher will be the $EVPI$. This is shown graphically in Figure 7–15, where we first assume X_b is the break-even point and then assume X_c is the break-even point. If $\bar{X}$, the prior mean, is close to X_b, perfect information is more likely to change the decision as to which

FIGURE 7–15

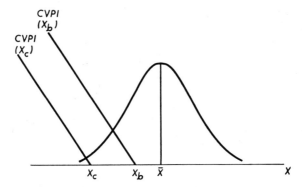

is the best act than if $\bar{X}$ is relatively far from X_b. Remember that for perfect information to have any value, it is necessary for the optimum act to change in the light of the new information.

Summarizing, assuming normal priors, the $EVPI$ depends on the following three factors:

1. The standard deviation, σ_X. This is a measure of how "uncertain" the estimator is about the prior mean.
2. The distance of the prior mean from the break-even point $(X_b - \bar{X})$. This is important because it helps determine how likely the decision maker is to change his decision because of new evidence.
3. The absolute value of the slope of the $CVPI$ line, C. The slope of the line is a measure of how rapidly the loss increases as the hours saved decrease below the break-even point.

It is at this point that we employ one of the more useful features of the normal distribution. The computation of the $EVPI$ can be reduced to a straightforward formula calculation where the components of the formula are those listed above. This formula is:

$$(7\text{–}3) \qquad EVPI = C \cdot \sigma_X \cdot N(D).$$

C is the absolute value of the slope of the $CVPI$ line or the loss constant; σ_X is the standard deviation of the normal prior distribution; D of $N(D)$ is defined as follows:

$$D = \frac{|X_b - \bar{X}|}{\sigma_X}.$$

Thus, D is a measure of the distance of the mean from the break-even point, measured in number of standard deviations. The vertical bars in the formula for D should be read as "absolute value." The quantity $N(D)$ may be obtained from Table D (in the Appendix at the end of the text). It may be interpreted as a loss function for the standard normal curve, valued for the quantity D.

It should be noted that the higher the value of D, the lower the value of $N(D)$, and all other things being equal, the lower the $EVPI$. The lower $N(D)$ results from the fact that the larger the distance $(X_b - \bar{X})$, the less likely it is that perfect information will change the optimum decision.

In the example of this chapter, $EVPI$ is calculated as follows:

$$C = \$4.00$$
$$\sigma_X = 300$$
$$D = \frac{|2,150 - 2,300|}{300} = \frac{|-150|}{300} = \frac{1}{2} = 0.50$$
$$N(D) = N(0.50) = 0.1978$$
$$EVPI = C \cdot \sigma_X \cdot N(D)$$
$$EVPI = \$4.00 \cdot 300 \cdot 0.1978 = \$237.36.$$

The reader may recall from Chapter 3 the difficulty of computing $EVPI$ for the discrete case. The use of the normal distribution simplifies computations substantially in most business applications. In the above example, we have computed the expected value of perfect information, \$237 (which is also the opportunity loss of the best act), and the expected profit of the best act, \$600. The sum of these two measures, \$837, may be defined as the expected gross profit of the act. The expected gross profit may also be computed using the following relationship:[3]

$$\text{Expected Gross Profit} = C \cdot \sigma_X \cdot N(-D)$$
$$= \$4.00 \times 300 \times 0.6978 = \$837.$$

If we had a perfect predictor available, we would be willing to pay up to \$237 to use it. It is not likely that we have a *perfect* predictor; but in some instances, we shall be able to obtain helpful though imperfect information. The problems of determining optimum sample size and revising the prior normal distribution in the light of this additional information are introduced in the following chapters. For a more advanced discussion the reader is referred to Schlaifer (1959).

BIBLIOGRAPHY

NATIONAL BUREAU OF STANDARDS. *Tables of the Normal Probability Functions.* Applied Mathematics Series 23. New York, 1953.

---

[3] $N(-D) = D + N(D)$
$N(-0.5) = 0.5 + 0.1978 = 0.6978.$

SCHLAIFER, R. *Probability and Statistics for Business Decisions*. New York: McGraw-Hill Book Co., Inc., 1959.

Also see the Bibliography of Chapter 2.

PROBLEMS

7-1. For the probability distribution of sales given below, write out the following cumulative mass functions:

Sales (S)	Probability
1 unit	0.10
2 units	0.15
3 units	0.20
4 units	0.30
5 units	0.20
10 units	0.03
15 units	0.02
	1.00

Required mass functions:

$$P(S \geq s)$$
$$P(S > s)$$
$$P(S < s)$$
$$P(S \leq s)$$

7-2. Find the following probabilities for a normally distributed random variable, X:

a) (*Mean of zero, standard deviation of one*):

$$P(X > 0.8)$$
$$P(X \leq 0.8)$$
$$P(X \geq -0.8)$$
$$P(-0.8 \leq X \leq 1.2)$$

b) (*Mean of six, standard deviation of two*):

$$P(X > 8)$$
$$P(X \leq 8)$$
$$P(X \geq -8)$$
$$P(-8 \leq X \leq 12)$$

c) (*Mean of six, standard deviation of one*):

$$P(X > 8)$$
$$P(X \leq 8)$$
$$P(X \geq 4)$$
$$P(4 \leq X \leq 12)$$

7-3. Find the value of the following normally distributed random variables, given each set of conditions:

 a) X is normal; mean, zero; standard deviation, one.

$$P(X > x) = 0.02068.$$

 What is x?

 b) X is normal; mean, eight; standard deviation, three.

$$P(U > u) = 0.1587.$$

 What is x? (U is the standardized value of X.)

 c) X is normal; mean, eight; standard deviation, three.

$$P(U \leq u) = 0.7224.$$

 What is x?

 d) X is normal; mean, ten; standard deviation, two.

$$P(U \geq u) = 0.2327.$$

 What is x?

7–4. A manufacturer is considering a modification in his product which will require a capital investment of $100,000. The product contributes an incremental profit of $5.00 per unit on a present value basis. The increased sales will result from the product modification making the product attractive to five thousand new retail stores. Without the modification, these retail stores would not handle the product. The sales manager feels that the mean sales per new store will be about six units. However, he thinks there is a 50–50 chance that the mean sales could be less than five or more than seven units. Excess inventory can be sold to cover incremental costs.

 a) Fit a normal distribution to the above situation.

 b) Calculate the expected profit of the best act. Should the investment be made?

 c) Calculate the *EVPI*.

7–5. In the situation of Problem 7–4, suppose the sales manager feels that the mean sales per store will be six units but that there is a 50–50 chance that the actual mean sales could be less than four or greater than eight units. Calculate the *EVPI*, and explain why it is greater than in Problem 7–4.

7–6. In each of the following situations a normal distribution is considered to be a good prior probability distribution. However, in each case, different characteristics of the distribution are assumed.

 a) Calculate the *EVPI*.

 b) Explain the difference in *EVPI* between each situation and situation 1.

  1) Mean—10 units:

   Break-even mean—seven units

   Standard deviation—two units

   C, the loss constant—$5,000 per unit

2) Mean—10 units:
   Break-even mean—seven units
   Standard deviation—five units
   C, the loss constant—$5,000 per unit
3) Mean—10 units:
   Break-even mean—nine units
   Standard deviation—two units
   C, the loss constant—$5,000 per unit
4) Mean—10 units:
   Break-even mean—seven units
   Standard deviation—two units
   C, the loss constant—$10,000 per unit

7-7. A manufacturer is considering a capital investment necessary to enter a new market territory. The required investment is $100,000, and he feels that the mean present value of the cash flows is $150,000. However, he thinks there is a 50–50 chance that the mean present value could be less than $80,000 or more than $220,000. The $150,-000, $80,000, and $220,000 figures are before subtracting the $100,-000 investment.

a) Should the investment be made?

b) Calculate the *EVPI*, using a normal prior distribution.

7-8. A mail-order firm is considering inserting color advertising in its catalogue, which is mailed to 100,000 customers. Current purchases of those receiving black-and-white catalogues are $6.00 per customer. With the color catalogue, management thinks that "most probably" sales would be increased to $7.00 per customer, but the probability distribution of sales has a standard deviation equal to one.

The company makes an average profit of 20 per cent on sales. It costs 25 cents more to print a color catalogue than a black-and-white one.

a) Should the company use the color catalogue?

b) What is the *EVPI?*

7-9. The ABC Company is considering the sale of a new product. There are $1,750 of fixed costs associated with undertaking the project. The product will sell for $4.00 a unit, and the variable costs are $1.50. It is expected that one thousand units will be sold, but the demand has a normal probability distribution, with a σ of 150.

a) How many units have to be sold to break even?

b) What is the expected profit if the product is handled?

c) What is the expected opportunity loss if the product is handled?

d) What is the expected gross profit?

7-10. The ABC Company is currently selling a product for $3.00 per unit. The incremental fixed costs associated with the product are $50,000 per unit time. The variable costs are $2.00 per unit. There is excess capacity, and up to 250,000 units can be produced with no additional fixed costs or changes in marginal costs.

The following schedule has been prepared for the purposes of analyzing a possible price change:

	Current Price	Information for:	
		Price after Decrease	Price after Increase
Price.................	$3.00	$2.50	$4.00
Expected sales.........100,000 units		250,000 units	60,000 units
Standard deviation of sales distribution... 10,000 units		75,000 units	35,000 units

Required:
a) Compute the expected profit for each price.
b) Compute the break-even number of units for each price.
c) Compute the expected opportunity loss for each price.
d) Compute the expected gross profit for each price.

Chapter 8

REVISION OF NORMAL PROBABILITIES

In Chapters 2 and 5, we discussed the idea of revising subjective probabilities in the light of new or experimental evidence. Chapter 2 introduced the Bayes theorem for probabilities, and in Chapter 5 the general framework for including experimental or sample evidence was considered. It is the purpose of this chapter and the next to extend this analysis and apply it in a specific decision situation.

We shall use a problem to illustrate the concepts that are involved. Suppose a manufacturer is considering introducing a new product. He will market this product through a chain of 5,000 stores. The manufacturer is uncertain about the level of sales for the product and has not been able to decide whether or not to market the product.

The first source of information that the manufacturer can tap in making this decision is his judgement and experience (including analysis of similar product introductions in the past). This experience may be represented by a subjective probability distribution for the total sales of the new product. Suppose the manufacturer believes that a normal distribution with a mean of two million units and a standard deviation of 150,000 units adequately describes his uncertainty about *total* sales of the product. We can convert this to a distribution concerned with average or *mean sales per store* by dividing by 5,000 (the number of stores). Thus the expected mean sales per store is 400.

With no other evidence the manufacturer would make his decision using the above subjective probabilities. However, he may be able to experiment and obtain additional information. Experimentation could take the form, in this example, of a market research study in which a sample is taken from the 5,000 stores. The new product could be introduced into these selected stores and sales of the product measured. The results could then be used as estimates for all 5,000 stores.

The sample evidence itself is subject to some uncertainty. There may be a bias in the evidence.[1] In addition, there is random or sampling error, due to the fact that we have experimented with a sample and not with the entire group of stores. Hence, we should not use sample evidence as the only basis for making this decision.

Using the Bayes theorem, we can combine the subjective probabilities of the manufacturer with the sample evidence to give a revised or posterior subjective distribution. This posterior distribution is then the basis for decision making.

In this chapter, we are concerned with the revision of the mean and the standard deviation of a normal prior distribution in the light of sample evidence. In the next chapter, we shall discuss whether or not it is desirable to obtain the sample evidence, assuming the sampling process has a cost.

To understand the revision of the prior normal probability distribution, it is necessary clearly to visualize the several distributions which are encountered.

THE PROBABILITY DISTRIBUTIONS

We shall use five probability distributions in the analysis:

1. *The population distribution, where σ_p = the standard deviation and u = the mean.* This distribution reflects the characteristics of the individual components of the population from which the sample is to be drawn.

For example, we might be interested in the probability distribution of sales per store for the population of all 5,000 stores. We could array the number of stores making sales of different amounts and divide these numbers by the total number of stores, so that the sum of the proportions is equal to one. A possible empirical distribution of the sales of stores in the population is presented in Figure 8–1.

There would be a small proportion of stores with large sales, but most stores are expected to sell less than $60. This distribution, as is typical of many distributions of economic data, is skewed to the right (i.e., has a long right tail), and a normal distribution would be a poor

---

[1] We shall concern ourselves in this book only with sampling error. For a discussion of how some forms of bias may be treated, see Schlaifer (1959), chap. xxxi.

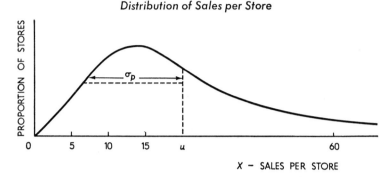

FIGURE 8-1

Population Distribution
Distribution of Sales per Store

X − SALES PER STORE

approximation to the curve in Figure 8–1. The manufacturer is assumed to have a reasonably good estimate of σ_p, the standard deviation of the empirical distribution of store sales. It may be that studies of this type have been made in the past; and although the true mean in any particular study is unknown, the deviations of the sales per store from this true mean (whatever it is) are known.

Frequently, σ_p and u are unknown, and the mean and the standard deviation of the sample are used as estimates of σ_p and u.

2. *The Distribution in the Sample.* Each store in the sample would have given sales. A frequency distribution, somewhat similar to that above, could be made for the elements in the sample, that is, a distribution of sales by store. Certain relationships exist between this distribution and the population distribution. In particular, let X_i be the sales of the ith store in the sample of n stores. Then the sample mean is

$$\bar{X} = \frac{\sum_{i=1}^{n} X_i}{n}$$

and is an unbiased estimate of the population mean u.[2]

The sample variance is:

$$\sigma_s^2 = \frac{\sum_{i=1}^{n} (X_i - \bar{X})^2}{n - 1}$$

---

[2] A sample statistic is unbiased if the expected value of that statistic is equal to the appropriate population parameter. In particular, $E(\bar{X}) = u$ and $E(\sigma_s^2) = \sigma_p^2$. In simple terms, the sample mean is unbiased since, on the average, it will equal the population mean.

and is an unbiased estimate of the population variance σ_p^2. The sample standard deviation is σ_s and is an estimate of σ_p.

3. *The Distribution of Sample Means.* There are many possible samples that could be selected from a given population, and each sample will have a mean $\bar{X}$. Considering all possible samples, $\bar{X}$ itself is a random variable and has a probability distribution with mean $E(\bar{X})$ and standard deviation $\sigma_{\bar{X}}$. $E(\bar{X})$ and $\sigma_{\bar{X}}$ are unknown; however, the population distribution and the distribution of sample means are connected by the following relationships:

$$E(\bar{X}) = u$$

(8-1)
$$\sigma_{\bar{X}} = \frac{\sigma_p}{\sqrt{n}}.$$

It should be remembered that X represents the mean of a particular sample and $E(\bar{X})$ is actually an average of means of samples.

For large samples the distribution of sample means is approximately normal.[3] Normality of this distribution is important in subsequent analysis. We shall assume in this book that a large enough sample has been taken to assure normality.[4]

4. *The Prior Distribution of the Population Mean.* Before a sample is taken, there is a prior (or betting) distribution of the mean of the population. This is a subjective probability distribution of the decision maker. The mean of this prior distribution is $\bar{u}_0$. The standard deviation of this prior distribution is σ_0, where σ_0 is the standard deviation of the prior probability distribution of the estimate of the population mean (it is *not* an estimate of the population standard deviation σ_p).

The random variable in the prior distribution (and also in the posterior distribution) is u, the population mean. While the actual population distribution has a given mean (as in Figure 8–1), this mean is unknown to the decision maker and, to him, is a (subjective) random variable.

The subscript zero of the symbols $\bar{u}_0$ and σ_0 indicates a prior distribution. The subscript one will be used to indicate a posterior distribution.

---

[3] This is the result of the central limit theorem of statistics. See any text on statistical theory, such as Hoel (1963).

[4] The question of how large a sample is necessary to assure normality of the sampling distribution of $\bar{X}$ is not simple. If the population distribution is symmetric, very small samples are adequate. For extremely skewed distributions, very large samples are needed. For practical purposes, samples of 30 to 50 items are usually considered adequate. For more discussion of this, see Schlaifer (1959), chap. xvii.

5. *The Posterior Distribution of the Population Mean.* After the sample is taken, the betting distribution of the population mean is adjusted to obtain the posterior distribution with $\bar{u}_1$, the mean, and σ_1, the standard deviation.

If the prior distribution is normal, and if the distribution of the sample mean is normal, then the posterior distribution will also be normal.

REVISING THE BETTING DISTRIBUTION

Assume the prior distribution of a population mean is normal and has a mean of $\bar{u}_0$ and a standard deviation of σ_0. A sample is taken; the sample mean is $\bar{X}$, and the standard deviation of the sample is σ_s (σ_s is an estimate of σ_p, the standard deviation of the population).

To simplify the formulas which we shall use, we introduce the symbol I to represent the amount of information contained in a distribution, and define I as being equal to the reciprocal of the variance, i.e.:

$$I_0 = \frac{1}{\sigma_0{}^2}$$

(8–2)
$$I_{\bar{X}} = \frac{1}{\sigma_{\bar{X}}{}^2} = \frac{n}{\sigma_p{}^2}$$

$$I_1 = \frac{1}{\sigma_1{}^2}.$$

The mean of the revised distribution $\bar{u}_1$ is the weighted average of the prior mean and the sample mean, where the weights are the amounts of information of the distributions:

(8–3)
$$\bar{u}_1 = \frac{I_0 \bar{u}_0 + I_{\bar{X}} \bar{X}}{I_0 + I_{\bar{X}}}.$$

Equations 8–3 and 8–5 (below) are the equivalent of the Bayes theorem for normal prior and sampling distributions. They determine the mean and the standard deviation of the posterior normal distribution.

Example

Our manufacturer, who is considering the introduction of a new product, has a normal prior distribution of sales per store for the product with mean $\bar{u}_0 = 400$ units and a standard deviation of $\sigma_0 = 30$ units. There are 5,000 stores, and a sample of 100 stores is drawn at random. The product is introduced in the 100 stores, and sales records are kept. The average sales per store for the 100 stores is 420 units, i.e. $\bar{X}$ (the sample mean) = 420. The sample standard deviation is 40 units, i.e. $\sigma_s = 40$.

Using σ_s as an estimate of the standard deviation of the population σ_p, we can estimate $\sigma_{\bar{x}}$, employing equation 8–1:

$$\sigma_{\bar{x}} = \frac{\sigma_p}{\sqrt{n}} = \frac{\sigma_s}{\sqrt{n}} = \frac{40}{\sqrt{100}} = \frac{40}{10} = 4.$$

The values of information are:

$$I_0 = \frac{1}{\sigma_0{}^2} = \frac{1}{900}$$

$$I_{\bar{x}} = \frac{1}{\sigma_{\bar{x}}{}^2} = \frac{1}{16}.$$

The revised mean, using equation 8–3, is:

$$\begin{aligned}
\bar{u}_1 &= \frac{\dfrac{1}{900} \times 400 + \dfrac{1}{16} \times 420}{\dfrac{1}{900} + \dfrac{1}{16}} \\[2em]
&= \frac{\dfrac{400}{900} + \dfrac{420}{16}}{\dfrac{1}{900} + \dfrac{1}{16}} = \frac{400 \times 16 + 420 \times 900}{16 + 900} \\[2em]
&= \frac{384{,}400}{916} = 419.7.
\end{aligned}$$

The mean of the prior distribution was 400, but since the standard deviation ($\sigma_0 = 30$) was relatively large compared to $\sigma_{\bar{x}}$, the amount of information in the prior distribution ($I_0 = \frac{1}{900}$) was small. The mean of the sample was 420; and since the standard deviation of the sample mean was relatively small ($\sigma_{\bar{x}} = 4$), the amount of information in the sample ($I_{\bar{x}} = \frac{1}{16}$) was relatively large. Thus the sample information overwhelmed the prior information; and the revised mean, 419.7, was very close to the sample mean of 420.

If the prior betting distribution has a relatively large standard deviation, the prior mean will be lightly weighted and will not significantly affect the posterior (or revised) mean.

Note that $I_{\bar{x}} = \dfrac{n}{\sigma_p{}^2}$; therefore the amount of information in the sample is directly related to sample size. Since very large samples tend to be quite accurate, the prior distribution will tend to have little effect upon the posterior distribution and hence upon the decision.

On the other hand, for smaller samples the prior distribution can have important effects, particularly if the population standard deviation (σ_p) is large.

REVISION OF THE STANDARD DEVIATION

The information in the revised distribution is equal to the sum of the information in the prior distribution plus the information in the sample:

(8-4) $$I_1 = I_0 + I_{\bar{x}}.$$

Example

In the example of the previous section the values of I_0 and $I_{\bar{x}}$ were:

$$I_0 = \frac{1}{900}$$

$$I_{\bar{x}} = \frac{1}{16}.$$

The value of I_1 is:

$$I_1 = \frac{1}{900} + \frac{1}{16} = \frac{916}{14,400}.$$

The standard deviation of the revised distribution may be computed using the definition of I_1:

$$I_1 = \frac{1}{\sigma_1^2}$$

$$\frac{1}{\sigma_1^2} = \frac{916}{14,400}$$

$$\sigma_1^2 = \frac{14,400}{916} = 15.7$$

$$\sigma_1 = \sqrt{15.7} = 3.96.$$

The revised standard deviation, 3.96, is very close to the estimate of the standard deviation of the same means, 4.0, since the prior distribution had little information (the standard deviation σ_0 was large compared to $\sigma_{\bar{x}}$).

Instead of using the above formula, which makes use of I_1, we can develop a variation of the formula which uses only the relevant standard deviations:

$$\frac{1}{\sigma_1{}^2} = \frac{1}{\sigma_0{}^2} + \frac{1}{\sigma_{\bar{x}}{}^2}$$

$$\frac{1}{\sigma_1{}^2} = \frac{\sigma_{\bar{x}} + \sigma_0{}^2}{\sigma_0{}^2 \quad \sigma_{\bar{x}}{}^2}$$

$$\sigma_1{}^2 = \frac{\sigma_0{}^2 \times \sigma_{\bar{x}}{}^2}{\sigma_{\bar{x}}{}^2 + \sigma_0{}^2}.$$

The standard deviation is equal to:

(8–5)
$$\sigma_1 = \sqrt{\frac{\sigma_{\bar{x}}{}^2 \times \sigma_0{}^2}{\sigma_0{}^2 + \sigma_{\bar{x}}{}^2}}$$

Using this equation to solve the example:

$$\sigma_1 = \sqrt{\frac{16 \times 900}{16 + 900}} = \sqrt{\frac{14{,}400}{916}} = \sqrt{15.7} = 3.96$$

which agrees with the previous solution.

If σ_p, the standard deviation of the population, is known, then instead of estimating $\sigma_{\bar{x}}$ with $\frac{\sigma_s}{\sqrt{n}}$, we can compute $\sigma_{\bar{x}}$ using the relationship $\sigma_{\bar{x}} = \frac{\sigma_p}{\sqrt{n}}$.

THE POSTERIOR NORMAL DISTRIBUTION AND DECISION MAKING

The posterior distribution results from a combination of the prior subjective probabilities and sample evidence. The posterior distribution is itself a betting or decision-making distribution. Since it is normal, the techniques introduced in Chapter 7 are applicable. Let us briefly illustrate some of these points.

Suppose our manufacturer who is considering the introduction of a new product has the following economic information. The cost of machinery and promotion for the new product is $520,000. The variable profit (or contribution) per unit sold is 25 cents. And the number of stores is five thousand.

The posterior random variable is u_1 — the mean sales per store. The profit equation, in terms of u_1, is:

$$\text{Profit} = \pi = -520{,}000 + (0.25)(5{,}000)u_1$$
$$= -520{,}000 + 1250u_1.$$

The break-even value is:

$$u_b = \frac{520{,}000}{1.250} = 416.$$

Since the posterior mean $\bar{u}_1 = 419.7$ is greater than u_b, the manufacturer should market the product. His expected profit is:

$$E(\pi) = -520,000 + 1250\bar{u}_1 = \$4,625.$$

We might also determine the $EVPI$ for the posterior distribution:

$$EVPI = C \cdot \sigma \cdot N(D)$$

where $\sigma = \sigma_1$; in this case:

$$C = 1,250$$
$$D = D_1 = \frac{\bar{u}_1 - u_b}{\sigma_1} = \frac{419.7 - 416}{3.96} = 0.935$$
$$N(D_1) = 0.09415$$
$$EVPI = (1,250)\ (3.96)\ (0.09415) = \$465.$$

BIBLIOGRAPHY

CHERNOFF, H., and MOSES, L. E. *Elementary Decision Theory*. New York: John Wiley & Sons, Inc., 1959.

HOEL, P. G. *Introduction to Mathematical Statistics*. 3d ed. New York: John Wiley & Sons, Inc., 1963.

RAIFFA, H., and SCHLAIFER, R. *Applied Statistical Decision Theory*. Boston: Graduate School of Business Administration, Harvard University, 1961.

SCHLAIFER, R. *Introduction to Statistics for Business Decisions*. New York: McGraw-Hill Book Co., Inc., 1962.

——————. *Probability and Statistics for Business Decisions*. New York: McGraw-Hill Book Co., Inc., 1959.

WEISS, L. *Statistical Decision Theory*. New York: McGraw-Hill Book Co., Inc., 1961.

QUESTIONS AND PROBLEMS

8–1. Given a normal prior distribution with $\bar{u}_0 = 10$ and $\sigma_0 = 2$. A sample of size $n = 36$ is taken, with $\bar{X} = 12$ and $\sigma_s = 6$. Compute the mean and the standard deviation of the posterior distribution.

8–2. Given a normal prior distribution with $\bar{u}_0 = 500$ and $\sigma_0 = 30$. A sample of size $n = 441$ is taken, with $\bar{X} = 450$ and $\sigma_s = 210$. Compute the mean and the standard deviation of the posterior distribution.

8–3. Given a normal prior distribution with $\bar{u}_0 = 20$ and $\sigma_0 = 4$. A sample of size $n = 25$ is taken, with $\bar{X} = 24$ and $\sigma_s = 15$. Calculate the mean and the standard deviation of the posterior distribution.

8–4. Which sample contains the most information:
  a) A sample of 100 from a population with a standard deviation of 50, or

b) A sample of 64 from a population with a standard deviation of 40? Explain.

8–5. Management has a normal prior distribution with a mean of 200 and a standard deviation of 10. The population from which a sample is to be taken has a standard deviation of 100. How large a sample must be taken so that the standard deviation of the posterior distribution is five?

8–6. An auditor believes that the average credit card balance outstanding is probably over \$10. More precisely, his feelings about the average balance can be represented by a normal distribution with a mean of 12 and a standard deviation of two. A sample of twenty-five accounts is drawn at random, and the average balance on these accounts is \$9.00. The standard deviation of the balances in the sample is \$5.00. What should be the auditor's posterior distribution? What probability would he assign to the possibility that the average balance is less than \$10?

8–7. Refer to Problem 7–8. Suppose that before making the decision as to which catalogue to use, one hundred color catalogues were printed and mailed to a sample of one hundred customers. Average sales for these customers were then \$7.40, with a standard deviation of \$5.00. Utilizing this information and the prior probabilities of Problem 7–8, what decision should be made? What is the posterior *EVPI?*

Chapter 9

DECISION MAKING WITH
NORMAL PROBABILITIES

IN THE preceding chapter, we discussed the use of normal prior probabilities and how the normal prior distribution is changed in the light of additional sample information. Companion analytical problems discussed in this chapter are how to decide when sampling is appropriate and also how large a sample should be taken. The analysis in this chapter differs from that of the previous chapter in that it is prior to (before) rather than posterior to (after) the sample.

THE INITIAL SITUATION

Assume the change in profit per unit resulting from decision d_1 is C (the profit function is linear) and the break-even amount is u_b. The mean of the prior betting distribution is $\bar{u}_0$.

Figure 9–1 indicates decision d_1 is desirable. The mean $\bar{u}_0$ is to the right of u_b, the break-even point; and the investment has a positive expected value equal to $C(\bar{u}_0 - u_b)$. However, there is a possibility that the true value of u is to the left of u_b.

The expectation of the loss for decision d_1 is:

(9-1) Expected Opportunity Loss $= C \cdot \sigma_0 \cdot N(D_0)$

where

$$D_0 = \frac{|\bar{u}_0 - u_b|}{\sigma_0}.$$

Equation 9–1 also measures the expected value of perfect information, since d_1 is the optimum decision. Before sampling, this value

FIGURE 9–1

The Prior Distribution of Population Means

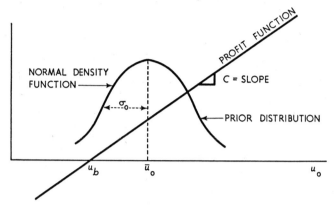

is based on the subjective feelings of the decision maker expressed in terms of a probability distribution for the population mean.

Example

Assume the break-even number of sales for a new product being considered is 800 units. Profits increase $15 for every unit the true mean is to the right of the break-even amount. The prior mean, $\bar{u}_0$, is equal to 1,000 units; the prior standard deviation, σ_0, is 100.

The optimum act based on the prior probabilities is to accept the new product. However, the expected opportunity loss of the act (the expected value of perfect information) is:

$$EVPI = C\sigma_0\, N(D_0)$$
$$D_0 = \frac{|\bar{u}_0 - u_b|}{\sigma_0} = \frac{1,000 - 800}{100} = 2$$
$$N(D_0) = N(2) = 0.0085$$
$$EVPI = 15 \times 100 \times 0.0085 = \$12.75.$$

THE EXPECTED POSTERIOR DISTRIBUTION

Before taking the sample, we can estimate the change which will take place in the betting distribution. That is, we can obtain some idea of the posterior distribution before actually taking the sample and revising our prior betting distribution. We do not know beforehand the sample mean $\bar{X}$ and hence do not know exactly what the mean of the posterior distribution will be. However, if we can obtain some measure of the sample precision, we can estimate the posterior variance and the information in the posterior distribution. Recall that the sampling error (the standard deviation of the distribution of $\bar{X}$'s) is

$$\sigma_{\bar{X}} = \frac{\sigma_p}{\sqrt{n}}.$$

Hence, we need a measure of the standard deviation of the population distribution (σ_p) to estimate the precision of a sample of a given size n. Such an estimate of σ_p could come from past studies, from an educated guess, or from a pilot sample of the population.

We shall use σ_*^2 to indicate the amount of revision in the variance from the prior to the posterior distribution. That is:

(9–2) $$\sigma_*^2 = \sigma_0^2 - \sigma_1^2$$

From equation 8–5, we have:

$$\sigma_1^2 = \frac{\sigma_{\bar{X}}^2 \cdot \sigma_0^2}{\sigma_0^2 + \sigma_{\bar{X}}^2}$$

and substituting in equation 9–2:

$$\sigma_*^2 = \sigma_0^2 - \frac{\sigma_{\bar{X}}^2 \cdot \sigma_0^2}{\sigma_0^2 + \sigma_{\bar{X}}^2} = \frac{\sigma_0^2 \cdot \sigma_0^2}{\sigma_0^2 + \sigma_{\bar{X}}^2}$$

and

(9–3) $$\sigma_* = \sqrt{\sigma_0^2 \cdot \frac{\sigma_0^2}{\sigma_0^2 + \sigma_{\bar{X}}^2}}.$$

THE EXPECTED VALUE OF SAMPLE INFORMATION

The economic value of a sample results from the fact that it reduces the posterior expected loss. That is, the sample, by supplying additional information, reduces the probability of a wrong decision. The expected value of sample information—$EVSI$—is computed in a manner similar to the $EVPI$, with σ_* used as the standard deviation. Thus:

(9–4) $$EVSI = C\sigma_* N(D_*)$$

where

$$D_* = \frac{|u_b - \bar{u}_0|}{\sigma_*}.$$

THE SAMPLING DECISION

For the example above, let us consider the possibility of taking a sample of size $n = 100$. Recall that $EVPI = \$12.75$. Even if the cost of the sample is less than this, we are not sure that the sample is worth while, since the sample gives only imperfect information.

Assume that $\sigma_p = 500$ (we know this from past experience). With a sample size of 100, the standard deviation of sample means is:

$$\sigma_{\bar{X}} = \frac{\sigma_p}{\sqrt{n}} = \frac{500}{10} = 50.$$

The value of σ_* is:

$$\sigma_* = \sqrt{\frac{\sigma_0^2 \times \sigma_0^2}{\sigma_0^2 + \sigma_{\bar{X}}^2}}$$

$$= \sqrt{\frac{100^2 \times 100^2}{100^2 + 50^2}} = \sqrt{\frac{100,000,000}{12,500}}$$

$$= \sqrt{8,000}$$

$$= \quad 89 \text{ (approximately)}$$

$$EVSI = C\sigma_* N(D_*)$$

$$D_* = \frac{|1,000 - 800|}{89} = 2.2$$

$$N(D_*) = 0.005$$

$$EVSI = 15 \times 89 \times 0.005 = \$6.68.$$

Sample information has a very low value; and in this situation, sampling of 100 units would not be undertaken if the cost of sampling 100 units were greater than $6.68.

Now, assume the break-even number of units is 955 (it was previously 800; it is now easier to make an incorrect decision). The expected value of perfect information is:

$$EVPI = C\sigma_0 N(D_0)$$

$$D_0 = \frac{|1,000 - 955|}{100} = \frac{45}{100} = 0.45$$

$$N(D_0) = N(0.45) = 0.2137$$

$$EVPI = 15 \times 100 \times 0.2137 = \$320.55.$$

The expected value of sample information is:

$$EVSI = C\sigma_* N(D_*)$$

$$D_* = \frac{|1,000 - 955|}{89} = 0.50$$

$$N(0.5) = 0.1978$$

$$EVSI = 15 \times 89 \times 0.1978 = \$264.$$

If the cost of sampling 100 units is less than $264, then sampling is desirable.

The expected value of sample information has been made much larger in this second example by reducing the difference between the expected number of units and the break-even number of units. The expected value of sample information would also have been larger if σ_0 had been larger (hence more uncertainty about the true u), thus increasing the likelihood of making the wrong decision.

Now, assume σ_0 is 300 (it was previously 100) and σ_p is still 500. The computations would become:

$$\sigma_{\bar{X}} = \frac{\sigma_p}{\sqrt{n}} = \frac{500}{10} = 50$$

$$\sigma_* = \sqrt{\frac{\sigma_0^2 \times \sigma_0^2}{\sigma_0^2 + \sigma_{\bar{X}}^2}} = \sqrt{\frac{300^2 \times 300^2}{300^2 + 50^2}} = \sqrt{\frac{90,000 \times 90,000}{92,500}}$$
$$= \sqrt{87,600} \quad = \quad 296.$$

Assuming the break-even number of units is still 955, the $EVSI$ is now:

$$EVSI = C\sigma_* N(D_*)$$
$$D_* = \frac{|1,000 - 955|}{296} = \frac{45}{296} = 0.15$$
$$N(D_*) = N(0.15) = 0.3284$$
$$EVSI = 15 \times 296 \times 0.3284 = \$1,460.$$

The $EVSI$ is now higher than in either of the previous two illustrations.

If σ_p were smaller than 500 units, two tendencies would be established. The sample would give more information, since the items would be picked from a less spread-out population. This would tend to increase the value of the information. However, the value of D would increase, thus making a loss less likely and tending to decrease the expected value of sample information.

In many situations, σ_p will not be known. An estimate of σ_p can be obtained by taking a small preliminary sample and using the relationship:

$$\sigma_s = \sigma_{p \text{ est.}} = \sqrt{\frac{\Sigma(X - \bar{X})^2}{n - 1}}.$$

We can then determine whether further sampling is desirable, using σ_s to compute $\sigma_{\bar{X}}$:

$$\sigma_{\bar{X}} = \frac{\sigma_s}{\sqrt{n}}.$$

OPTIMUM SAMPLE SIZE

The difference between the value of a sample of a given size ($EVSI$) and its cost is defined to be the expected net gain from sam-

FIGURE 9–2

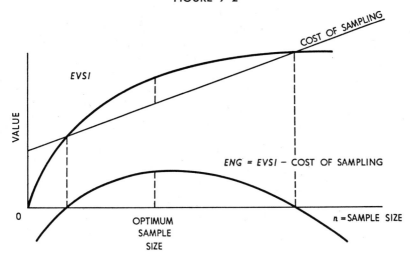

pling (ENG). As the size of the sample increases, its value ($EVSI$) increases, but at a decreasing rate. Obviously, the $EVSI$ can never be greater than the value of perfect information ($EVPI$). The cost of sampling is directly related to sample size. In general, the larger the sample, the larger its cost. These relationships are graphed in Figure 9–2.

The expected net gain (ENG) rises at first and then declines. The value of n which maximizes ENG is the optimum sample size. A sample larger than this would have less net value: a sample smaller than this optimum could profitably be increased in size.[1]

A Comprehensive Example

Assume a manufacturer of toys is considering the production of a new toy. The investment necessary to undertake production and distribution of the toy is $500,000 for one year. The incremental profit (selling price less variable cost) is $1.00 per toy. If the manufacturer is to break even, he must sell at least 500,000 units in the one year.

The product will be sold to 50,000 retail sport stores to which the company is selling its present products. The break-even sales per store, u_b, are 10 units per store ($500,000 \div 50,000$). After careful examination of his intuition the manufacturer feels that the mean sales per store will be 12 units (i.e., $\bar{u}_0 = 12$), and he assigns a 50–50

---

[1] Under certain circumstances, the determination of the optimum sample size can be reduced to a mathematical formula. See, for example, Schlaifer (1959), chap. xxxvi. In this chapter, we shall determine approximate optima by trial and error.

FIGURE 9-3

The Prior Subjective Distribution of Mean Sales per Store

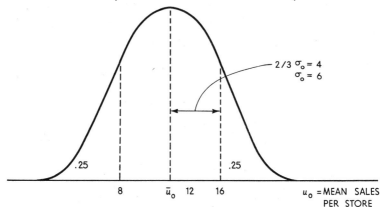

probability that mean sales will be less than eight or greater than 16. If he is willing to accept a normal distribution as an indication of his prior subjective probabilities, the distribution may be roughly fitted as shown in Figure 9–3.

The mean of the distribution $\bar{u}_0$ is equal to 12 units, and the standard deviation, σ_0, is six units. This is a distribution showing the likelihoods of the different possible values of mean sales.

Under the above conditions, the best act is to introduce the new toy. This is because the required break-even sales per store, $u_b = 10$, is less than the estimated mean of 12. The cost of uncertainty, or the *EVPI*, is $76,650.

$$EVPI = C\sigma_0 N(D)$$
$$= \$50,000 \times 6 \times 0.2555$$
$$= \$76,650.$$

$$D = \frac{|\bar{u}_0 - u_b|}{\sigma_0} = \frac{|12 - 10|}{6} = 0.333$$
$$C = \text{One Toy} \times 50,000 \text{ Stores}$$
$$\times \$1.00 \text{ per Toy}$$
$$= \$50,000.$$

We must determine whether sampling is worth while and, if it is, how large a sample should be taken.

Let us first consider whether our action will be changed after we have obtained the sample information. If we take a sample and observe its mean, we shall then revise the mean of our prior subjective distribution. If the revised mean is greater than 10 (the break-even mean), we shall still choose to market the toy, and the sample information would turn out to have had zero value. On the other hand,

FIGURE 9–4

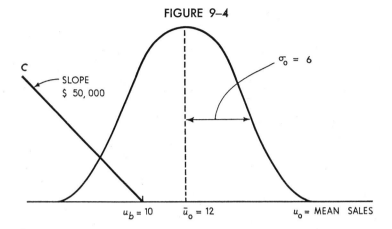

if the sample mean is sufficiently below 10 so that the revised mean is also lower than 10, we would choose not to market the toy, and the sample would have value. Hence the value of the sample depends to a great extent on the value of the revised mean.

The above discussion is illustrated in Figure 9–5. If the revised mean, $\bar{u}_1$, falls to the right of $u_b = 10$, we shall choose the same act as we would have chosen without the sample. On the other hand, if it falls at t, we would have avoided a loss of C^* by sampling. Before taking the sample, we do not know what $\bar{u}_1$ will be, so we shall treat it as a random variable. The best estimate of the revised mean is the mean of the prior distribution, since $\bar{u}_0$ is the most likely value of $\bar{u}_1$.

Assume that $\sigma_p = 10$, i.e., the standard deviation of the distribution of purchases of the many individual stores is 10. The standard deviation of the population, σ_p, is an important ingredient in the sample decision. If σ_p is large, it means the purchases of individual stores are widely dispersed from the mean sales of all stores. In such a case a sample would not give as much information as if σ_p is small.

FIGURE 9–5

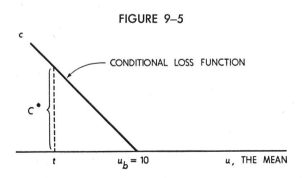

To take an extreme case, if $\sigma_p = 0$, then a sample of one store will tell the manufacturer the amount of sales to each store in the population, for if $\sigma_p = 0$, then all stores in the population will purchase the same amount. On the other hand, if σ_p is very large, a small sample will give very little information, since we may be obtaining observations from the extremes of the population distribution.

We must now compute the square root of the change in the variance of the prior probability distribution. The manufacturer has estimated σ_p, the standard deviation of this population, to be 10. Assume a sample size of 25. The standard deviation of sample means $\sigma_{\bar{x}}$ is:

$$\sigma_{\bar{x}} = \frac{\sigma_p}{\sqrt{n}} = \frac{10}{5} = 2$$

and

$$\sigma_{\bar{x}}^2 = 4.$$

We need to compute σ_*:

$$\sigma_* = \sqrt{\frac{\sigma_0^2}{\sigma_0^2 + \sigma_{\bar{x}}^2} \cdot \sigma_0^2} = \sqrt{\sigma_0^2 \cdot \frac{\sigma_0^2}{\sigma_0^2 + \sigma_{\bar{x}}^2}}$$

where σ_0^2 is the prior variance; in our example, its value is 36, and $\sigma_{\bar{x}}^2$ is the variance of the sample means. The calculations are as follows:

$$\sigma_* = \sqrt{36 \cdot \frac{36}{36 + 4}} = \sqrt{36 \cdot \frac{36}{40}} = \sqrt{32.4} = 5.69.$$

The estimate of σ_* is 5.69. Remember, this estimate is made before the sample is taken. With a sample size of 25 the expected value of the sample information is:

$$D_* = \frac{|12 - 10|}{5.69} = 0.351$$
$$EVSI = C \cdot \sigma_* \cdot N(D_*)$$
$$= \$50,000 \times 5.69 \times 0.248$$
$$= \$70,556.$$

As can be seen from the above calculation, the $EVSI$ with $n = 25$ is quite large. If the cost of sampling each store is $100, the cost of the sample is $2,500. The expected net gain (ENG) from sampling 25 units is the $EVSI$ less the cost of sampling. Hence:

$$ENG_{25} = EVSI - \text{Cost of Sampling}$$
$$= 70,556 - 2,500 = \$68,056.$$

Since the ENG is positive, it is desirable to take a sample of 25. However, we may be able to increase the ENG by adjusting the sample size. We can approximate the optimal n by iterative procedures (trial and error), making calculations on either side of $n = 25$ and converging on the best n until we maximize the ENG. As we increase n, we shall increase the $EVSI$, but the sample cost will also increase. Hence, we must find the proper balance between the value of the additional information and the increased cost caused by increasing the sample size, n.

TABLE 9–1
Calculation of Optimal Sample Size

Sample Size n	$\sigma_{\bar{X}}^2$ Variance of Sample Means $\dfrac{\sigma_p^2 = 100}{n}$	$\dfrac{}{n}$	σ_*	D^* $\dfrac{\lvert 12 - 10 \rvert}{\sigma_*}$	$N(D_*)$	$EVSI$ $50{,}000\,\sigma_* N(D_*)$	Sample Cost	ENG $(EVSI -$ Sample Cost$)$
20........	5.00	5.62	0.356	0.246	$69,126	$2,000	$67,126
25........	4.00	5.69	0.351	0.248	70,556	2,500	68,056
35........	2.85	5.75	0.346	0.250	72,125	3,500	68,625
40........	2.50	5.77	0.345	0.251	72,739	4,000	68,739
45........	2.22	5.80	0.344	0.251	73,099	4,500	68,599

Table 9–1 shows the calculation of ENG from sampling for several sample sizes between 20 and 45. The ENG rises until the sample size reaches approximately 40 and then begins to decline. The optimal size is therefore between 35 and 45. Actually, the change in the ENG is quite small even when the sample size is doubled. In this example the ENG is not sensitive to changes in sample size.

CONCLUSION

The last three chapters have considered decision making with normal probabilities and linear loss functions. While these assumptions of normality and linearity imply that we have considered a special case, the applications appear widespread. Other methods have been developed for different distributions and loss functions. However, except for Chapters 12 and 13, which deal with the binomial distribution, these methods are beyond the scope of this book. The normal distribution–linear loss function case illustrates the concepts involved in Bayesian decision making under uncertainty.

Bibliography

See the Bibliography at the end of Chapter 8.

Questions and Problems

9-1. Suppose that the total cost of taking a sample of any size was a fixed amount, K. What would be the optimum sample size?

9-2. Assume a normal prior distribution with $\bar{u}_0 = 20$ and $\sigma_0 = 10$. Also, $\sigma_p = 20$. The cost of sampling $= 10 + 2n$, $u_b = 15$, and $C = \$100$.

   a) Compute the $EVPI$ before the sample.

   b) Compute the $EVSI$ for $n = 10$, $n = 25$, and $n = 50$.

   c) What is the optimum sample size (of the three items above), and what is its ENG?

9-3. Refer to Problem 7-8. Suppose that the mail-order firm can print a few color catalogues and mail them to a sample of customers. The purchases of these customers could be measured and some information about the effect of the color catalogue obtained. From past experience the standard deviation of customer purchases is known to be about $5.00. Suppose that the cost of sampling is $500 plus $5.00 per item sampled. What is the optimum sample size? (To simplify the problem, consider only the following values of n: $n = 0$ [no sample], $n = 64$, $n = 100$, and $n = 225$.)

9-4. Refer to Problems 7-8, 8-7, and 9-3 above. Consider only a sample of size $n = 100$. Does the difference between the $EVPI$ prior to the sample (Problem 7-8) and the $EVPI$ posterior to the sample (Problem 8-7) equal the expected value of sample information ($EVSI$ in Problem 9-3 above)? Should it? Explain.

9-5. A major magazine publisher was considering publishing a hard-cover volume of pictorial selections from its magazine. The pictorial volume would be sold largely by mail solicitation of the persons on the magazine's large mailing list. This list included not only subscribers but persons considered potential subscribers. Management felt that the volume would sell a considerable number of copies because of the reputation of the magazine and because the pictorial essays had received wide acclaim when they appeared in the magazine. In fact, many persons wrote in suggesting that a volume of this type be considered.

Some of the cost of publishing the volume had already been incurred when the photographs and text were prepared for the magazine. However, it was estimated that additional costs of $10,000 would be incurred. In addition, it was estimated that the costs of designing and printing the advertising material and the costs of the repeated mailings would amount to about $250,000. (The mailing list contained two million names—some, of course, were duplicates. Two mailings were contemplated, with a cost per individual name of 5 cents per mailing. In addition, there was about $50,000 involved in the development of the advertising material.)

The variable manufacturing cost of the proposed book was estimated to be $2.00 per volume. The selling price was fixed at $3.00.

Because of the high initial costs, management was undecided about the publishing venture. The best guesses centered at about 250,000 sold. Management felt (two chances out of three) that the sales would be somewhere between 200,000 and 300,000.

Management was somewhat reluctant completely to abandon the project because of the possible prestige value of such a volume. Therefore the possibility of doing some market survey work prior to making the final decision was considered. It was a fairly simple task to select a sample of individuals from the mailing list and test the salability of the volume on these persons. The mailing costs and other variable costs for each of the individuals in the sample amounted to 25 cents per person. However, it was necessary to design and print some special advertising literature, and this would cost about $13,000, regardless of the number of persons sampled. A sample of 2,000 persons was considered an appropriate sample size. The company statistician estimated that the standard error for the sample of 2,000 persons would be 10,000 books (that is $\sigma_{\bar{x}} = 10,000$).

a) Based upon the prior information only, what is the expected profit from publishing the volume? Disregarding any possibility of fringe benefits, such as prestige value, should it be published? What is the expected value of perfect information ($EVPI$)?

b) What is the expected value of sample information ($EVSI$)? What is the net gain from sampling ($EVSI$ − cost of sample)? Should the sample be taken?

c) Suppose that spending the $13,000 on advertising literature would reduce the estimated development cost of $50,000 to $40,000 if the complete mailing is undertaken (i.e., $10,000 of the $13,000 is recoverable if the book is published). The break-even point is now 250,000 books. What is the $EVSI$ in this case? What is the net gain from sampling? Hint: Note that if the sample is taken, the posterior profit function and hence the posterior break-even point are changed.

Chapter 10

INVENTORY CONTROL AND

UNCERTAINTY—A MARGINAL APPROACH

CHAPTER 3 suggested a method of solving inventory problems making use of conditional and expected value tables. In many situations, that method of analysis requires an excessive amount of clerical effort. An alternative procedure is to make use of marginal analysis and find the "last" unit worthy of being ordered.

It should be noted that this chapter deals with inventory control problems where the problems of order size, in conjunction with frequency and timing of orders, are *not* present. We are concerned only with the problem of how much should be ordered if we are faced with a demand with known probabilities and *reordering is not possible.*

We shall divide the problem to be analyzed into three classifications:

1. Fixed demand under certainty—i.e., the exact number of units to be sold is known and is always one amount.
2. Changing demand under certainty—i.e., the exact number of units to be sold may change. However, the number is known in advance. The probabilities of selling different numbers of units is known, and we know which event has occurred before we make a decision. This is analogous to knowing that a coin will come up either a tail or a head, the rewards being different for a head and a tail, and knowing which has come up on the most recent toss of the coin before making our bet. We have perfect information about the outcome.
3. Demand with a probability distribution—i.e., with uncertainty as to the demand of the next period. This is analogous to knowing that a fair coin has a tail and a head, but not knowing which will come up on the next toss.

FIXED DEMAND UNDER CERTAINTY

With fixed demand under conditions of certainty, the number of units to be used in each period is known in advance, and the same number of units is used in each period. In terms of probabilities, the probability of the demand occurring is 1.0. Examples of reasonably fixed known demand would be the number of meals served during a weekday at the United States Naval Academy once the academic year has started. Another example is the demand for a text required for a course after it has been assigned by an instructor (assuming no used copies are available). Under a fixed demand the order size will be made equal to the number of units required. This classification of the situation will occur very infrequently in practice. The profit in any time period will be equal to the sales price minus the incremental costs times the fixed number of sales.

UNCERTAINTY AND PERFECT INFORMATION

In most situations, sales will not be fixed but will vary from period to period. Thus the sales of a product may vary in successive weeks from 1,000 to 400 to 2,000. If the amount of sales is not fixed, and if we know prior to placing our order the total amount of the sale for the next time period, then we may speak of inventory decision making under perfect information and uncertainty.

Let us assume that the demand for the product is known to have the distribution shown in Table 10–1 (the net profit earned on each unit sold is $3.00).

The profit may be zero, $3.00, $6.00, or $9.00, depending on the number of units demanded. Before we obtain the perfect prediction of the sales for the next period, we do not know what the profit will be.

The decision policy would be to order the number of units to be sold. The number sold will be known, but it could vary from zero to three units. Thus, sales are known with certainty before the purchase decision, but the resulting profits will vary from period to pe-

TABLE 10–1

Sales	Probability	Conditional Profit Assuming Sales Are Known ($3.00 · Demand)
0	0.10	$0.00
1	0.30	3.00
2	0.40	6.00
3	0.20	9.00
	1.00	

riod. The uncertainty is with respect to the number of units to be sold before we receive this information, since the number demanded in each period will not always be the same. Imagine two dice being thrown where the rewards will be equal to the sum of the numbers appearing on the dice (2, 3, . . . , 12). Assume that the price of playing the game is $4.00 and you do not have to play or pay until after the dice are rolled and you have been informed of the result. You can only play once. There is certainty, in a sense, for you know the results before you have to take action; but before the dice are rolled, there is no assurance of the amount you will win, and you can be sure the amount appearing will change with a known probability distribution. This is what is meant by our description of "uncertainty with perfect information."

TABLE 10–2

1 Sales	2 Probability	3 Conditional Profit for Each Demand	4 Expected Profit (Col. 2 · Col. 3)
0.................	0.10	$0.00	$0.00
1.................	0.30	3.00	0.90
2.................	0.40	6.00	2.40
3.................	0.20	9.00	1.80
	1.00		$5.10

With perfect information, the amount to be ordered is calculated directly, since it is equal to the amount to be sold (which we learn with certainty). The amount of profit will be equal to $3.00 times the number of units sold. There is one complication which did not exist when we talked of a fixed demand. The amount of profit which we expect to make is not known with certainty before the perfect information is received. For example, the expected value of the profit may be found by multiplying the conditional profit for each demand by the probability of the event taking place (see Table 10–2).

The expected profit, assuming that the demand is known before ordering, is $5.10 for any period. But the profit for that period may be zero, $3.00, $6.00, or $9.00. Thus, if we know that zero units will be demanded, we shall order no units and sell none, making zero profits. If we know that three units will be demanded (as they will be 0.20 of the time), we shall order and sell three units, making $9.00 profit. But the weighted average of these and the other events is such that we expect, on the average, a profit of $5.10.

UNCERTAINTY—NO INFORMATION

The third case being discussed is where there is a probability distribution of demand and we do not have perfect information. For example, we know that two dice may appear with some number between two and 12, and we know the probabilities of each number occurring, but we have to make our bet before the dice are rolled. In like manner, we know the probability distribution of demand for our product, but we do not know before the period begins how much will be demanded in this period. In this situation, how many units should be ordered?

TABLE 10–3
Computation of Expected Profit*

Event: Demand	Probability of Demand	Order One Unit		Order Two Units		Order Three Units	
		Conditional	Expected	Conditional	Expected	Conditional	Expected
0........	0.10	$(2.00)	$(0.20)	$(4.00)	$(0.40)	$(6.00)	$(0.60)
1........	0.30	3.00	0.90	1.00	0.30	(1.00)	(0.30)
2........	0.40	3.00	1.20	6.00	2.40	4.00	1.60
3........	0.20	3.00	0.60	6.00	1.20	9.00	1.80
	1.00						
Expected Profit..............			$ 2.50		$ 3.50		$ 2.50

* Negative amounts are in parentheses.

One possibility would be to compute the different expected profits which would occur with different ordering plans. This is the procedure followed in Chapter 3. Table 10–3 presents this computation. Remember that if no units are purchased, no units may be sold; if one unit is purchased, no more than one unit may be sold, even if the amount demanded is greater. Assume that units cost $2.50 each and that leftovers may be sold for salvage for 50 cents. The sales price is $5.50 per unit.

The optimum act is to order two units, since the expected profit will be $3.50, which is higher than the expected profits resulting from any other strategy. Note that the expected profit of $3.50 following the optimum strategy is less than the $5.10 expected profit which we computed assuming *known demand* (perfect information). This decrease in expected profit occurs since at the time of ordering we no longer know with certainty how many units will be demanded.

We only know the probability that different demands will occur. The value of perfect information is $5.10 minus $3.50, or $1.60.

A MARGINAL APPROACH

In the above analysis, we computed the different total profits which would be expected following different ordering policies. An alternative solution uses a marginal approach. We compute the effect on profit of adding one more unit to the order size.

Let the probability of selling an additional unit (or more) of product be designated p, and the amount of conditional incremental profit to be earned by each unit be designated MP ($3.00 in the example). The probability of not selling the additional unit or more is $(1 - p)$. The $(1 - p)$ results since the probabilities of selling and not selling the unit sum to one, and the probability of selling the unit is p.

If the incremental unit is not sold, the net conditional loss will be the decrease in value of the inventory, which we shall call ML ($2.00 in the example). We can compute $p \cdot (MP)$, or the expected increase in profits, and $(1 - p) \cdot (ML)$, or the expected increase in costs (the marginal loss). The decision maker will continue to order additional units of the product provided the expected increase in profit is greater than the expected increase in cost of leftovers. This rule enables him to maximize net profits.[1] As more units are added to the order size, p will decrease and $(1 - p)$ will increase; thus, sooner or later, the expected marginal increase in the cost of leftovers (the marginal expected loss) will become equal to the expected marginal increase in profit. This is the optimum order size; it would not be desirable to purchase more units. The probability p will decrease, since p is the probability of selling an additional unit. The probability of selling one unit (demand will be one or more) will be 0.90 in the example developed above (there is 0.10 probability of sales of zero). Let us consider increasing the order from one to two units. The probability of selling both units is 0.60, or the sum of the probabilities of selling two units or more. Thus, p decreases as each additional unit is added to the order size; and as it decreases, the expected gross profit resulting from stocking each additional unit decreases. We shall continue to increase the order size as long as the expected in-

---

[1] See Chapter 22 for a proof that profits are maximized when marginal costs are equated with marginal revenues. It follows that expected profits are maximized when the expected marginal functions are equated if second-order conditions are also satisfied.

FIGURE 10–1

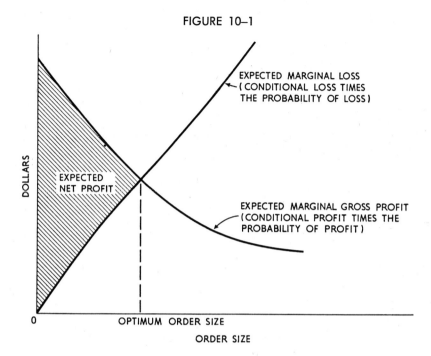

crease in gross profits is greater than the expected increase in the costs of leftovers. This may be written in the form:

$$p \cdot (MP) > (1 - p) \cdot (ML)$$

or

Expected Marginal Gross Profits > Expected Marginal Loss

Net profits will be maximized when

$$p \cdot (MP) = (1 - p) \cdot (ML)$$

for some order size; larger orders cause expected net losses.

As long as expected marginal gross profits are greater than expected marginal costs, we should try adding one more unit to the order size. Figure 10–1 shows this graphically. Orders less than the optimum order size yield smaller expected net profits. Expected net profits also are decreased by orders in excess of the optimum order size.

OPTIMUM ORDERING

We have to find the value of p (probability of selling one or more additional units) for which the maximizing equation holds.

TABLE 10–4

Sales	Probability of Sales	Cumulative Probabilities (p)
0.........	0.10	1.00
1.........	0.30	0.90
2.........	0.40	0.60
3.........	0.20	0.20
	1.00	

Solving the equation $p(MP) = (1 - p)ML$, for p, we obtain:

$$p_c = \frac{ML}{ML + MP}$$

where p_c is the "critical" probability of selling the next unit.

If the events are not continuous (for example, demand can be either 1,000 or 2,000 units, but not in between), it is not always possible to find the marginal sale with a probability of p_c. The following rule is useful in approximating the optimum adjustment in the discrete case:

1. As long as the probability of selling one or more additional units is greater than p_c, the critical ratio, we should order that unit.
2. If the probability of selling the additional unit is equal to p_c, we are indifferent to including it in our order or leaving it out.
3. If the probability is less than p_c, do not order that unit.

In the example being considered, ML equals \$2.00, and MP equals \$3.00; thus:

$$p_c = \frac{ML}{ML + MP} = \frac{2}{2 + 3} = \frac{2}{5} = 0.40.$$

The probabilities of selling an additional unit are shown in Table 10–4.

The column headed Cumulative Probabilities is p, since it indicates the probability of selling zero or more (1.00), one or more (0.90), two or more (0.60), or three or more (0.20) units. It is the right tail of the probability distribution.

The critical ratio p_c is 0.40. Thus, we would not order three units, since $p < p_c$ for the third unit. We would order more than one, since $p > p_c$. It is interesting to compute the expected additional profit and expected marginal loss in going from one to two units:

$$
\begin{aligned}
p \cdot (MP) &= 0.60 \cdot \$3.00 = \$\ 1.80 \\
(1 - p) \cdot (ML) &= 0.40 \cdot \$2.00 = \underline{(0.80)} \\
& \$\ 1.00, \text{ the marginal expected profit of} \\
& \text{ordering the second unit.}
\end{aligned}
$$

TABLE 10–5

Ordering Policy	Expected Profit	Expected Marginal Profit (or Loss)
0........	$0.00	....
1........	2.50	$ 2.50 (going from 0 to 1)
2........	3.50	1.00 (going from 1 to 2)
3........	2.50	(1.00) (going from 2 to 3)

The probability of selling the second unit is 0.40 (the probability of selling two) plus 0.20 (the probability of selling three), or 0.60. The probability of not selling the second unit is 0.40 (one minus p). Comparable computations for going from zero to one and from two to three units are:

Going from zero to one:

$$p \cdot (MP) = 0.90 \cdot \$3.00 = \$ 2.70$$
$$(1 - p) \cdot (ML) = 0.10 \cdot \$2.00 = \underline{(0.20)}$$
$$\text{Marginal Expected Profit}\ldots\ldots\$ 2.50$$

Going from two to three:

$$p \cdot (MP) = 0.20 \cdot \$3.00 = \$ 0.60$$
$$(1 - p) \cdot (ML) = 0.80 \cdot \$2.00 = \underline{(1.60)}$$
$$\text{Marginal Expected Loss}\ldots\ldots\$(1.00)$$

It would not be desirable to stock three units, since there is an expected marginal loss of $1.00 associated with the third unit.

The expected marginal profit can also be obtained by comparing the expected profit (see Table 10–3) following different ordering policies, as shown in Table 10–5.

In the special type of situation illustrated in Table 10–5, the optimum order size may be computed directly by solving for p_c in the above formula. It should be noted that linearity assumptions were made regarding gross profits per unit and leftover costs per unit. Frequently, these assumptions are not realistic; and more appropriate, but complex, functions for the marginal gross profits and marginal losses are available. Say $MP = f(Q)$ and $ML = g(Q)$, where f stands for the marginal gross profit function, g for the marginal loss function, and Q for sales. Then the optimum inventory order is characterized by one whose last unit meets the requirement

$$p \cdot f(Q) = (1 - p) \cdot g(Q).$$

COST OF UNCERTAINTY

In the example of the inventory decision under uncertainty with perfect information, we found that the expected profit was $5.10.

This means that we would expect, on the average, to make $5.10 a period if we knew in advance the sales of the period (eliminating the possibility of leftover units). We found that the optimum strategy under conditions of uncertainty without information yields an expected profit of $3.50. Hence, there is a cost of uncertainty of $5.10 less $3.50, or $1.60. It may be possible to reduce this cost of uncertainty by obtaining information. Thus a geologist may reduce the uncertainties of drilling for oil, and market research may reduce the uncertainties of marketing a new product. The costs of this information must be measured against the cost of uncertainty, taking into consideration the amount of uncertainty which will remain after the information has been obtained.

COST OF OVER- AND UNDERORDERING

Up to this point, we have computed the optimum order size using either total expected profits or marginal expected profits (making use of the formula $p_c = \dfrac{ML}{ML + MP}$). It is possible to modify the model by introducing new variables. For example, we could include hidden costs of underordering, such as the costs of customer ill will resulting from not finding the goods on hand. It is necessary that an estimate of this factor be made in terms of the present value of future profits lost because of each ordering policy and that the expected value of this figure be included in computing the expected profit of each act.

Continuing the example of this chapter (MP equals $3.00, and ML equals $2.00), let us assume there is a cost of 75 cents associated with every unit of demand not filled because of an inventory shortage. Consider these definitions and data:

C_o = Cost of overage per unit of overage.
C_u = Cost of underage per unit of underage.
C_o = $2.00. The $2.00 is the difference between the cost per unit and the distress sale price for each unit not sold.
C_u = $3.75. The $3.75 is equal to the sum of the gross profit lost by underordering a unit and the cost of ill will for each unit of underage, i.e., when there is demand and there are no units to sell.

The inventory decision of whether to increase the order by a marginal unit may now be considered in terms of the additional expected cost of underage if the unit is not ordered (pC_u) and the additional expected cost of overage if the unit is ordered [$(1 - p)C_o$].

Some cost is incurred in any event; increased orders reduce the total cost of underage, but increase the total cost of overage. Our objective is to minimize the sum of such costs (or regrets, as they are sometimes called). This is done by ordering every unit where

$$pC_u > (1 - p)C_o$$

and discontinuing the order for that unit where the inequality sign is reversed. It follows that regret is minimized when $pC_u = (1 - p)C_o$, or

$$p_c = \frac{C_o}{C_o + C_u}$$

since another unit would cause regret to increase. In our example:

$$p_c = \frac{C_o}{C_o + C_u} = \frac{2}{2 + 3.75} = 0.35.$$

The increased penalty of not filling an order has had the same effect as an increase in the profit margin (i.e., an increase in the regret of not having a unit on hand when a unit is demanded), and it will tend to increase the size of the order by decreasing p_c.

USING A CONTINUOUS PROBABILITY DISTRIBUTION

Instead of assuming that sales can take on only a few discrete values, we can make use of a continuous probability distribution. Such a distribution will make it possible to consider all feasible values of the random variable, demand. For illustrative purposes, assume that the random variable, tomorrow's demand, is normally distributed.

As in the previous section on the discrete case, we begin by computing p_c, where p_c is the critical probability. This critical probability is the probability of selling the last unit which is advantageous to the company and which should result in an increase in order size. In terms of the normal distribution, p_c can be represented by the shaded area as shown in Figure 10–2. It should be noted that p_c is the right tail of the distribution.

Figure 10–2 shows an optimum order size of 50 units. If less than 50 units are ordered, p, the probability of selling an additional unit or more, will be greater than p_c; the same arguments presented for the discrete case hold in the continuous case.

In the computation of optimum order size, the first step is to find d, the number of standard deviations from the mean, that will

FIGURE 10–2

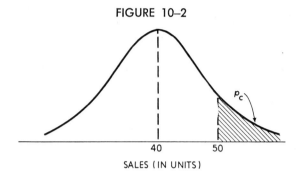

SALES (IN UNITS)

equate the right tail of the normal density function and p_c. It is then necessary to convert d to units by multiplying d by the standard deviation of the sales distribution. This number of units is then added to mean sales, if $p_c < 0.50$ (as shown in Figure 10–2), or subtracted, if $p_c > 0.50$. If $p_c = 0.50$, then $d = 0$.

Example 1

Assume that the distribution of demand is normal, C_o is equal to 64 cents, and C_u is equal to \$3.36. The critical probability is:

$$p_c = \frac{C_o}{C_o + C_u} = \frac{0.64}{0.64 + 3.36} = 0.16.$$

The 0.16 probability is the right tail of a normal distribution. Referring to Table B (in the Appendix to the book), we find that the left tails are given. The left-tail complement of a 0.16 right tail is 0.84, and this is approximately one standard deviation from the mean (with one standard deviation, the value in the table is 0.8413). If we move out beyond one standard deviation to the right of the mean, the probability of making an additional sale will be equal to or less than 0.16.

Example 2

Assume mean sales for the coming period are 40 units and the standard deviation of the prior distribution is 10. Assume p_c is 0.16. We want to increase the order size until the probability of making an additional sale is equal to or less than 0.16. We have to move one standard deviation to the right of the mean ($d = 1$) in order to make the right tail of the distribution equal 0.16. In order to convert d to units, we multiply by the standard deviation:

$$d\sigma = 1 \cdot 10 = 10 \text{ units}$$

Since $p_c < 0.50$, we have to add the 10 units to the mean sales to obtain Q, the optimum order size 50. We can write the following equation:

$$Q = \text{Mean Sales} \pm d\sigma$$
$$= 40 + 10 = 50.$$

The sign is plus if $p_c < 0.50$ and minus if $p_c > 0.50$.

Example 3

Assume that demand has the same normal distribution as above. Suppose we have now computed p_c and found it to be 0.84. Figure 10–3 shows this situation.

FIGURE 10–3

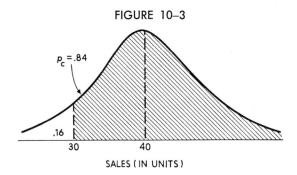

SALES (IN UNITS)

Again, $d = 1$, but the optimum order size is now 30, calculated as follows:

$$Q = \text{Mean Sales} - d\sigma$$
$$= 40 - (1 \cdot 10) = 30.$$

CONCLUSION

We have developed an example of the application of probability concepts to business decision making under uncertainty. The next chapter will treat the same problem, but where more factors are considered. In this chapter the possibility of reordering was excluded from consideration; inventory decision models with reordering will be introduced in the next chapter.

BIBLIOGRAPHY

CHURCHMAN, C. W.; ACKOFF, R. L.; and ARNOFF, E. L. *Introduction to Operations Research.* New York: John Wiley & Sons, Inc., 1957.

MAGEE, J. F. "Guides to Inventory Policy, No. 1: Functions and Lot Size," *Harvard Business Review,* January-February, 1956.

Magee, J. F. *Production Planning and Inventory Control.* New York: McGraw-Hill Book Co., Inc., 1958.

Saaty, T. L. *Mathematical Methods of Operations Research.* New York: McGraw-Hill Book Co., Inc., 1959.

Schlaifer, R. *Probability and Statistics for Business Decisions.* New York: McGraw-Hill Book Co., Inc., 1959.

Whitin, T. M. "Inventory Control Research: A Survey," *Management Science*, October, 1954.

————. *The Theory of Inventory Management.* Princeton: Princeton University Press, 1953.

Problems

10–1. The probability distribution of the demand for a product has been estimated to be:

Sales	Probability of Sales
0	0.05
1	0.15
2	0.30
3	0.35
4	0.10
5	0.05
6	0.00
	1.00

Each unit sells for $100, and the total incremental costs per unit (including selling incentives) are $60. If the product is not sold, it is completely worthless. The purchase costs of a unit are $10.

a) Assuming no reordering is possible, how many units should be purchased?

b) If the customer ill will is estimated to be $65 for every unit for which there is unfilled demand, how many units should be ordered?

c) Assume the purchase costs are $60 (i.e., equal to the total incremental costs). If the product is not sold, it is completely worthless. Assume no costs of customer ill will. How many units should be purchased?

10–2. Assume that our estimate of the sales of the next period is a normal distribution with a mean of 50 units and a standard deviation of 10 units. Reordering is not possible. Compute the optimum order sizes for the different p_c's given below:

	p_c
a)	0.40
b)	0.50
c)	0.55
d)	0.60
e)	0.78
f)	0.90
g)	0.98

10–3. Given the following information, compute the optimum order size (reordering is not possible):

Sales price...$100
Incremental cost per unit sold......................... 70
Purchase cost per unit................................ 50
Salvage value (if not sold)............................ 10
Loss in good will for each unit of demand not satisfied..... 50

The probability distribution of sales is normal; mean, 140; standard deviation, 20.

10–4. Refer to Problem 10–3. Recompute the optimum order size, assuming the standard deviation of the probability distribution is 50.

10–5. Refer to Problem 10–3. Recompute the optimum order size, assuming there is *no* loss in good will with unfilled orders.
a) Assume a standard deviation of 20.
b) Assume a standard deviation of 50.
c) Compare the above answers with those of Problems 10–3 and 10–4.

10–6. A wholesaler of stationery is deciding how many desk calendars to stock for the coming year. It is impossible for him to reorder, and leftover units are worthless. The following table indicates the possible demand levels and the wholesaler's prior probabilities:

Demand (in Thousands)	Probability of Demand
100	0.10
200	0.15
300	0.50
400	0.25
	1.00

The calendars sell for $100 per thousand, and the incremental purchase cost is $70. The incremental cost of selling (commissions) is $5.00 per thousand.
a) Use the analysis of this chapter to find how many calendars should be ordered.
b) Check this calculation by preparing conditional and expected value tables and computing expected values for each act. Also, calculate the *EVPI*.
c) How much of an ill-will cost would have to exist to justify an order of 400,000 calendars?

Chapter 11

INVENTORY CONTROL—MINIMIZING
COST WHEN THERE IS REORDERING

In the previous chapter, inventory control was discussed in a situation where there were only one-shot orders. That is, the order was placed, and then the event occurred, but there was no opportunity for reordering. An illustration of this type of situation is the ordering of the food and drink for a company picnic. In the majority of business situations, we are not restricted to one-shot orders. Items may be reordered as the stock runs low.

ADDITIONAL DECISIONS

With the ability to reorder, there are two operating decisions to be made:

1. When to place an order. We shall assume the order point is determined by the units on hand rather than a passage of calendar time (for example, placing an order every month).
2. The size of the order. We shall assume there are no discontinuous quantity discounts.

The objective is to maximize the difference between revenue and cost associated with maintaining an inventory.

There are three general types of costs to be considered:

K = Cost of placing one order.
k_c = Cost of carrying one unit in inventory, one unit of time.
k_u = Cost of being out of stock one unit (cost of underage).

The optimum order size and optimum order point will, in general, be a function of these three costs plus the intensity or rate of use (quantity used during a unit time period). In Chapter 10, C_o and C_u were used as follows:

142

C_o = Per unit cost of overage (without reference to time).
C_u = Per unit cost of underage (without reference to time).

Thus, C_o and C_u measure a penalty without reference to time. On the other hand:

k_c = Carrying cost per unit, per unit of time.
k_u = Underage cost per unit, and the number of units of underage will be a function of time.

To simplify the analysis (which will soon get too complex, in any event), we shall assume the lead time (time between placing an order and receiving the product) is known with certainty.

INVENTORY CONTROL WITH KNOWN DEMAND

We shall first investigate inventory control when we know the demand. We assume that both the lead time and the demand are known. With this assumption, the computation of the order point is not complicated. If the usage rate is 0.25 units per day, and the lead time is 40 days, we would set an order point of 40 · 0.25, or 10 units. This allows us no room for error, but it is consistent with the assumptions of known demand and known lead time.

The optimum order size analysis is also simplified because the cost of underage will be zero. This follows from the assumption of known parameters. The total cost (TC) for a period will be equal to the sum of the ordering costs (or setup costs) plus the costs of carrying the inventory during the period.

Let:

K = Incremental cost of placing an order (or setting up production).
D = Total usage (demand) in units during time period T.
Q = Optimum order size in units (the unknown).

$\dfrac{D}{Q}$ = Number of orders during T.

$\dfrac{Q}{2}$ = Average inventory (assuming linear usage).

Then:

$$\frac{Q}{2}k_cT = \text{Cost of carrying inventory during the period } T \text{ (average inventory}$$

times k_c, the cost per unit per unit time, times the length of time T)

$\dfrac{D}{Q}K$ = Cost of placing orders (number of orders, $\dfrac{D}{Q}$, times the cost of placing an order, K)

$TC = \dfrac{Q}{2}k_cT + \dfrac{D}{Q}K.$

The optimum order size, Q, is:[1]

(11–1)
$$Q = \sqrt{\dfrac{2KD}{k_cT}}.$$

An example follows:

$T = 30$ days
$D = 300$ units (expected demand during T)
$k_c = 25$ cents per unit, per day
$K = \$5.00$ per order

$$Q = \sqrt{\dfrac{2KD}{k_cT}} = \sqrt{\dfrac{2 \cdot 5 \cdot 300}{0.25 \cdot 30}} = \sqrt{400} = 20 \text{ units.}$$

The optimum order size is 20 units. If D is measured in dollars instead of units, then Q will also be in terms of dollars. If k_c is in terms of costs per time period and D is the units needed for the same time period, then the formula simplifies to:

(11–2)
$$Q = \sqrt{\dfrac{2KD}{k_c}}.$$

Even when the demand is not known with certainty, the above model may be helpful in approximating a solution for the problem of optimum order size.

INVENTORY CONTROL WITH UNCERTAINTY

Instead of assuming that the demand is known, let us hypothesize that we only know the probability distribution of demand, but not

[1] Take the first derivative with respect to Q, set it equal to zero, and solve for Q:

$$TC = \dfrac{Q}{2}k_cT + \dfrac{DK}{Q}$$
$$\dfrac{dTC}{dQ} = \dfrac{1}{2}k_cT - \dfrac{DK}{Q^2} = 0.$$

Since

$$\dfrac{d^2TC}{dQ^2} = \dfrac{2DK}{Q} > 0$$

this solution is for a minimum TC.

$$Q = \sqrt{\dfrac{2KD}{k_cT}}$$

the actual demand. When we set the order point, there is some probability that we shall run out of inventory and encounter a cost of underage (compare with the earlier case where demand was known). The optimum order point is no longer a simple computation. The cost of underage will be affected by the choice of both the optimum order point and the optimum order size. It is interesting to look at the interaction between the various costs and the two variables (optimum order point and optimum order size):

Action	*Result*
Decrease order-point size (i.e., place order when fewer units on hand), *or* decrease optimum order size.	Decrease carrying costs of inventory, and increase expected cost of underage.
Increase order-point size, *or* increase optimum order size.	Increase carrying costs of inventory, and decrease expected cost of underage.

A change in optimum order size changes the frequency of reaching the ordering point (thus the frequency of encountering a chance of underage). A change in the optimum order point changes the likelihood of underages and changes the optimum number of times the order point should be encountered. Thus the total cost is affected by both the order point and the order size, and the optimum order point and the optimum order size are related.

FIGURE 11–1

Illustration of Overlap

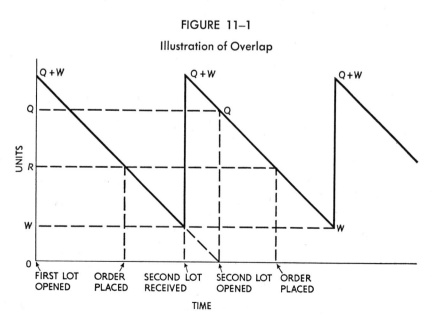

Again, we want to minimize the total cost incurred during a given time period. There are now four costs to consider:

1. Cost of placing orders.
2. Cost of carrying inventory during the overlap period. Overlap is defined as the period of time from the receipt of an order to complete utilization of the stock already on hand when the order was received.
3. Cost of carrying an inventory of size Q from the time it is first used to the time it is totally consumed.
4. Cost of running out of inventory (cost of underages).

Figure 11–1 shows a situation where there is a base safety stock, W, and therefore a need of including a cost factor to cover the cost of carrying this amount of inventory (cost of overlap). Unfortunately, there is no easy way of using the total cost function for this model to compute the optimum order point and the optimum order size.[2] We shall make simplifying assumptions.

A SIMPLIFIED INVENTORY MODEL

In most business situations an approximate solution to the problems of optimum order point and optimum order size will be satisfactory. Even the more sophisticated models generally assume a known lead time and known intensity of demand. Thus, we shall move toward a more workable and somewhat less involved model.

THE ASSUMPTIONS

We shall first assume that the choice of the order point does not affect the optimum order size (i.e., the amount ordered will be computed using $Q = \sqrt{\dfrac{2KD}{k_c}}$, equation 11–2 developed earlier in this chapter). This ignores the effect the order point has on carrying costs. Fortunately, the effect of order point on optimum order size is generally small. If it is significant, this model may not apply.

Secondly, the rate of demand during the overlap period (the period when the new stock has been received but there is still old stock on hand) is assumed to be at a constant rate, D, rather than a random variable with a probability distribution function. L, the lead time, is also a constant.

---

[2] It is possible to find the optimum by the use of higher mathematics, but the solution becomes too complex for an introductory work. See Appendix 2 to this chapter for a possible method of solution.

The third assumption is that M, the sales during the lead time, is normally distributed. This assumption is the least essential of the three assumptions and may be changed; it is chosen to simplify the computations.

THE MODEL

Let:

R = Order point

R^* = Optimum order point

M = Amount demanded during the lead time ($\bar{M}$, mean amount), a random variable

Q = Optimum order size

D = Demand per unit of time (a year)

$R - M$ = Units unsold when new units are received

$\dfrac{R - M}{D}$ = Time of overlap (number of units on hand at time of receipt of new order, divided by rate of demand, gives the time of overlap in terms of a fraction of a year)

k_o = Cost of overage per unit, per unit of time

$k_o\dfrac{(R - M)}{D}$ = Cost of overlap per unit (unit cost times the time of overlap)

$Qk_o\dfrac{(R - M)}{D}$ = Cost of overlap for Q units (it will be useful to rewrite the expression as follows):

$$Qk_o\frac{(R - M)}{D} = \frac{Qk_o}{D}(R - M).$$

In most cases, k_c may be used interchangeably with k_o. The exception would be where special costs of obsolescence are incurred with overage. The costs of overage, k_o, and the rate of usage, D, must apply to the same time period. If k_o is for a year, then D must also be for a year.

k_u = Cost per unit for sales lost

$M - R$ = Amount by which demand during lead time exceeds order-point amount.

The conditional costs (see Figure 11–2) are:

$$\text{Cost of Overage} = \frac{Qk_o}{D}(R - M)$$
$$\text{Cost of Underage} = k_u(M - R).$$

The total expected costs are equal to the conditional costs expected over all values of M. That is, the costs for different values of

FIGURE 11–2

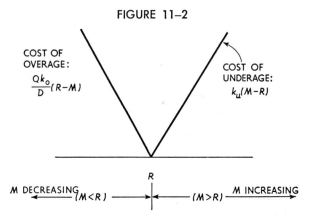

M are multiplied by the probability density of the events; each value of the two cost lines is multiplied by the height of the probability distribution of M for the same value of M to find the expected cost.[3] See Figure 11–3.

FIGURE 11–3

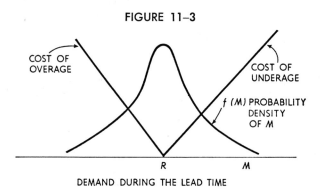

DEMAND DURING THE LEAD TIME

A derivative is then taken of the expected cost equation and set equal to zero to find the optimum order point, R^*. We find:

(11-3)
$$F(R^*) = \frac{k_u}{k_u + k_o \dfrac{Q}{D}}$$

The term $F(R^*)$ is read: "Set R^* so that there is $\dfrac{k_u}{k_u + k_o \dfrac{Q}{D}}$ probability of M being equal to or less than R^*."[4]

---

[3] See Appendix 1 (at the end of this chapter) for the derivation of the formula explained in this section.

[4] $F(R^*)$ is the *left* tail of a probability distribution, i.e., the $P(M \leq R^*)$

FIGURE 11-4

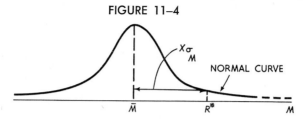

Let X be the number of standard deviations we must go from the mean sales, $\overline{M}$, before the probability is $F(R^*)$ that the demand, M, is equal to or less than R^*. We can obtain R^*, the optimum order point, as follows (see Figure 11–4).

$$(11\text{–}4) \qquad\qquad R^* = \overline{M} \pm X\sigma_M.$$

Use the plus if $\dfrac{k_u}{k_u + k_o \dfrac{Q}{D}} > 0.50$, otherwise the minus.

An example follows:

Let:

$$D = 100 \text{ units}$$
$$Q = 50 \text{ units}$$
$$k_o = \$40 \text{ per unit per year}$$
$$k_u = \$80 \text{ for each unit short}$$
$$k_o\frac{Q}{D} = \$20$$
$$\overline{M} = 20$$
$$\sigma_M = 5$$
$$F(R^*) = \frac{80}{80 + 20} = 0.80.$$

Referring to Table B (in the Appendix at the end of the text), we find $X = 0.84$.

The optimum order point is:

$$R^* = \overline{M} + X\sigma_M = 20 + (0.84)(5)$$
$$R^* = 20 + 4.2 = 24.2$$

With an order point of 24.2 units, we shall not run out 80 per cent of the time (remember the mean demand is 20 units).

SUMMARY

Assuming known demand and known lead time of supply, the solution for optimum order size and order point is relatively easily obtained.

Instead of knowing demand (that is, knowing the exact number of units which will be used), we may only know the probability distribution of demand, where demand is treated as a random variable. In this type of situation, solutions are possible but not easy. We are unable to compute simple formulas for obtaining the optimum order size and order point. It is in this type of problem that simulation has application, since it may be faster to simulate answers on a computer than to solve them mathematically.

We have assumed that the optimum order size was independent of the optimum order point, and that sales during the lead time were normally distributed. These assumptions enabled us to arrive at the formulas $F(R^*) = \dfrac{k_u}{k_u + k_o\dfrac{Q}{D}}$ and $R^* = \overline{M} \pm X\sigma_M$, where R^* is the optimum order point in number of units. While not exact (few computations are exact when relating to inventory), these computations will give reasonable answers to very complex phenomena.

Appendix 2 to this chapter gives an improved model which requires more computational time but gives somewhat better results.

APPENDIX 1

DERIVATION OF OPTIMUM ORDER POINT

The symbols used in this Appendix are the same as used in the chapter.

FIGURE 11–5

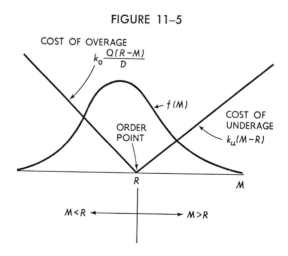

We shall show that R^*, the optimum order point, may be determined by setting the left tail of the standard normal curve equal to:

$$\frac{k_u}{k_u + k_o\dfrac{Q}{D}}$$

$$F(R^*) = \frac{k_u}{k_u + k_o\dfrac{Q}{D}}.$$

The total cost is the sum of the expected cost of overage and the expected cost of underage. Let $K_o = k_o\dfrac{Q}{D}$; then:

$$\text{Total Cost} = \int_{-\infty}^{R} K_o(R - M)f(M)dM + \int_{R}^{\infty} k_u(M - R)f(M)dM$$

$$= K_oR\int_{-\infty}^{R} f(M)dM - K_o\int_{-\infty}^{R} Mf(M)dM +$$

$$k_u\int_{R}^{\infty} Mf(M)dM - k_uR\int_{R}^{\infty} f(M)dM$$

$$= K_oRF(R) - K_o\overset{R}{\underset{-\infty}{E}}(M) + k_u\overset{\infty}{\underset{R}{E}}(M) - k_uRG(R)$$

where $\overset{R}{\underset{-\infty}{E}}(M)$ is the partial expectation of M for values of M from $-\infty$ to R and $\overset{\infty}{\underset{R}{E}}(M)$ is the partial expectation of M for values of M from R to ∞.

Since $F(R)$ plus $G(R)$ equals one:

$$G(R) = 1 - F(R)$$

and since $\overline{M} = \overset{\infty}{\underset{-\infty}{E}}(M)$:

$$\overset{\infty}{\underset{R}{E}}(M) = \overline{M} - \overset{R}{\underset{-\infty}{E}}(M)$$

we can substitute in the equation for total cost; and after arranging terms, we obtain:

$$\text{Total Cost} = (K_o + k_u)[RF(R)] - (K_o + k_u)\overset{R}{\underset{-\infty}{E}}(M) + k_u(\overline{M} - R).$$

To find the minimum, we take the first derivative of total cost and set it equal to zero:

$$\frac{d \text{ Total Cost}}{dR} = (K_o + k_u)[F(R) + Rf(R)] - (K_o + k_u)Rf(R) - k_u$$

$$= (K_o + k_u)F(R) - k_u.$$

Setting the derivative equal to zero:

$$(K_o + k_u)F(R) - k_u = 0$$

$$F(R^*) = \frac{k_u}{K_o + k_u} = \frac{k_u}{k_u + k_o\dfrac{Q}{D}}$$

where R^* is the optimum order point. The second-order condition is satisfied, since $(K_o + k_u)f(R) > 0$.

APPENDIX 2

An Improved Inventory Model

The use of the equation $Q = \sqrt{\dfrac{2DK}{k_c}}$ for the optimum order size ignores the effect that the order point has on the order size. The following equation takes this interaction into consideration (we shall assume $k_c = k_o$).

$$(11-5) \qquad Q = \sqrt{\frac{2D[K + k_u \int_R^\infty (M - R)\,f(M)dM]}{k_c}}.$$

Note that R, obtained by using the equation $F(R) = \dfrac{k_u}{k_u + k_c\dfrac{Q}{D}}$, is

in the above formula, and Q is in the equation for R.[5] The two equations must be solved simultaneously. This may be done by the use of an iterative procedure which starts with an estimate of Q, solves for R, then solves for a new Q, and repeats this process until a Q and an R are found to satisfy both equations.

Equation 11–5 can be converted into a form which is more susceptible to computation. We make use of the fact that if $f(M)$ is normally distributed and if R is larger than the expected sales during the reorder period, then:

$$\int_R^\infty (M - R)f(M)dM = \sigma N(R)$$

---

[5] The formula for the right tail of the demand distribution is:

$$G(R) = \frac{k_c\dfrac{Q}{D}}{k_u + k_c\dfrac{Q}{D}} = \frac{k_c}{k_c + k_u\dfrac{D}{Q}}$$

FIGURE 11–6

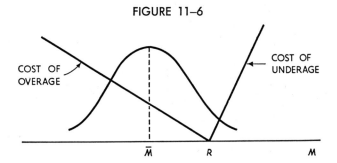

$N(R)$ is the unit normal loss integral valued for R (R converted to standard deviations from the mean). The σ is the standard deviation of the distribution of demand during the reorder period.

Equation 11–5 now becomes:

$$(11\text{–}6) \qquad\qquad Q = \sqrt{\frac{2D[K + k_u\sigma N(R)]}{k_c}}.$$

Figure 11–6 shows the probability distribution of demand and the loss functions for overage and underage.

It is necessary that D, the rate of usage, and k_c, the cost of carrying one unit for one time period, be in the same units. To satisfy this requirement, we shall assume they both refer to one year.

THE TOTAL COST

The total cost of a policy involving a specific order size, R, and an optimum order quantity, Q, is equal to the sum of the costs of ordering, the costs of being out of stock, and the costs of carrying inventory.

$$(11\text{–}7) \quad \text{Total Cost } (R, Q) = K\left(\frac{D}{Q}\right) + \left[k_u\int_R^\infty (M - R)\, f(M)dM\right]\frac{D}{Q} +$$

$$\left[\frac{Q}{2} + \int_{-\infty}^R (R - M)\, f(M)dM\right]k_c$$

where $K\left(\dfrac{D}{Q}\right)$ is the cost of ordering, K is the cost per order, and $\dfrac{D}{Q}$ is the number of orders.

$\left[k_u\displaystyle\int_R^\infty (M - R)\, f(M)dM\right]\dfrac{D}{Q}$ is the cost of being out of stock. k_u is the cost per unit. The integral is the expected number of units out of

FIGURE 11–7

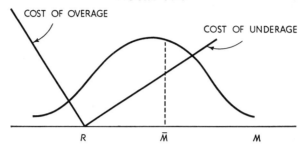

stock. $\dfrac{D}{Q}$ is the number of replenishment cycles, i.e., the number of

orders. $\left[\dfrac{Q}{2} + \displaystyle\int_{-\infty}^{R} (R - M)\, f(M)dM\right] k_c$ is the cost of carrying inven-

tory. k_c is the cost of carrying one unit for one time period (say a year). The remainder of the term is the average inventory; the integral is the expected number of leftover units; and this is added to $\dfrac{Q}{2}$ the average inventory, assuming no units on hand when the order is received.

The equations for Q and $F(R)$ are obtained from equation 11–7, the equation for the total cost, by taking the partial derivatives with respect to R and with respect to Q and setting them equal to zero.

The equation for total cost can be simplified (assuming $R > \bar{M}$) by making use of the fact that $f(M)$ is assumed to be a normal density function:

Expected underage:

$$\int_{R}^{\infty} (M - R)\, f(M)dM = \sigma N(R), \text{ if } R > \bar{M}$$

Expected overage:

$$\int_{-\infty}^{R} (R - M)\, f(M)dM = \sigma N(-R), \text{ if } R > \bar{M}$$

(11–8)   Total Cost $(R, Q) = \left[K + k_u \sigma N(R)\right]\dfrac{D}{Q} + \left[\dfrac{Q}{2} + \sigma N(-R)\right]k_c.$

$N(R)$ is associated with the cost of underage and $N(-R)$ with the cost of overage if the order point is larger than the mean demand (see Figure 11–6). If the order point is less than the mean demand, then $N(-R)$ is associated with the cost of underage and $N(R)$ with the cost of overage (see Figure 11–7).

Example

The following example illustrates the computation of the optimum order size and order point.

The amount expected to be used (D) is 1,800 units per year.

The cost of making one order (K) is \$10.

The cost of carrying one unit for one year is \$60 (this is k_c).

The order time is twenty days; and the mean usage, $\overline{M}$, during the order time is 100 units, with a standard deviation of 30 units, and is normally distributed.

The cost of underage is \$5.00 per unit out of stock (this is k_u).

Using the following equation, we can determine the first estimate of Q:

$$Q = \sqrt{\frac{2KD}{k_c}} = \sqrt{\frac{2 \times 10 \times 1,800}{60}} = \sqrt{600} = 24.49 \text{ units, or 24 units.}$$

$$F(R) = \frac{k_u}{k_u + k_c \times \dfrac{Q}{D}} = \frac{5}{5 + 60 \times \dfrac{24}{1,800}} = \frac{9,000}{10,440} = 0.862.$$

Referring to a table of cumulative probabilities for the normal distribution, $F(R) = 0.862$ is equivalent to:

$d = 1.09$ standard deviations
$R = 100 + 1.09 \times 30 = 133$ units (this is the order point).

The next step is to insert the value for the order point in the more exact formula for the optimum order size. We shall need to know that $N(R) = N(1.09) = 0.07$.

$$Q = \sqrt{\frac{2D[K + k_u\sigma N(R)]}{k_c}}$$

$$= \sqrt{\frac{2 \times 1,800[10 + 5 \times 30 \times 0.07]}{60}}$$

$$= \sqrt{60(20.5)} = \sqrt{1,230} = 35.$$

We now return to the optimum order point formula:

$$F(R) = \frac{5}{5 + 60 \times \dfrac{35}{1,800}} = 0.811$$

$d = 0.88$ standard deviations to the right of the mean
$R = 100 + 0.88 \times 30 = 126$ units.

If a new optimum order point is computed and the procedure is repeated several times, we finally obtain values which satisfy both equations:

$$F(R) = 0.785$$
$$d = 0.79 \text{ standard deviations}$$
$$N(0.79) = 0.1223$$
$$Q = 41 \text{ units (optimum order size)}$$
$$R = 100 + 0.79 \times 30 = 124 \text{ units (order point)}$$

$$Q = \sqrt{\frac{2 \times 1,800 \, [10 + 5 \times 30 \times 0.1223]}{60}} = \sqrt{1,698} = 41$$

$$F(R) = \frac{5}{5 + 60 \times \dfrac{41}{1,800}} = 0.785.$$

The total cost of a policy of ordering 41 units at an order point of 124 units is:[6]

$$TC(R, Q) = \left[K + k_u \times \sigma \times N(0.79) \right]\frac{D}{Q} + \left[\frac{Q}{2} + \sigma \times N(-0.79) \right] k_c$$

$$TC(R, Q) = \left[10 + 5 \times 30 \times 0.1223 \right]\frac{1,800}{41} + \left[\frac{41}{2} + 30 \times 0.9123 \right] 60$$

$$= (28.3)43.9 + (47.4)60 = 1,242 + 2,844 = \$4,086.$$

If we had used the decision rule we obtained on the first trial, $R = 133$ units and $Q = 24$ units, the total cost would be:[7]

$$TC(R, Q) = \left[10 + 5 \times 30 \times 0.07 \right]\frac{1,800}{24} + \left[\frac{24}{2} + 30 \times 1.16 \right]60$$

$$= (20.5)75 + (46.8)60$$
$$= 1,538 + 2,808 = \$4,346.$$

The more exact decision rule results in an expected cost which is approximately \$260 less than the decision rule which assumes the order quantity is not affected by the order point.

BIBLIOGRAPHY

See the Bibliography of Chapter 10.

PROBLEMS

11–1. The costs of placing an order are \$6.00 per order. It is estimated that 1,000 units will be used in the next 12 months. The carrying cost per unit per year is \$30.

Compute the optimum order size.

---

[6] $N(-D) = D + N(D)$; therefore, $N(-0.79) = 0.79 + 0.1223 = 0.9123$.
[7] $N(1.09) = 0.07$ and $N(-1.09) = 1.09 + 0.07 = 1.16$.

11-2. The costs of placing an order are \$150 per order. It is estimated that 1,000 units will be used in the next 12 months. The carrying cost per unit per month is \$2.50.

Compute the optimum order size.

11-3. The following information relates to an item in inventory:

k_u = \$2.00 cost per unit for sales lost
L = 18 days (lead time)
$\bar{M}$ = 50 mean sales during the lead time
σ_M = 10 units
D = 1,000 units per year (estimated demand)
K = \$6.00 per order (ordering costs)
k_c = \$30 (cost of carrying a unit in inventory for one year)

The distribution of M is assumed to be normal. Assume independence of order size and order point (i.e. order size does not affect the order point).

a) Compute Q, the optimum order size.

b) Compute $F(R^*)$; and determine R^*, the optimum order point.

11-4. A retailer feels that the mean demand for a unit of inventory for the coming year is 1,800 units. The lead time on orders is 20 days, and the mean demand during the lead time is 100 units. The lead time demand is assumed to be normally distributed, with $\sigma = 30$ (there is a 50–50 chance that the lead time demand could be less than 80 units or more than 120 units). The cost per unit of lost sales is \$5.00 per unit, the cost of placing an order is \$10, and the cost of carrying a unit in inventory for one year is \$60. Assume independence of order size and order point (i.e. order size does not affect the order point).

a) Compute Q, the optimum order size (round to nearest whole unit).

b) Compute R^*, the optimum order point.

11-5. The mean demand for a unit of inventory for the coming year is 40,000 units. The lead time is 36 days, and the mean demand during the lead time is 4,000 units. The lead time demand is assumed to be normally distributed with $\sigma = 500$. The cost per unit of shortages is \$10, the cost of placing an order is \$64, and the cost of carrying a unit in inventory for one year is \$2.00. Assume independence of order size and order point (i.e. order size does not affect the order point).

a) Compute the optimum order size (round to the nearest whole unit).

b) Compute the optimum order point.

Chapter 12

THE DECISION TO BUY IMPERFECT INFORMATION: AN EXAMPLE USING BINOMIAL PROBABILITIES

ONE OF the primary problems facing a decision maker is whether to act based on information already available or whether to delay action and gather more information. The advantage of gathering more information (sampling) is to reduce or, ideally, to eliminate the expected cost of uncertainty. Hence, when the expected opportunity loss of the optimal act (expected cost of uncertainty) is high, it will frequently pay to sample. If the decision maker does sample, the problem becomes one of choosing the best sampling plan, interpreting the information, and acting on this information.

In order to incorporate the additional information, the decision maker must revise the prior probabilities and act in accordance with the revised set of priors. This process was introduced in Chapter 5 and expanded in Chapters 8 and 9 for the normal distribution.

In this chapter, we shall illustrate, by means of an example, the decision problem for the binomial distribution. This chapter is based to a large extent on an example from Robert Schlaifer's book, *Probability and Statistics for Business Decisions* (1959), with the kind permission of the author. A brief description of both the binomial probability distribution and a Bernoulli process was given in Chapter 2. Those readers who need a more complete description of this background material are referred to Schlaifer's book or the mathematical statistics books listed in the Preface.

To summarize, the example to follow will illustrate:

1. The best action based on the prior probabilities
2. The decision of whether to sample
3. The determination of optimal sample size

158

4. The revision of prior probabilities in the light of additional information.

Example Using Binomial Probabilities

Suppose a manufacturer is concerned with a production process which has the characteristics of a Bernoulli process. If grade A raw material is used in the process, the run characteristic or the fraction defective (D) will be as follows:

D: Characteristic	Probability of Occurrence
0.01 defective....................	0.25
0.05 defective....................	0.25
0.10 defective....................	0.50
	1.00

Before the material is processed, we do not know its characteristic (i.e., whether it will result in 0.01, 0.05, or 0.10 defectives). On the other hand, if grade AA material is used, the defective rate is certain to be 0.01.

The raw material arrives in homogeneous batches and produces a certain fraction defective, and the occurrence of good and defective product is independent from piece to piece. Hence the manufacturer feels that the process can be treated as a Bernoulli process for purposes of analysis. Each production run consists of 500 pieces.

The problem facing the manufacturer is to decide whether to use grade A or grade AA material. If grade A material is used, when should a switch be made to a new batch of grade A material or to grade AA material? Assume there are other uses of grade A material in the plant.

The cost situation is as follows:

1. For every defective piece, it costs 50 cents to rework the product to make it usable.
2. If grade AA material is used, it will cost $12.50 *more* for material for the run of 500 pieces than if grade A is used.

BEST ACTION WITHOUT SAMPLING

As can be seen from the above data, if the grade A material turned out to have a run characteristic of 0.01, the manufacturer would prefer grade A to grade AA material. The former act costs $12.50 less than the latter. We can compute a break-even fraction defective—i.e., the fraction defective that would make the manufacturer indifferent between the two acts on a cost basis. The computation is as follows:

1. *Grade A Material.* The cost to rework a defective piece is 50 cents, and the total cost per run is therefore 50 cents times the fraction defective times the length of run, 500 pieces.

2. *Grade AA Material.* If grade AA material is used, it will cost $12.50 more for material cost, and the cost of rework will be

$$(0.01)(500)(\$0.50) = \$2.50.$$

Note that under this act, the manufacturer is certain that 0.01 will be the run characteristic.

$$(0.01)(\$0.50)(500) + \$12.50 = \$15.00 = \text{Incremental Cost per Run}$$
$$\text{Using Grade AA.}$$

3. *Break-Even Point.* The break-even point D^* (fraction defective) which equates the cost of the two acts is:

$$(\$0.50)(D^*)(500) = \$15.00$$
$$\$250D^* = \$15.00$$
$$D^* = 15.00/250$$
$$D^* = 0.06$$

The above calculations show that if grade A material was used and the fraction defective was *either* 0.01 or 0.05, it would be cheaper to use grade A than to use grade AA material. Grade AA material is preferred if the use of grade A material gives a fraction defective of 0.10.[1]

With this background, let us now compute the expected cost of each act to see which act is better, given the information at hand. Table 12–1 summarizes the situation. It indicates that if we have to make the decision without additional sample evidence, the best act is to use grade AA material—this act has a $15.00 expected cost as compared with $16.25 for the other act. However, the manufacturer has another course of action to consider. Basically, it is a question of whether to act now on the basis of available information or to delay action, gather more information (sample), and then act. In our example the manufacturer could start using grade A material and take a sample of products as they come off the machine. Depending on what the sample shows, he might then decide whether to continue the run or change to grade AA material.

---

[1] For simplicity, we are assuming only discrete events are possible; otherwise, grade AA would be preferred for any fraction defective larger than 0.06. In this example, 0.06 is not considered to be possible.

TABLE 12–1

Event D (Fraction Defective)	Probability of Event	Act			
		Grade A Material		Grade AA Material	
		$CV*$	EV of Cost†	CV	EV of Cost
0.01 defective........	0.25	$ 2.50	$ 0.625	$15.00	$ 3.75
0.05 defective........	0.25	12.50	3.125	15.00	3.75
0.10 defective.......	0.50	25.00	12.500	15.00	7.50
	1.00		$16.250		$15.00

* The conditional cost, as derived above, is ($0.50)($D$)(500).
† The EV of cost is the probability of the event times the conditional value.

The manufacturer can carry out the above plan by starting a run and inspecting a number of pieces. Let us assume that the sample will cost 5 cents for each piece inspected.

The first step in the analysis is to see what additional information is worth. We need, in other words, to calculate the $EVPI$, as this will set an upper limit on the values of additional information. Let us modify Table 12–1 and calculate the *expected cost under certainty* (see Table 12–2).

TABLE 12–2

Expected Cost under Certainty

Event D (Fraction Defective)	Probability of Event	Best Conditional Cost, Given Each Event	Best Act	Expected Cost
0.01 defective.......	0.25	$ 2.50	Grade A	$ 0.625
0.05 defective.......	0.25	12.50	Grade A	3.125
0.10 defective.......	0.50	15.00	Grade AA	7.500
	1.00			$11.250

The cost of uncertainty is $3.75, i.e., $15.00 − $11.25, and this sets the value of *perfect* information to the manufacturer. If the sample costs 5 cents per part inspected, we would not choose a sample of more than 75 pieces ($3.75/$0.05), since its cost would be greater than $3.75. Hence the $EVPI$ sets a firm limit on the sample size (assuming that sampling costs are directly proportional to sample size).

Let us consider the following sample plan. We shall use grade A material and run off a certain number of pieces—say, five. We shall then count the number of defectives; and if we find less than a certain number (say, one), we shall allow the run to proceed. If we find

FIGURE 12–1

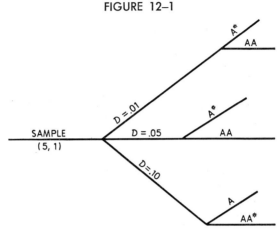

* Optimum act.

one or more defectives in the sample of five, we shall use the batch of A elsewhere and switch to grade AA material.[2] We shall denote this particular decision (sample) rule as (5, 1), which means:

1. Take a sample of five.
2. If one or more defects are found, reject the batch and switch to AA.
3. If less than one defect is found, allow the run to proceed.

In general, this rule will be denoted as (n, c), which means: "Take a sample of n pieces, and if the defectives are less than some criterion, c, accept the run; but reject the run if c or greater defects are found."

Our task is to choose the best n (sample size) and c (criterion number). The larger the n, the more information we get, but the larger the cost. Hence, we have a balancing problem. Let us begin by evaluating an arbitrary decision rule—say (5, 1)—and then compare this with some other rule. After this is done, a procedure for solving the entire problem will be established.

If we use grade A material, the fraction defective may be 0.01, 0.05, or 0.10. These possibilities are shown in the first three branches of the tree shown in Figure 12–1. Given each of these possibilities, we have to accept or reject the run. If we accept it, we shall allow the run to continue, using grade A material. If we reject it, we shall switch to grade AA material. These possibilities are shown in the last six branches of the tree. The best act, given each D or run characteristic, is starred. If the actual characteristic is either 0.01 or 0.05,

---

[2] We shall assume no further batches of grade A material are immediately available.

we should like to accept it; if the characteristic is 0.10, we should like to reject it. Since our sample will not give perfect information, the particular rule we have chosen might possibly lead us to a wrong decision. Our task is to determine the probabilities of taking the right or wrong action, given each possible characteristic. Since the process is Bernoulli, we can use binomial tables to establish these probabilities.

For example, suppose the actual probability of a defective is 0.01, the probability of accepting the run [given a (5, 1) rule] is the probability of finding less than one defective in a sample of five, given that $p = 0.01$. The probability of *rejecting* is the probability of finding one or more defectives in a sample of five. These probabilities can be read out of binomial tables as follows:

0.01 Defective Characteristic

P (Accepting) $= P(R < 1 | p = 0.01, n = 5) = 0.95$
P (Rejecting) $= P(R \geq 1 | p = 0.01, n = 5) = 0.05.$

If the actual characteristic turns out to be 0.05 or 0.10, the following statements are true:

0.05 Defective Characteristic

P (Accepting) $= P(R < 1 | p = 0.05, n = 5) = 0.77$
P (Rejecting) $= P(R \geq 1 | p = 0.05, n = 5) = 0.23.$

0.10 Defective Characteristic

P (Accepting) $= P(R < 1 | p = 0.10, n = 5) = 0.59$
P (Rejecting) $= P(R \geq 1 | p = 0.10, n = 5) = 0.41.$

Remember, the correct acts are:

Accept if 0.01 defective; i.e., use A.
Accept if 0.05 defective; i.e., use A.
Reject if 0.10 defective; i.e., use AA.

The (5, 1) rule gives a probability of 0.95 of taking the correct action if the actual characteristic is 0.01; but if the actual characteristic is 0.10, it gives a 0.59 probability of making an error (accepting the run using A when we should switch to AA).

At this point, we may now redraw our tree and fill in the probabilities of each branch occurring (see Figure 12–2). We now know the probabilities of the (5, 1) rule leading to certain actions, but we also need to know the costs of errors. The conditional costs of each act are summarized in Table 12–3. It will be recalled that the opportunity loss is the amount by which the best act, given each event, is better than every other possible act. Table 12–4 shows opportunity losses of the two acts.

FIGURE 12–2

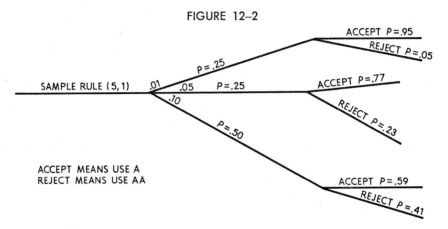

If the manufacturer switches to grade AA when the actual run characteristic using grade A is 0.01, he is $12.50 worse off than if he had allowed the run to continue. Likewise, the manufacturer incurs a $10.00 loss by allowing a run to continue when the run characteristic is actually 0.10 defective.

TABLE 12–3

Conditional Costs

Event D	Act	
	Grade A Material	Grade AA Material
0.01 defective.......	$ 2.50	$15.00
0.05 defective.......	12.50	15.00
0.10 defective.......	25.00	15.00

TABLE 12–4

Opportunity Losses

Event D	Act	
	Grade A Material	Grade AA Material
0.01 defective.......	$ 0.00	$12.50
0.05 defective.......	0.00	2.50
0.10 defective.......	10.00	0.00

We are now prepared to evaluate a (5, 1) sample rule against action without sampling. The tree diagram of Figure 12–3 illustrates the possible outcomes. The manufacturer, at the start, may decide not to sample. If he makes this choice, he can (1) use A material

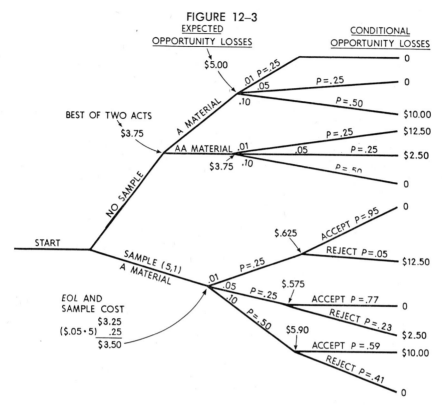

FIGURE 12–3

(with a $5.00 *EOL*) or (2) use AA material (with a $3.75 *EOL*). As a third alternative, the manufacturer may decide to start with A material and then sample to decide whether or not to allow the run to proceed. If he makes his sample decision based on our arbitrary (5, 1) sample rule, sampling and then acting has a loss of $3.50, which is 25 cents better than the best act without sampling; hence, he should sample. Let us now go into detail on how the opportunity loss of $3.50 is computed.

Referring to the branch marked "Sample," the characteristic of the A material may be 0.01, 0.05, or 0.10 defective (with probability 0.25, 0.25, and 0.50, respectively). Given a (5, 1) sample rule, the manufacturer can make an error; and if he does, he will incur an opportunity loss. The sample rule will be in error if:

1. The actual run characteristic is 0.01 and the sample produces one or more defects (in which case the run will be rejected). This error involves a loss of $12.50, since we switch to AA when A is good. The conditional probability of an error is 0.05, since this is the probability of one or more defects in a sample of five, given a 0.01 characteristic.

The *joint* probability of the characteristic being 0.01 *and rejecting this setting* is $0.25 \cdot 0.05 = 0.0125$.

2. The actual characteristic is 0.05, and the sample produces one or more defects. The cost of error in this case is $2.50, and the joint probability of incurring this loss is $0.25 \cdot 0.23 = 0.0575$.

3. The actual characteristic is .10, and the sample *produces less* than one defective. In this case the run will be accepted when it should be rejected, and a loss of $10.00 will be incurred. The joint probability of incurring this loss is $0.50 \cdot 0.59 = 0.295$.

The *EOL* of the (5, 1) sample rule is shown in Table 12–5.

TABLE 12–5

Run Characteristic	Conditional Opportunity Loss	Joint Probability	Expected Opportunity Loss
0.01 defective.............	$12.50	0.0125	$0.15
0.05 defective.............	2.50	0.0575	0.15
0.10 defective.............	10.00	0.2950	2.95
Total *EOL*...			$3.25
Sampling cost (5 pieces times $0.05).............................			0.25
Total *EOL* and Sampling Costs................................			$3.50

Instead of using opportunity losses to determine the desirability of sampling, we could have used conditional costs of the various outcomes and taken their expectations. We would have found the expected cost of not sampling to be $15.00 and the expected cost of sampling with a (5, 1) sample rule to be $14.75 (including the 25-cent cost of the sample). The difference in the two expected costs is 25 cents, which is the same difference we get if we compare the expected opportunity losses of the two acts (the two acts are "Sample" and "No sample").

THE BEST SAMPLE RULE

The above calculations indicate that the manufacturer should sample. The *EOL* of the best act without sampling is $3.75, and this can be reduced by 25 cents with a (5, 1) sample plan. The question is: Will any other sample plan reduce the *EOL* more? The answer is yes, and we shall now turn our attention to finding the optimal sample plan.

The procedure will be as follows:

1. For each sample size used, find the best *c* (criterion) number.
2. Then, compare sample sizes to find the one with the lowest opportunity loss.

FINDING THE BEST CRITERION NUMBER

We have concluded that a (5, 1) sample rule is a good plan but perhaps not the best. Let us now consider a (5, 2) rule to see if a c number of two is better than one.

The calculation of expected cost is shown in Figure 12–4.

FIGURE 12–4

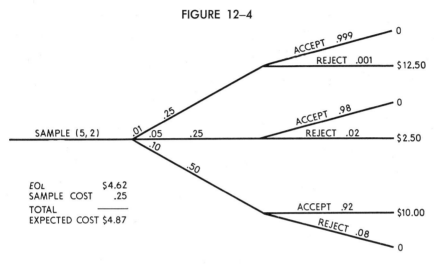

The probabilities for "Accept" in Figure 12–4 are the binomial probabilities $P(R < 2|n = 5, p)$. The expected cost of $4.87 leads us to conclude that the (5, 2) rule is inferior to the (5, 1) rule, which has an expected cost of $3.50. The (5, 2) rule makes it more difficult to reject the process and gives more weight to the $10.00 loss if the actual run characteristic is 0.10. This plan gives better error control when the run characteristic is 0.01 and 0.05 but inferior error control if the run characteristic is 0.10, as shown in Table 12–6.

TABLE 12–6

Run Characteristic	Probability of Error	
	Rule (5, 1)	Rule (5, 2)
0.01 defective.........	0.05	0.001
0.05 defective.........	0.23	0.02
0.10 defective.........	0.59	0.92

Use of a c of three, four, or five would be even less desirable, and we can conclude that, given a sample size of five, the best possible c number is one; there is no need to compute losses for (5, 3), (5, 4), and so forth. The reason for this is that raising the c number makes it even more difficult to reject the process; hence, more weight will be given to the $10.00 loss involved in the event "the run characteristic is 0.10."

THE BEST SAMPLE SIZE

The objective is to balance the additional cost of sampling against the additional (better) information obtained by a larger sample. The procedure will be to choose three samples of different sizes, find the best criterion number for each sample size, and try to "straddle" the minimum EOL plus sampling cost. Let us now examine the procedure.

We have shown above that the total loss using a (5, 1) sample rule is $3.50. Suppose we test a sample size of 14 and 20 units. The method of calculation is exactly the same as above, and is shown in Tables 12–7 and 12–8.

TABLE 12–7
Sample Size of 14

| Run Characteristic | Prob- abilities | Conditional Losses | Probability of Error | | EOL | |
			(14, 1)	(14, 2)	(14, 1)	(14, 2)
0.01 defective.....	0.25	$12.50	0.131	0.01	$0.41	$0.03
0.05 defective.....	0.25	2.50	0.512	0.15	0.32	0.09
0.10 defective.....	0.50	10.00	0.229	0.59	1.14	2.95
	1.00					
EOL..					$1.87*	$3.07*
Sampling cost ($0.05 times 14 units)........................					0.70	0.70
Total Loss...					$2.57	$3.77

* Calculation of *EOL:*
  $1.87 = [$12.50(0.25)(0.131) + $2.50(0.25)(0.512) + $10.00(0.50)(0.229)]$
  $3.07 = [$12.50(0.25)(0.01) + $2.50(0.25)(0.15) + $10.00(0.50)(0.59)]$

TABLE 12–8
Sample Size of 20

| Run Characteristic | Prob- abilities | Conditional Losses | Probability of Error | | EOL | |
			(20, 1)	(20, 2)	(20, 1)	(20, 2)
0.01 defective.....	0.25	$12.50	0.182	0.02	$0.57	$0.06
0.05 defective.....	0.25	2.50	0.642	0.26	0.40	0.16
0.10 defective.....	0.50	10.00	0.122	0.39	0.61	1.95
	1.00					
EOL..					$1.58	$2.17
Sampling cost ($0.05) times 20 units)........................					1.00	1.00
Total Loss...					$2.58	$3.17

The calculations show that the best criterion number for sample sizes of 14 and 20 is one. Now, let us compare the expected costs of using sample sizes of five, 14, and 20. The loss goes down as the sample size increases to 14 and then increases for a sample of 20. This means that a sample size of 20 results in increased sample costs and the value of increased information is not as large. The best sample size seems to be around 14, and our problem now is to test sample sizes on each side of 14. This is done in Table 12–9; it can be seen

TABLE 12–9
Expected Costs of Sample Rule (n, c)

Sample Rule (n, c)	Expected Opportunity Loss	Sample Cost	Total
(5, 1)...........	$3.25	$0.25	$3.50
(10, 1)...........	2.31	0.50	2.80
(12, 1)...........	2.03	0.60	2.63
(13, 1)...........	1.95	0.65	2.60
(14, 1)...........	1.87	0.70	2.57
(15, 1)...........	1.80	0.75	2.55
(15, 2)...........	2.86	0.75	3.61
(16, 1)...........	1.73	0.80	2.53 ← optimum plan
(16, 2)...........	2.69	0.80	3.49
(17, 1)...........	1.69	0.85	2.54
(17, 2)...........	2.57	0.85	3.42

that (16, 1) is the best sample rule, with an expected loss of $2.53. By using this rule, the manufacturer can reduce the loss from $3.75 (the lowest *EOL* without sampling) to $2.53. Since the $2.53 includes the sampling cost, the manufacturer has increased the expected profit of the best act by $3.75 − $2.53 = $1.22 by sampling.

Using the above procedure, we would make the computations before the sample was taken and would arrive at a sample rule such as the (16, 1) rule just derived. A sample would then be taken and a decision made without any further computation. In the following section a procedure is developed where computations are made to determine the best act after the sample evidence is obtained. This procedure assumes the absence of a predetermined decision rule.

SAMPLING AND THE REVISION OF PRIOR PROBABILITIES

In the preceding section, we discussed the conditions under which sampling is appropriate and also showed a method for determining the best sample rule. This analysis is performed *before* the sample is taken. The problems are whether or not to sample and, if sampling is desirable, how large a sample should be taken. Sample information has value if it reduces the cost of uncertainty; this cost, in turn, depends on the original prior probabilities used to evaluate the expected value of the best act.

In this section, we shall discuss the problem of revising prior probabilities as a result of a sample and thus incorporate additional information into the analysis. Specifically, we shall assume that a sample has been taken, and we now must determine the best act. To calculate the expected value of the various acts after the sample, we must revise our prior probabilities to incorporate the additional evidence and then compute expected values using these revised prior probabilities.

In the example of the previous section, the expected cost of using grade A material is $16.25 versus an expected cost of $15.00 of using grade AA material. From this, we conclude that the best act, based on available information, is to use grade AA material.

However, it would be possible to use grade A material, run off a small sample, and then decide whether the batch of grade A material is inferior, and thus shift to the use of grade AA material. Let us assume that a sample of 16 pieces *has been* taken and that two defectives have been found. We shall now consider the question of how the original prior probability distribution should be revised, and we shall verify that the best act is to switch to grade AA raw material.

In analyzing the sample information, the first step is to compute the probability of getting two defectives in a sample of 16 pieces. This probability is a *conditional* probability, in the sense that it depends on what the state of the process is, i.e., 0.01, 0.05, or 0.10 defective. Thus, we must compute three conditional probabilities. The R represents the result of the sample—in this case the number of defectives in the sample of 16 pieces.

$P(R = 2|p = 0.01, n = 16)$ Conditional probability of two defectives, given a sample of 16 and a fraction defective of 0.01.

$P(R = 2|p = 0.05, n = 16)$ Conditional probability of two defectives, given a sample of 16 and a fraction defective of 0.05.

$P(R = 2|p = 0.10, n = 16)$ Conditional probability of two defectives, given a sample of 16 and a fraction defective of 0.10.

A simpler form of presentation is $P(R = 2|0.01, 16)$.

These conditional probabilities can be calculated from the binomial tables (Table E in Appendix at the end of the text) as follows:

$$P(R = 2|0.01, 16) = P(R \geq 2|0.01, 16) - P(R \geq 3|0.01, 16)$$
$$= 0.0109 - 0.0005 = 0.0104$$
$$P(R = 2|0.05, 16) = P(R \geq 2|0.05, 16) - P(R \geq 3|0.05, 16)$$
$$= 0.1892 - 0.0429 = 0.1463$$
$$P(R = 2|0.10, 16) = P(R \geq 2|0.10, 16) - P(R \geq 3|0.10, 16)$$
$$= 0.4853 - 0.2108 = 0.2745.$$

The conditional probabilities rise as the assumed fraction defective rises. This is reasonable, since if the run characteristic was 0.10, we would expect an average of 1.6 defectives in 16 trials ($16 \cdot 0.10 = 1.6$). The actual number of defects in the sample of 16 is two. Hence the conditional probability rises as the fraction defective rises from 0.01 to 0.10. The conditional probabilities would eventually begin to fall if we allowed the fraction defective to continue to rise above 0.10.

TABLE 12–10

State	Prior Probabilities (a Summary of Information before the Sample Is Taken)	Conditional Probabilities (a Summary of the Sample Information)
0.01 defective............	0.25	0.0104
0.05 defective............	0.25	0.1463
0.10 defective............	0.50	0.2745
	1.00	

Let us now summarize our information. This is done in Table 12–10. We now have two sets of probabilities—a set of prior probabilities (0.25, 0.25, 0.50) and a set of conditional probabilities (0.0104, 0.1463, 0.2745). We can calculate a *joint* probability for each state by multiplying each prior probability by each conditional probability. Refer to equation 2–3 of Chapter 2:

$$P(B|A) = \frac{P(AB)}{P(A)}$$
$$P(AB) = P(B|A) \cdot P(A).$$

The joint probabilities are calculated for each state. The joint probability for the first state is the probability of a 0.01 defective lot *and* finding two defectives in a sample of 16 pieces. Table 12–11 is a table of joint probabilities. The states have been labeled A_1, A_2, and A_3, or, in general, A_i. In the example $P(B)$ is equal to $P(R = 2)$.

The sum of the joint probabilities is 0.1765. This is the *marginal* probability of getting two defectives in a sample of 16 pieces using raw material grade A:

$$P(B) = P(R = 2) = 0.1765$$

TABLE 12–11
Table of Joint Probabilities

State A_i	$P(A_i)$ Original Prior Probabilities	$P(B\|A_i)$ Conditional Probabilities	$P(A_iB)$ Joint Probability $P(R = 2$ and A_i Defective)
$A_1 = 0.01$ defective.....	0.25	0.0104	0.0026
$A_2 = 0.05$ defective.....	0.25	0.1463	0.0366
$A_3 = 0.10$ defective.....	0.50	0.2745	0.1373
	1.00		$P(R = 2) = 0.1765$

The remaining question is how to revise the prior probabilities in the light of the sample information. What we are looking for is the *probability of the various run characteristics* or states (A_1, A_2, and A_3), *given a sample of 16 pieces where we found two defectives*. This is a conditional probability, so we shall use a formula. The formula can be expressed in words as follows:

The Probability of A_i Characteristic, *Given* Two Defectives in a Sample of 16 Pieces $=$ The Joint Probability of A_i Characteristic *and* Two Defectives in a Sample of 16 Pieces / The Marginal Probability of Two Defectives in a Sample of 16 Pieces

This is a variant of the same conditional probability formula we have worked with, namely:

$$P(A|B) = \frac{P(AB)}{P(B)}.$$

The new set of revised prior probabilities is calculated in Table 12–12. The new set of revised probabilities is given in column 3. It

TABLE 12–12
Computation of Revised Prior Probabilities

State A_i	(1) Joint Probability $P(A_i$ and Two Defectives in 16 Pieces) $P(A_iB)$	(2) Marginal Probability P(Two Defectives in Sample of 16 Pieces with Grade A Material) $P(B)$	(3) Revised Prior Probability $P(A_i\|$Two Defectives in Sample of 16 Pieces) $P(A_i\|B) = \dfrac{P(A_iB)}{P(B)}$
$A_1 = 0.01$ defective	$0.0026 = P(A_1B)$	0.1765	$P(A_1\|B) = \dfrac{0.0026}{0.1765} = 0.015$
$A_2 = 0.05$ defective	$0.0366 = P(A_2B)$	0.1765	$P(A_2\|B) = \dfrac{0.0366}{0.1765} = 0.207$
$A_3 = 0.10$ defective	$0.1373 = P(A_3B)$	0.1765	$P(A_3\|B) = \dfrac{0.1373}{0.1765} = 0.778$
	0.1765		1.000

should be noted that they sum to one. Using these revised prior probabilities, we can calculate the expected cost of continuing to use the batch of grade A raw material and decide whether to allow the run to continue or use a different batch of grade AA raw material. This is done in Table 12–13. Based on the revised set of probabilities, it is desirable to switch to grade AA raw material. We shall shift to a

TABLE 12–13

Expected Cost Table Using Revised Probabilities

| | | Grade A Raw Material | |
State	Revised Probabilities	Conditional Cost	Expected Cost
0.01 defective...............	0.015	$ 2.50	$ 0.04
0.05 defective...............	0.207	12.50	2.59
0.10 defective...............	0.778	25.00	19.45
	1.000		$22.08

different batch of raw material, since we know that grade AA material has an expected cost of $15.00, which is less than $22.08, the expected cost of allowing the run to continue. We have assumed that our supply of grade A material is exhausted.

SUMMARY

Let us now summarize the method for revising prior probabilities to take account of additional information. We started out with prior probabilities on each run characteristic. Let us call these probabilities $P(A_1)$, $P(A_2)$, and $P(A_3)$, where $A_1 = 0.01$ defective, $A_2 = 0.05$ defective, and $A_3 = 0.10$ defective. We then found conditional probabilities, after taking the sample, as follows: $P(B|A_1)$, $P(B|A_2)$, $P(B_1A_3)$, where $P(B)$ equaled the probability of R equals two defectives in a sample of 16 pieces. We then computed the joint probabilities of *each* fraction defective *and* two defectives in a sample of 16:

$$P(BA_1) = P(B|A_1)P(A_1)$$
$$P(BA_2) = P(B|A_2)P(A_2)$$
$$P(BA_3) = P(B|A_3)P(A_3).$$

The marginal probability of finding two defectives, $P(B)$, is the sum of the joint probabilities, $P(B) = P(BA_1) + P(BA_2) + P(BA_3)$. The conditional probability of each run characteristic, $P(A_1|B)$, $P(A_2|B)$, $P(A_3|B)$, was then computed by dividing the marginal probability, $P(B)$, into each appropriate joint probability, $P(BA_1)$, $P(BA_2)$, and $P(BA_3)$:

$$P(A_i|B) = \frac{P(BA_i)}{P(B)} = \frac{P(BA_i)}{P(BA_1) + P(BA_2) + P(BA_3)}$$

$$P(A_1|B) = \frac{P(BA_1)}{P(B)}$$

$$P(A_2|B) = \frac{P(BA_2)}{P(B)}$$

$$P(A_3|B) = \frac{P(BA_3)}{P(B)}.$$

The general formula for $P(A_i|B)$ is known as the Bayes theorem. It is important to note that it is a definition of *conditional probability*. The Bayes theorem is the formal mathematical statement of the method we used in our example to revise the prior probabilities to take account of the new sample information.

BIBLIOGRAPHY

NATIONAL BUREAU OF STANDARDS. *The Tables of the Binomial Probability Distribution.* Applied Mathematics Series 6. New York, 1950.

ROMIG, H. G. *Binomial Tables.* New York: John Wiley & Sons, Inc., 1953.

Tables of the Cumulative Binomial Probability Distribution. Cambridge: Harvard University Press, 1955.

Also see the Bibliography of Chapter 2.

PROBLEMS

12–1. *A manufacturer is faced with a problem of deciding how to inspect a particular part as it comes off the assembly line. The parts can be either good or defective, and the manufacturer can choose between two inspection systems. Both inspection systems will give perfect performance on good parts; that is, a good part will never be classified as defective. The two systems differ on classifying defectives. The first device, which is mechanical, will misclassify at a rate of 0.01, 0.05, 0.10, or 0.15, depending on how it is adjusted at the beginning of each production run. A rate of 0.01 means that 0.01 of the lot remains defective after inspection, and so on. Because of the nature of the production run, once the machine is adjusted, it cannot be readjusted until the next run. The adjustment record for the past one thousand adjustments is as follows:

---

* This problem requires a relatively large amount of time.

Fraction Defectives Misclassified	Number of Occurrences
0.01	100
0.05	300
0.10	500
0.15	100
	1,000

The alternative inspection system is to place a workman on the assembly line, and the experience in the past has been that this system produces only 0.01 misclassifications.

If the workman is used, the incremental cost over the machine will be $25 per production run (a run is 1,000 pieces). However, when a defective is classified as good, there is a cost of reworking the subassembly when the part is used. This cost is 50 cents per part misclassified.

a) Under what conditions would the inspection process be a Bernoulli process?
b) Assuming the conditions in (a) are fulfilled, calculate:
   1) The EMV of the best act
   2) The expected cost under certainty
   3) The $EVPI$
c) Suppose the machine could be adjusted and a sample of up to 50 parts taken to check the adjustment, and then the machine could continue to be used or a workman could be placed on the assembly line for the remainder of the run.
   1) Would a sample of 10 parts be worth while if the cost of sampling is 10 cents per part? What is the best criterion number for a sample of 10?
   2) Is a sample of 20 better than a sample of 10?
   3) What is the maximum sample that would be taken, based on the $EVPI$?

12–2. *A manufacturer produces a special type of gear casting in a process which can be considered a Bernoulli process. His regular machine is in need of repair, but he has a stand-by machine which in the past, after proper adjustment, has had the following defect record:

Fraction Defective	Historical Frequencies
0.01	100
0.05	100
0.10	800
	1,000

For the current run the manufacturer can subcontract the work at a cost of $10.30 per part (500 parts in the run). The incremental

---

* This problem requires a relatively large amount of time.

cost of production is $10, and it costs $5.00 to rework a defective piece.

a) What is the best act without sampling if the historical frequencies are considered prior probabilities? What is the opportunity loss of each act?

b) If it costs 1 cent per piece to sample, would it pay to sample 20 pieces and then decide whether to continue the run on subcontract? What is the best sample rule for a sample of 20?

12–3. A coin is to be flipped, and the probability of a head is unknown. The following prior probabilities are assigned:

Event (Probability of Head on One Toss)	Probability of Event
0.30	0.10
0.40	0.10
0.50	0.80
	1.00

The coin is flipped five times, and four heads occur. Revise the prior probabilities to take account of the new evidence.

12–4. Assume the same situation as given in Problem 12–3, except that in five tosses no heads appear. Revise the prior probabilities. Compare the revised process of Problem 12–3 with Problem 12–4. Does the comparison seem reasonable? Explain.

12–5. A manufacturer assigns the following prior probabilities to the fraction defective in a production process considered Bernoulli:

Event	Probability of Event
0.01 defective	0.20
0.05 defective	0.30
0.10 defective	0.50
	1.00

The rework cost of a defective is 50 cents; the length of run is 1,000 pieces.

a) Compute the expected cost of using the process for a run of 1,000 pieces.

b) A sample of 10 pieces is run off, and two defectives are found. Revise the probabilities to take account of the new information. Compute the expected cost of using the process.

12–6. In the situation of Problem 12–5, suppose the sample of 10 produced no defectives. Revise the priors to take account of this information. Compare the revised priors of Problems 12–5 and 12–6 for reasonableness.

12–7. You produce a product on ten machines. When these machines are in proper adjustment, they produce with 8 per cent defective, and this level of quality is acceptable to your customers. The product is stored in your warehouse in lots of 1,000 units, each lot containing units from the same machine. You have just discovered that one of your machines has been out of adjustment for several days, and has gone undetected because an inexperienced tester has been assigned to that machine. The machine, while it was out of adjustment, produced 40 per cent defective parts. One tenth (10 per cent) of the lots that are stored in your warehouse are 40 per cent defective; and since lots are mixed up on being transferred from factory to warehouse, you have no way of knowing, without testing, which are the good lots (8 per cent defective) and which lots are bad (40 per cent defective).

Your customers will balk at receiving a lot which turns out to be bad when they try to use the product, and you value the cost of sending a customer a bad lot (40 per cent defective) at $500 per lot (cost of replacing defectives and lost customer good will).

You could sell the lots as being of inferior quality, but you would receive $100 per lot less than if they were sold as good quality.

Your assistant has suggested taking a sample of one item from each lot, and deciding upon the basis of the sample whether to sell the lot as a good-quality or inferior-quality one. Sampling involves destruction of the product, and the cost is $15 per item sampled.

Assume three alternatives:

a) Sell all the lots as good-quality lots, and incur the cost of $500 on those that turn out bad.

b) Sell all the lots as inferior-quality lots at a discount of $100 from the price of a good lot.

c) Take a sample of one item from each lot. Decide on the basis of the sample whether the lot is good or inferior, and sell it as such.

   1) Draw up a pay-off table for the first two alternatives. Without sampling, what would be your decision?

   2) Assume you sample. If the sampled item is not defective, should the lot be sold as being of good or inferior quality? What should be done if the sampled item is defective?

   3) What is the expected cost of each of the three alternatives above? Which should be selected?

Chapter 13

DECISION MAKING WITH

A BERNOULLI PROCESS

DECISION making in many situations may depend upon knowing or estimating p, the parameter or characteristic of a Bernoulli process. In the previous chapter the process characteristic, p, was allowed to take on only selected discrete values. These values were assigned prior probabilities, which were then revised based upon sample evidence. The probability function of p is now allowed to be a continuous probability distribution function rather than a discrete mass function, and p may take on any value $(0 \leq p \leq 1)$. This results in a simplification of some of the computations made previously, though it does require the introduction of additional symbols and terms.

THE BETA PROBABILITY DISTRIBUTION

The beta distribution is a probability distribution of the following form:[1]

(13-1) $\qquad f_B(x|a, b) = \dfrac{(b - 1)!}{(a - 1)!(b - a - 1)!} x^{a-1}(1 - x)^{b-a-1}$

where x is the random variable $(0 \leq x \leq 1)$, and a and b are parameters of the distribution (a and b are both $\geq$ zero). The mean or expected value of x is $E(x) = \dfrac{a}{b}$. The distribution function can take on many shapes over the range $0 \leq x \leq 1$, as shown in Figures 13-1

---

[1] The beta distribution is often written as:
$$f(x) = \frac{(\alpha + \beta + 1)!}{\alpha! \, \beta!} \times x^{\alpha}(1 - x)^{\beta}$$
but can be put in the above form by letting $\beta = b - a - 1$ and $\alpha = a - 1$.

FIGURE 13–1

The Beta Distribution for Various Values of a and b

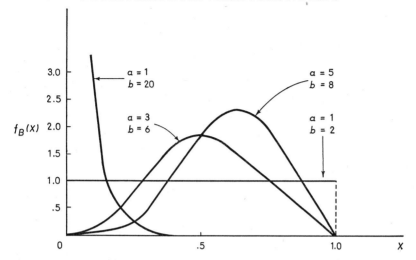

and 13–2. Note that the variance of the distribution decreases as b increases $\left[$ for a given $E(x) = \dfrac{a}{b}\right]$, as shown in Figure 13–2. The beta distribution is symmetric only for $E(x) = 0.5$. However, as b becomes large, the distribution becomes more symmetric for any value of $E(x)$.

We wish to use the beta distribution as a prior probability dis-

FIGURE 13–2

Beta Distribution for Various Values of a and b with E(x) = 0.5

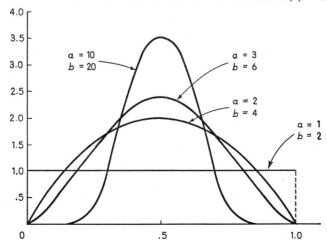

tribution for the unknown value of p—the Bernoulli process characteristic. First, we shall examine the beta distribution in more detail.

Example 1

Assume that the parameters of the Beta distribution are $a = 3$ and $b = 4$. The computation for $f_B(x = \frac{1}{4})$ is:

$$f_B\left(\frac{1}{4}\Big|3, 4\right) = \frac{(4-1)!}{(3-1)!(4-3-1)!}\left(\frac{1}{4}\right)^{3-1}\left(\frac{3}{4}\right)^{4-3-1}$$
$$= \frac{3\cdot 2}{2} \times \left(\frac{1}{4}\right)^2 \times \left(\frac{3}{4}\right)^0$$
$$= \frac{3}{16}.$$

Example 2

Assume $a = 1$ and $b = 2$. The value of the beta density function for any value of x:

$$f_B(x|1, 2) = \frac{(2-1)!}{(1-1)!(2-1-1)!}x^{1-1}(1-x)^{2-1-1} = 1.$$

The results of Example 2 are important. A prior probability distribution which is rectangular (all possible values have equal likelihood) can actually be represented by a beta distribution with a equal to one and b equal to two.

EVALUATING BETA PROBABILITIES

For continuous distributions, it is generally more useful to evaluate areas under the density function rather than the height of the function itself. Accordingly, we shall evaluate the area in the tails of the beta distribution. The left tail of the beta distribution is related to the right tail of the binomial distribution, and we can utilize binomial tables (Table E at the end of this volume) to evaluate beta probabilities.[2]

Because of certain relationships which we shall consider later in revising the beta distribution, it is convenient to use the equivalent binomial symbols p, n, and r in the beta function. Thus, we can rewrite the beta function as:

---

[2] This can be done, of course, only for integer values of a and b, since the binomial distribution is restricted to integer values for r and n. The beta function is defined for noninteger values of a and b, but more detailed tables are needed. See K. Pearson, "Tables of the Incomplete Beta-Function," *Biometrika*, 1948 (London).

(13-2) $f_B(p|r, n) = \dfrac{(n-1)!}{(r-1)!(n-r-1)!}p^{r-1}(1-p)^{n-r-1}$

where p is the random variable. It is important to understand that n and r, as used above, are simply parameters of the beta function. Using these new symbols, we can evaluate beta values as follows:

For $p \leq \frac{1}{2}$:

(13-3) $F_B(p|r, n) = G_b(r|p, n-1) = \text{Prob}(R \geq r|p, n-1)$

and for $p \geq \frac{1}{2}$:

(13-4) $F_B(p|r, n) = 1 - G_b(n-r|1-p, n-1)$
$= 1 - \text{Prob}(R \geq n - r|1 - p, n - 1)$

where F_B represents the cumulative (left-tail) beta probability as shown in Figure 13-3 and G_b is the cumulative (right-tail) binomial probability (in Table E). (The subscript B refers to the beta distribution and the subscript b to the binomial.)

Example

Given a beta distribution with $r = 3$ and $n = 6$, find the probability that p is less than or equal to 0.3:

$$\text{Prob}(p \leq 0.3) = F_B(0.3|r = 3, n = 6).$$

Using equation 13-3, the required probability is:

$$F_B(0.3|r = 3, n = 6) = G_b(r = 3|p = 0.3, n - 1 = 5)$$

and the latter term is the binomial probability $\text{Prob}(R \geq 3|0.3, 5)$, which is 0.1631 from Table E.

FIGURE 13-3

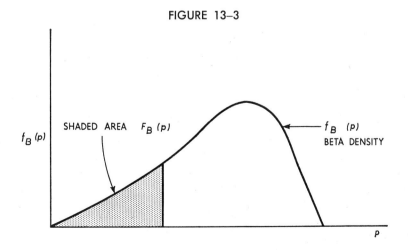

THE BETA FUNCTION AS A PRIOR DISTRIBUTION

The beta function will be used to represent the decision maker's uncertainty about the value of p—the Bernoulli process characteristic. As such, it is primarily a subjective distribution (although historical evidence may be implicitly included). We shall consider how the decision maker could convert his judgment into a specific beta distribution. Note that the mean or expected value of the distribution is given by:

$$(13\text{--}5) \qquad\qquad E(p) = \frac{r}{n}.$$

The mode, or highest point, of the beta density is given by:

$$(13\text{--}6) \qquad\qquad \text{Mode} = \frac{r-1}{n-2}.$$

Thus, if the decision maker can estimate the most likely value of p (the most likely value equals the mode) and can make some estimate of the average or expected value of p, he can solve the above two equations for the beta parameters n and r.

Note that if the distribution is symmetric [i.e., $E(p) = \frac{1}{2}$], the above procedure breaks down, since the mean equals the mode. However, if the decision maker can make an estimate of the variance of p, he can use equation 13–7 below, together with equation 13–5, to obtain values of r and n.

$$(13\text{--}7) \qquad\qquad \text{Var}(p) = \frac{r(n-r)}{n^2(n+1)}.$$

Example 1

Suppose the prior most likely value of p is one fourth but the prior expected p is one third. That is:

$$E(p) = \frac{r}{n} = \frac{1}{3}.$$

and

$$\text{Mode} = \frac{r-1}{n-2} = \frac{1}{4}.$$

From the first equation, $n = 3r$. Substituting in the second gives:

$$4r - 4 = 3r - 2.$$

Solving gives $r = 2$ and $n = 6$.

Example 2

The decision maker sets the expected value of p at one half and Var(p) at 0.05. We have:

$$\text{Var}\,(p) = \frac{r(n-r)}{n^2(n+1)} = 0.05$$

and

$$E\,(p) = \frac{r}{n} = \frac{1}{2}.$$

From the second equation, $n = 2r$. Substituting in the first gives:

$$r(2r - r) = 0.05(2r)^2\,(2r+1).$$

Dividing by $0.05r^2$ gives:

$$20 = 8r + 4.$$

Solving gives $r = 2$ and $n = 4$.

The decision maker should check that the probabilities associated with the values of r and n derived from the above techniques correspond with his intuitive judgments. Thus, in Example 2 above, the probability that p is less than one fourth is:

$$F_B(\tfrac{1}{4}|r = 2, n = 4) = G_b(2|\tfrac{1}{4}, 3) = 0.1563 \text{ (from Table E)}$$

Before accepting the parameters of $r = 2$, $n = 4$, the decision maker should agree that the above probability is consistent with his judgment.

THE POSTERIOR BETA DISTRIBUTION

The prior beta distribution was concerned with the value of p, the Bernoulli process characteristic. To obtain additional information about p, we can take a sample. The random variable of the sample is the number of successes obtained and is binomially distributed. The prior distribution can then be revised to obtain a posterior distribution used for decision-making purposes.

Let us designate the parameters of the prior beta distribution by r_0 and n_0. (The zero subscript is associated with the prior distribution and the subscript one with the posterior distribution.)

Then, n trials from the Bernoulli process are taken (i.e., a sample of size n is taken), and r successes are found (no subscripts with the sample values).

Then *the posterior distribution will be a beta distribution with parameters r_1 and n_1, where:*

(13–8)
$$r_1 = r_0 + r$$

and

(13–9)
$$n_1 = n_0 + n.$$

Example 1

The prior distribution of p is a beta distribution with $r_0 = 5$ and $n_0 = 10$. A sample of 10 items is taken, and three are successes (i.e., $r = 3, n = 10$). The posterior distribution is then a beta distribution with parameters

$r_1 = r_0 + r = 5 + 3 = 8$ and $n_1 = n_0 + n = 10 + 10 = 20.$

Example 2

A certain politician assigns a beta distribution with parameters $r_0 = 4$ and $n_0 = 10$ to p, the percentage of votes he will receive in the forthcoming election. A random sample of 10 voters are queried, and seven indicate an intention of voting for the politician. What probability should the politician assign his winning [i.e., $\text{Prob}(p \geq 0.5)$]? Now:

$$r_1 = r_0 + r = 4 + 7 = 11$$

and

$$n_1 = n_0 + n = 10 + 10 = 20.$$

$E(p) = \dfrac{11}{20} = 0.55$ for the posterior distribution. His expected

majority is 55 per cent. Using equation 13–4, we have:

$$F_B(\tfrac{1}{2}|r_1 = 11, n_1 = 20) = G_b(11|\tfrac{1}{2}, 19) = 0.3238$$

Hence the politician should estimate his probability of winning at 0.6762 (i.e., $1 - 0.3238$).

Once we have determined the above rule for revising beta distributions, an alternative method for setting the initial prior distribution is apparent. The prior distribution with $r_0 = 1$ and $n_0 = 2$ is a rectangular distribution, with all values of p equally likely (see Figure 13–1). Any other prior can be broken down into two parts: (a) the rectangular prior and (b) a fictitious sample with $r_0 - 1$ successes in $n_0 - 2$ trials. For example, if the decision maker set $r_0 = 4$ and $n_0 = 10$, it could be said that this choice was the same as if he started with a rectangular distribution and then sampled and found three successes ($r_0 - 1 = 3$) in eight trials ($n_0 - 2 = 8$). Thus the decision maker can select his prior beta distribution based on a fictitious sample.

DECISION MAKING WITH LINEAR LOSS FUNCTIONS

Let us assume that the economic costs or losses are a linear function of p, the unknown Bernoulli characteristic. The decision will depend upon the relative position of p_b, the break-even value of p, and $E(p)$, the expected value. An example will help to illustrate this. A certain lot of 1,000 items contains an unknown percentage defective, denoted by p. Suppose that a defective causes rework costs of 50 cents. A new lot (with no defectives) could be purchased for $100. If the lot is 20 per cent defective, the cost of using the old lot would be the same as purchasing the new lot. Thus, $p_b = 0.20$. If $p \leq 0.20$, the old lot is preferable. The loss function can be written as:

$500(p - 0.2)$ if $p \geq 0.2$ and the old lot is used

or

$500(0.2 - p)$ if $p \leq 0.2$ and the new lot is used.

Suppose the decision maker has a beta prior distribution for p with parameters $r_0 = 1$, $n_0 = 8$. The prior $E(p) = \dfrac{r_0}{n_0} = \dfrac{1}{8} = 0.125$; and since this is less than $p_b = 0.20$, the optimum action (a priori) is to use the old lot. Suppose a sample of ten items is taken from the lot and three defectives are found. The posterior beta parameters are:

$$n_1 = n_0 + n = 8 + 10 = 18$$
$$r_1 = r_0 + r = 1 + 3 = 4$$

and the posterior $E(p) = \dfrac{r_1}{n_1} = \dfrac{4}{18} = 0.22$. Since 0.22 is greater than the break-even p of 0.2, the new lot should be purchased.

The expected value of perfect information ($EVPI$) can be computed at any stage in the decision process by the following formulas:

If $p_b \leq E(p)$:

(13–10) $EVPI = C[p_b F_B(p_b|r, n) - E(p)F_B(p_b|r + 1, n + 1)]$

If $p_b \geq E(p)$:

(13–11) $EVPI = C[p_b F_B(p_b|r, n)$
$$- E(p)F_B(p_b|r + 1, n + 1) - (p_b - E(p))]$$

where C is the economic loss per unit of p, p_b is the break-even value of p, and r and n are the parameters of the beta distribution.

Example

In the illustration above, we can compute the $EVPI$ for the prior distribution: $C = \$500$, $r_0 = 1$, $n_0 = 8$, and $p_b = 0.2$. Since $p_b \geq E(p)$, we use equation 13–11:

$$EVPI = 500[0.2F_B(0.2|1, 8) - 0.125F_B(0.2|2, 9) - (0.2 - 0.125)]$$

where

$$F_B(0.2|1, 8) = G_b(1|0.2, 7) = 0.7903$$

and

$$F_B(0.2|2, 9) = G_b(2|0.2, 8) = 0.4967$$

giving

$$EVPI = 500[(0.2)(0.7903) - (0.125)(0.4967) - 0.075] = \$10.50.$$

Posterior to the sample, $p_b \leq E(p)$; and equation 13–10 is appropriate, with $r_1 = 4$ and $n_1 = 18$:

$$EVPI = 500[0.2F_B(0.2|4, 18) - 0.222F_B(0.2|5, 19)]$$

where

$$F_B(0.2|4, 18) = G_b(4|0.2, 17) = 0.4511$$

and

$$F_B(0.2|5, 19) = G_b(5|0.2, 18) = 0.2836$$

giving

$$EVPI = 500[(0.2)(0.4511) - (0.222)(0.2836)] = \$13.63.$$

Note that the posterior $EVPI$ turns out to be greater than the prior $EVPI$. In general this would not be the case. Samples would generally reduce posterior $EVPI$. In this case the sample moved the posterior expected value closer to the break-even point than it had been previously.

ESTIMATING p: SQUARED ERROR LOSSES

Suppose that instead of a linear loss function, as above, the loss is some constant, C, times the square of the difference between our estimated p (say, p_e) and the true value of p(say, p_z). That is:

$$\text{Loss} = C(p_z - p_e)^2.$$

We would like to find an appropriate estimator, p_e. The estimator to minimize the above loss is $p_e = \dfrac{r_1}{n_1}$, where r_1 and n_1 are the parameters of the posterior beta distribution.

Previously, in discussing the linear loss function, it was assumed that a loss only occurred if the true p was less than the break-even p (when the loss sloped upward to the left) or larger than the true p (when the loss sloped upward to the right). The computations in this situation assume a loss if the estimate differs from the actual p, and the loss is not influenced by the direction of the difference.

The expected value of perfect information in this situation is:

$$(13\text{–}12) \qquad EVPI = C\frac{r_1(n_1 - r_1)}{n_1{}^2(n_1 + 1)} = C\,\mathrm{Var}(p).$$

The subscript one in the above equation refers to a posterior distribution. The $EVPI$ for a prior distribution can be obtained by replacing the one by a zero subscript.

There are actually two different approaches to decision making being discussed. One approach is to choose the better of two alternative acts. This decision was illustrated using the linear loss function. The second approach to the decision process is to make an estimate of p, with the losses being caused by the true p being different from the estimated p. With this second approach the estimate of p becomes the decision. In the first approach the information relative to the p is used indirectly to make an economic decision. Both approaches lead to a computation of the expected opportunity loss, which in turn may lead to a decision to gather more information.

Example

The decision maker has no prior information about p and assumes a rectangular prior distribution. The loss function is:

$$\$10{,}000(p_z - p_e)^2 = \text{Loss}$$

where p_e is the estimate of p, $\left(p_e = \dfrac{r_1}{n_1}\right)$, and p_z is the actual value of p. A sample is taken with three successes in six trials ($r = 3$, $n = 6$). The posterior beta parameters are

$$r_1 = r_0 + r = 1 + 3 = 4$$

and

$$n_1 = n_0 + n = 2 + 6 = 8$$

and the posterior $E(p) = \dfrac{r_1}{n_1} = \dfrac{4}{8} = 0.5$. The posterior expected value of perfect information is:

$$EVPI = C\frac{r_1(n_1 - r_1)}{n_1^2(n_1 + 1)} = \$10{,}000\frac{(4)(4)}{(8^2)(9)} = \$278.$$

DECISIONS NOT DISCUSSED

In the previous chapter, we solved problems involving the decision whether to buy imperfect information and, if so, how much. In this chapter, we have computed the expected value of perfect information (the expected opportunity loss) and revised information based on sample information, but have not attempted to quantify the value of expected information and determine the optimum sampling rule. This omission occurs because the calculations become very complex and are beyond the scope of this text. At this point the reader should know how to revise a beta distribution based on sample information and how to compute the expected opportunity loss (i.e., expected value of perfect information).

BIBLIOGRAPHY

RAIFFA, H., and SCHLAIFER, R. *Applied Statistical Decision Theory.* Boston: Graduate School of Business Administration, Harvard University, 1961. Many of the relationships described in this chapter are adapted from this book.

Also see the bibliographies of Chapters 2 and 12.

PROBLEMS

13-1. A beta distribution with random variable x has parameters $a = 2$, $b = 3$. Find:

a) $f_B(x = \frac{1}{2})$ d) $F_B(x = \frac{1}{2})$
b) $f_B(x = \frac{2}{3})$ e) $F_B(x = \frac{2}{3})$
c) $f_B(x = \frac{9}{10})$ f) $F_B(x = 1.0)$

13-2. A beta distribution with random variable p has parameters $r = 1$, $n = 5$. Find:

a) $f_B(p = \frac{1}{10})$ d) $F_B(p = \frac{1}{10})$
b) $f_B(p = \frac{1}{5})$ e) $F_B(p = \frac{1}{5})$
c) $f_B(p = \frac{1}{2})$ f) $F_B(p = \frac{1}{2})$

13-3. A decision maker decides upon a prior beta distribution for the random variable p, a Bernoulli process characteristic. The prior parame ters are $r_0 = 1$ and $n_0 = 5$. A sample of ten is taken, with two successes.

    a) Before the sample, what value has the decision maker assigned to Prob($p \leq 0.10$)?

    b) After the sample, what value should the decision maker assign to Prob($p \leq 0.10$)?

13–4. Indicate an appropriate beta distribution for the following cases (i.e., find the beta parameters):

    a) Expected value = $\frac{1}{4}$, mode = $\frac{2}{9}$

    b) Expected value = $\frac{1}{5}$, mode = $\frac{1}{8}$

    c) Expected value = $\frac{1}{2}$, variance = $\frac{1}{36}$

    d) Expected value = $\frac{1}{5}$, mode close to $\frac{1}{5}$, variance = 0.0016

13–5. The Outrageous Outboard Motor Company manufactured many of the components for its motors. Part No. 1317–C–19 was a newly designed needle valve assembly for the carburetor and was designed to fit with fairly close tolerances. This part was used at the rate of about 10,000 per year and was produced for inventory in lots of 1,000 each.

    A circular aluminum base was produced on an elaborate automatic aluminum-casting machine, and this part was frequently a source of malfunction. The difficulty arose from the fact that when the casting machine was not in perfect adjustment, the aluminum base did not fit properly, and the carburetor then caused the motor to idle improperly. A defect of this nature was discovered when the completed motor was tested; and when it occurred, the defective part had to be removed and replaced. (Defectives were scrapped and had no salvage value.) Each aluminum base cost 50 cents to manufacture. The labor

FIGURE 13–4

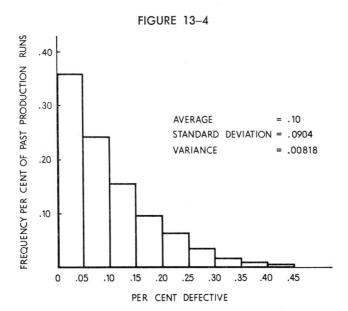

cost for removing and replacing each defective was an additional 50 cents.

The plant manager, Jim Dant, requested Ralph Richards, the plant engineer, to study the problem, suggest alternative courses of action, and recommend a policy.

Upon examining past production records, Richards plotted the histogram in Figure 13–4, showing the relative frequency of per cent defective for the casting machine. As can be seen from the chart, about 75 per cent of the time the casting machine had less than 15 per cent defective, but it occasionally produced as much as 40 per cent defective. The average number defective was 10 per cent, and the standard deviation was 9.04 per cent.

Richards checked with the local sales representative of the casting machine manufacturer and found that if the casting machine was very carefully checked and adjusted before use, it would operate perfectly for a run of over 1,000. Richards estimated this adjustment would cost $80.

Richards also considered the possibility of having the lot 100 per cent inspected. He estimated that a person could inspect an average of 100 per hour, and it would cost $4.00 per hour (including the inspector's hourly wage and other indirect—but traceable— expenses). All defective parts would be eliminated by the inspector.

a) What was the expected cost of each alternative? Which would you recommend?

b) What was the *EVPI* in this decision situation?

c) Suppose a sample of eight items were taken on a given day (before the complete production run) and zero defectives were found in the sample. Which action should be taken, and what would be its expected cost? Use $r_0 = 1$, $n_0 = 10$.

d) What was the posterior *EVPI* after the sample of eight items?

Chapter 14

UTILITY AS A BASIS FOR DECISION MAKING

ASSUME that you are given a choice in each of the following paired alternatives. You may select one of the A choices, one of the B choices, and one of the C choices. Make a note of the set of alternatives you choose.

A_1 = The certainty of a $100,000 gift, tax-free

or

A_2 = On the flip of a fair coin, nothing if it comes up heads, or a tax-exempt gift of $200,002 if the coin turns up tails.

B_1 = A certain loss of $10

or

B_2 = One chance out of 100 of incurring a $900 debt, but a $99/100$ chance of losing nothing.

C_1 = A gift of $10,000, tax-free

or

C_2 = A payment of 2^N cents, where N is the number of times a fair coin is flipped before tails comes up. If tails appears on the first toss, you receive 2 cents; if the coin shows heads on the first toss and tails on the second, you receive 4 cents; two heads in a row followed by tails yields 8 cents; and so forth. However, you are allowed to participate only once: The sequence stops with the first showing of tails.

Most people would choose the set A_1, B_1, and C_1. However, the mathematical expectation (or expected monetary value) favors the alternatives A_2, B_2, and C_2. The expected value of alternative A_2 is one half (the probability of the fair coin showing heads) times zero (the monetary value associated with heads) plus one half (the prob-

191

ability of tails) times $200,002, or $100,001. Since this expected value is $1.00 more than the expected value of choice A_1, you should have selected A_2 *if you wanted to maximize expected monetary value.*

Similarly, with B_2 the expected loss is 99/100 (the appropriate probability) times zero (the amount of loss) plus 1/100 times $900. This amount is $9.00, which is a smaller loss than the certain loss of $10 associated with B_1. If you made decisions so as to minimize expected monetary loss, you would accept the very small chance of a large loss.

The expected monetary value of the game described in C_2 is infinite. The chance of the first tails appearing on the first toss is one half; on the second toss, one fourth; on the third, one eighth; on the fourth, one sixteenth; and so on. The related rewards would be 2 cents, 4 cents, 8 cents, 16 cents, etc. The expected monetary value, by definition, is the sum of the monetary outcomes, weighted by the associated probabilities. In this case:

$$EMV = \tfrac{1}{2}(2\cent) + \tfrac{1}{4}(4\cent) + \tfrac{1}{8}(8\cent) + \tfrac{1}{16}(16\cent) + \ldots$$
$$= 1\cent + 1\cent + 1\cent + 1\cent \ldots = \infty\cent$$

The fact that no prudent man would choose this game in preference to the certainty of a modest amount provides the essentials of the famous St. Petersburg paradox. This paradox led Daniel Bernoulli to the first investigations of utility rather than the expectation of monetary value as a basis of choice making.

UTILITY

Since most people would choose A_1, B_1, and C_1 rather than the alternatives with greater monetary expectation, it seems reasonable to conclude that people do not always make decisions so as to maximize expected monetary value. What, then, is the proper criterion for decision making? Von Neumann and Morgenstern (1944) constructed a framework which was consistent with choices such as A_1, B_1, and C_1. They argued that decisions were made so as to maximize expected *utility* rather than expected monetary value. If you selected A_1 over A_2, we would conclude that alternative A_1 had more utility for you than alternative A_2. If you were indifferent between two alternatives—say, B_1 and B_2—we would conclude that each alternative offered the same expected utility (or, in this case, disutility) to you. Indifference might be defined as your willingness to take either result at random, or have some stranger make the choice for you. It is possible to derive generalizations about a person's utility function for some commodity (most often money) that are consistent with logic and observation of repeated decisions. It follows that it is reasonable to assume that people make decisions so as to maximize expected utility rather than expected value. This is not a painless choice, for expected monetary value is an unambiguous concept, and relatively easy to calculate. It would be quite convenient if we were able to associate expected monetary values with some index of the decision maker's utility. A complex set of alternatives then might be reduced to a set of expected values, which could be transformed into utility measures for purposes of decision making. It is our purpose in this chapter to relate money and a utility index, and to derive generalizations about this relationship in situations involving risk.

MEASURING UTILITY[1]

Is it possible to measure the utility of money? In an attempt to answer this question, we shall consider three different types of measurement scales:

1. Nominal
2. Ordinal
3. Cardinal

A nominal scale assigns a description to a set of elements. The elements may be a physical unit or a condition. The description may be a number, as in a numbering system for baseball players; or it may be an adjective, as when a person says he is hungry or not hungry. A nominal scale is very useful for decision analysis. For example, a set of possible returns might be divided into subsets of satisfactory and unsatisfactory returns. Investments may be divided into two classes, acceptable and unacceptable, on a nominal scale. A form of grading procedure could assign two grades, passing or failing. It is not difficult to conceive of nominal measures of utility. For example, acts could be classified as having negative utility (disutility) or positive utility.

An ordinal measure adds the concept of relative size. Objects become "more" or "less" than other objects. An ordering or ranking is possible. A person can declare a sound is louder than another sound. Different light sources may be ranked by brightness without a number

---

[1] The material presented in this section is to a great extent based on the authors' interpretation of the following two sources: Friedman and Savage (1948); and Luce and Raiffa (1957).

measure being placed on the amount of light. We can choose the winner of a race without the use of a stop watch. An attempt may be made to rank all investments according to their relative desirability (though this process may be easier to describe than to accomplish).

Ordinal measures of utility are used in analyzing situations with riskless choices. Indifference curve analysis collects alternatives with equal utility (i.e., a person is indifferent to these choices), and we compare any of these choices with the choices on another indifference curve which is higher (and more desirable) or lower (and less desirable). If we could rank investments, this would imply that we have an ordinal measure of desirability.

With a cardinal measure, a number is assigned which is a measure of a characteristic. Thus a piece of wood may be a number of inches long, a weight in pounds, and a volume in cubic inches. We can measure in a cardinal sense such things as distance, weight, light, sound, time, heat, and intelligence.

The von Neumann–Morgenstern measure of utility is a special type of cardinal measure (some would say it is a special type of ordinal measure). It measures utility in situations involving risk for the individual decision maker. The use of this utility measure allows us to predict which of several lotteries a person will prefer, and thus enables an employee to make the decision for the employer. Sometimes the employer will make decisions inconsistent with his utility function, but this type of inconsistency can generally be straightened out if the employer reconsiders his decisions.

One justification for the use of utility in investment situations evolves from the fact that other measures cannot adequately cope with uncertainty. Neither net present value nor rate of return are sufficient measures of the worth of an investment with uncertainty. An individual making his own investments will automatically apply his own utility function to the situation. He may do this without knowing that such a function exists. Making the decision helps determine the function. Formal utility analysis finds its most effective use in situations too complex for an individual's intuition, and where a manager is making decisions for his employer.

THE PSYCHOLOGICAL ASSUMPTIONS

The use of utility for purposes of making decisions in the manner described involves assumptions about how an individual reacts to choices. Since we are attempting to measure attitudes toward uncertain situations, it is important that the model used in making the decisions be consistent with the psychological make-up of people.

The following assumptions will be made:

1. With any two alternatives, we can decide whether we are indifferent to them or which one we prefer. This seems to be a trivial requirement, but it is very necessary. In fact, we may find that it is difficult to determine a specific unequivocal reaction to pairs of alternatives. For example, would you prefer $200 for certain or a 50–50 chance at getting zero dollars or $1,000? Change the $200 until your preference is different. Finding the exact point of indifference between the two lotteries is very difficult, and the answer is frequently indecisive.

2. Alternatives are transitive, i.e., if A is preferred to B, and B is preferred to C, then A is preferred to C. Also, if A equals B, and B equals C, then A is equal to C. It is possible, where the degree of preference is slight and the alternatives are many, for a person to give rankings of pairs that are intransitive. This means that on close decisions a person may be inconsistent. For example, a person might say that he prefers a trip to Nassau to a trip to Bermuda, and a trip to Bermuda to a trip to Hawaii, but then say that he prefers a trip to Hawaii to a trip to Nassau. This is intransitive, but it may result from the fact that all three trips sound fine; and while he is trying to give preferences, he is close to being indifferent between three choices. He should be able to eliminate this type of intransitivity by re-examining his decisions.

3. If a person is indifferent to two lotteries, then they may be substituted for each other for purposes of analysis. For example, we previously compared a 50–50 chance of zero dollars and $1,000 with $200 for certain. If you are indifferent between these two lotteries, then we can use the second lottery ($200 for certain) as a means of describing the first. Further, we can say the utilities of the two lotteries are equal.

4. If two lotteries have the same two possible outcomes, but the outcomes have different probabilities, then the lottery with the more favorable outcome having the higher probability is the preferred lottery.

Example

Assume the two lotteries shown in Table 14–1. Lottery A must be preferred.

TABLE 14–1

Possible Outcomes	Probability of Outcomes for Lottery:	
	A	B
$1,000.................	0.80	0.50
0.................	0.20	0.50

5. If A is preferred to B, and B is preferred to C, then there is some lottery involving A and C which is indifferent to B for certain.

Example

Let:

$$A = \$1,000$$
$$B = \$400$$
$$C = \text{Zero dollars}$$

We shall make up a lottery involving A with probability p and C with probability $(1 - p)$. The expected monetary value of the lottery is:

$$A(p) + C(1 - p) = 1,000p + 0(1 - p).$$

What is the value of p which will make you indifferent to the above lottery and B for certain? If there is some value, then assumption 5 is satisfied.

6. If A is preferred to B, and there is some third alternative, C, then any combination of A plus C is preferred to a combination of B plus C, provided the probability assignments are the same in both lotteries. It is required that the probability attached to C be less than one.

Example

Let:

$$A = \$1,000$$
$$B = \$400$$
$$C = \text{Zero dollars}$$

$A(p) + C(1 - p)$ is preferred over $B(p) + C(1 - p)$. If p equals 0.6, then $\$1,000 \times 0.6$ is preferred over $\$400 \times 0.6$; the expectation $\$600$ is preferred over $\$240$.

Assumption 6 can also be expressed as follows: If a combination of A plus C is preferred over a combination of B plus C, with C having

TABLE 14-2

Outcomes	Utility of Outcomes	Probability
A_1...............	$U(A_1)$	p_1
A_2...............	$U(A_2)$	p_2
....	.....	..
....	.....	..
A_n...............	$U(A_n)$	p_n

the same probability (less than one) in both combinations, then A is preferred to B.

7. The utility of a lottery is defined to be equal to the expected utility of its components.

The assumption that the utility of a lottery is the expectation of the component utilities is a convenient assumption for mathematical manipulation.[2] Let us assume a lottery, L, has the outcomes shown in Table 14-2, with each lottery assigned a utility measure and a probability of occurrence.

The utility of the lottery is defined as:

$$U(L_1) = p_1U(A_1) + p_2U(A_2) + \ldots + p_nU(A_n).$$

The lottery L_1 may itself have a probability of occurrence. Assume lottery L_1 has a probability of r and lottery L_2 has a probability of $(1 - r)$. The utility of the two lotteries is $U(L)$:

$$U(L) = rU(L_1) + (1 - r)U(L_2).$$

Example

Assume two lotteries (see Table 14-3):

$$U(L_1) = 0.6 \times 50 + 0.4 \times 0 = 30$$
$$U(L_2) = 1.0 \times 40 = 40.$$

Assume L_1 has a probability of 0.8 and L_2 has a probability of 0.2. The expected utility of the gamble (i.e., the two lotteries) is:

$$U(L) = 0.8 \times 30 + 0.2 \times 40 = 32.$$

Since our scale of utility is arbitrary, we can change the scale and origin without contradicting our assumptions. In particular, if a and b are any two constants, $b > 0$, and if $U(L)$ is a utility function, then $F(L)$ is also a utility function where:

$$F(L) = a + bU(L).$$

---

[2] See Dorfman, Samuelson, and Solow (1958), pp. 465-69, for a proof.

TABLE 14–3

Lottery	Outcomes	Utility of Outcomes	Probability
L_1.........	$1,000	50	0.6
	0	0	0.4
L_2.........	400	40	1.0

That is to say, we can add a constant to a utility function, or we can change the unit (or the slope). It is said that a utility function is unique up to an order preserving linear transformation.[3]

DERIVATION OF A UTILITY FUNCTION FOR MONEY

Assume that you have been assigned the task of evaluating your employer's utility for various possible monetary gains and losses. The purpose might be to provide you and other subordinates with a guide so that you may make decisions that are consistent with the interests of your employer. One procedure for approximating such a function follows.

Formulate an alternative which promises two different rewards (say, zero dollars and $10,000), with equal subjective probability to your employer (i.e., he would be indifferent between this opportunity and one where he would receive zero if a fair coin came up on one side or $10,000 if it came up on the other). Assign an arbitrary index to these amounts, the only restriction being that the index for $10,-000 be greater than the index for zero dollars. This is going to be the utility index, designated by U (some amount of money) = some number, representing the utility index of that amount of money. For convenience, let us choose $U(0) = 0$, i.e., the utility of zero dollars is zero. This is not necessary; we could let the utility index for zero dollars be -49, or -2, or any other real number—the zero point on the utility scale is arbitrary. Now, let $U(\$10,000) = 1$, to be read "the utility of $10,000 is one." Again, this is arbitrary; it could be 15, or one billion, or any other number larger than the index for zero dollars—so the unit of measurement of utility is not fixed. The expected utility of the formulated alternative now is the sum of the utility assignments to the possible events, weighted by the appropriate proba-

---

[3] The sense in which von Neumann and Morgenstern use the term "utility" differs somewhat from the traditional use in economics. Utility in the von Neumann sense is associated with choices involving uncertainty; in the older economic version, utility represented the intrinsic satisfaction possessed by a commodity. The distinction will be sharpened in the following discussion.

bilities. In this case (where we designate the formulated situation as A_1, for act 1):

$$E[U(A_1)] = \tfrac{1}{2}[U(0)] + \tfrac{1}{2}[U(\$10{,}000)] = \tfrac{1}{2}(0) + \tfrac{1}{2}(1) = 0.5.$$

Now, formulate an alternative line of action (A_2) which yields some amount of money with certainty—say, $5,000. You request your employer to choose between the two courses of action, A_1 and A_2. Say he chooses A_2, or $5,000 for certain. We infer that

$$U(A_2) > U(A_1) = 0.5,$$

or $U(\$5{,}000) > \tfrac{1}{2}U(0) + \tfrac{1}{2}U(\$10{,}000) = 0.5$; i.e., the utility of $5,000 is greater than one half. Because the $5,000 is preferred to A_1, we conclude that the utility index of A_2 is greater than one half. Assume next that you offered $2,000 for certain (A_3) and found that your employer preferred A_1. This would imply that the utility index associated with $2,000 should be less than one half. If your employer's patience held out, you could continue proposing alternative acts yielding sums of money with certainty until you discovered one that was exactly as attractive as A_1. Say this offer was in the amount of $3,000, so that we could infer that he was indifferent between $3,000 for certain and the original proposal. Thus the utility assignment to $3,000 should be:

$$U(\$3{,}000) = \tfrac{1}{2}[U(0)] + \tfrac{1}{2}[U(\$10{,}000)] = 0.5.$$

We now have three points through which your employer's utility function passes. Additional utility evaluations for sums of money between zero and $10,000 may be made in a similar manner. For example, pose an alternative which offers a 0.5 probability of $3,000 and a 0.5 probability of $10,000. Find the sum which must be offered with certainty to make your employer indifferent to the opportunity involving risk. Say this amount is $5,500. We could conclude that the appropriate utility assignment for $5,500 is:

$$U(\$5{,}500) = \tfrac{1}{2}[U(\$3{,}000)] + \tfrac{1}{2}[U(\$10{,}000)] = \tfrac{1}{2}(0.5) + \tfrac{1}{2}(1) = 0.75.$$

Alternatively, say you wanted to find the sum L such that your employer would be indifferent between the certainty of $3,000 and the risky alternative of a 0.5 probability of $5,500 and a 0.5 probability of L. By a process of trial and error, assume you found L to be $900. Then you could conclude:

$$U(\$3{,}000) = \tfrac{1}{2}U(\$5{,}500) + \tfrac{1}{2}(U\$900)$$
$$0.5 = \tfrac{1}{2}(0.75) + \tfrac{1}{2}U(\$900).$$
$$0.25 = U(\$900).$$

A consistent measure for sums in excess of $10,000 may be derived by a comparable process. Assume you wanted the relevant index for $100,000. You would contrive a choice for your employer between a certain sum whose utility index had been estimated (say, $5,500) and a chance prospect involving $100,000 and some other sum (say, zero) whose utility measure had been found. Notice that the amount to be received with probability one must fall within the range of the sums that are received with some uncertainty,[4] for our objective is to vary the probability assignments to the uncertain amounts until the state of indifference is obtained. Say that this occurred when your employer was offered either $5,500 for certain or a 0.5 probability of nothing and a 0.5 probability of $100,000. The equation

$$U(\$5,500) = \tfrac{1}{2}U(\$0) + \tfrac{1}{2}[U(\$100,000)]$$

now may be written. Substitute the known utility measures and solve for the single unknown:

$$0.75 = \tfrac{1}{2}(0) + \tfrac{1}{2}U(\$100,000)$$
$$1.50 = U(\$100,000).$$

The utility index to be assigned to losses may be derived in a similar way. To find a utility measure consistent with those already accumulated for a loss of $1,000, proceed as follows. Construct a choice between, say, $3,000 with a probability of one, and the prospect of, say, $p(-\$1,000) + (1 - p)$ ($10,000). You could vary the probability weights p and $(1 - p)$ until the desirability of the two alternatives was identical to your employer. Let us assume that this happened when $p = \tfrac{1}{3}$ (i.e., a proposition with a one-third chance of a $1,000 loss and a two-thirds chance of a $10,000 gain). We may form an equation containing the unknown utility and solve for the index:

$$U(\$3,000) = pU(-\$1,000) + (1 - p)U(\$10,000)$$
$$\tfrac{1}{2} = \tfrac{1}{3}U(-\$1,000) + \tfrac{2}{3}(1)$$
$$-\tfrac{1}{2} = U(-\$1,000).$$

As a variation, the probability weights might be fixed and your employer asked to choose between, say, zero dollars for certain or a 50–50 chance at either $100,000 or some unknown amount, L. The amount L would be varied until the desired state of indifference had

---

[4] This is a reflection of the principle of transitivity. See assumption 2, page 195.

been attained. Assume that this came about when $L = -\$2,000$. Then we could write:

$$\tfrac{1}{2}U(\$100,000) + \tfrac{1}{2}U(L) = U(\$0)$$
$$\tfrac{1}{2}(1.5) + \tfrac{1}{2}U(L) = 0$$
$$U(-\$2,000) = -1.5.$$

We may surmise that the disutility of a \$2,000 loss is -1.5 on the scale we are constructing for the employer.

Any number of utility-money pairs may be generated in this fashion. These pairs may be collected in a table and plotted on a graph.

TABLE 14–4

Expected Monetary Index	Utility Index
\$100,000	1.50
10,000	1.00
5,500	0.75
3,000	0.50
900	0.25
0	0.00
−1,000	−0.50
−2,000	−1.50

A line through the various points then approximates the utility function for money of the person being tested. This is done in Table 14–4 and Figure 14–1 for the employer.

USUAL CHARACTERISTICS OF UTILITY FUNCTIONS

Some generalizations about the usual shape of the utility function are possible. People usually regard money as a desirable commodity and prefer more of it to less of it. The utility measure of a large sum is expected to be greater than the utility measure of a small sum. The utility function rises over any relevant range of money.[5] We may say that the utility function has a positive slope over this relevant range. The slope in this case is the ratio of an incremental change in the utility index $[\Delta U(M)]$ as a result of an incremental change in the stock of money (ΔM). The incremental changes will always have the same sign, so we may write:

$$\text{Slope} = \frac{\Delta U(M)}{\Delta M} > 0.$$

---

[5] If money is acquired indefinitely, a saturation point is approached, and the utility function levels off—it is bounded from above. It is also bounded from below for large losses.

This measure is called the marginal utility of money. It should be noted that, except for the algebraic sign, this is an arbitrary measure. This follows from the utility function being unique only to a linear transformation.

The slope of the utility function is positive and probably does not vary in response to small changes in the stock of money. It follows that, for small changes in the amount of money going to an individual, his utility function over that range has approximately a con-

FIGURE 14–1

Utility for Money

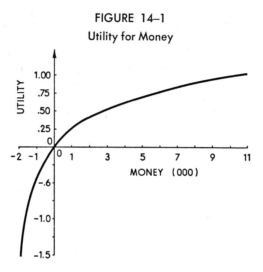

stant slope and may be regarded as linear. If the utility function is linear [$U(M)'$ in Figure 14–2], the person maximizes expected utility by maximizing expected monetary value. Thus, expected monetary value may properly be used as a guide in decision making only when there is reason to believe the pertinent utility function is linear over the range of possible outcomes. We have seen that for large variations in the amount of money, this is a most unlikely condition. At the extremes—for losses and for large gains—the utility function is almost certain to approach upper and lower limits. The slope of the curve usually will increase sharply as the amount of the loss increases, implying that the disutility of a large loss is proportionately more than the disutility of a small loss, but the slope will decrease as the loss becomes very large. Similarly, for large stocks of money, the slope of the utility function grows smaller with further additions to that stock. These observations are consistent with the traditional "diminishing marginal utility" view of consumer psychology. However, over some initial range of positive increments to the individual's stock of money, it now seems reasonable to assume the typical utility function to be concave upward.[6] The slope of the utility function increases over this initial range, up to a point of inflection, and decreases thereafter. The amount of money associated with the point of inflection of the utility function is defined as the individual's level of aspiration for money (Siegel [1957]). Psychologists have shown that people experience a sense of failure if they receive less than the amount of reward associated with the inflection point in

FIGURE 14–2

Utility for Money

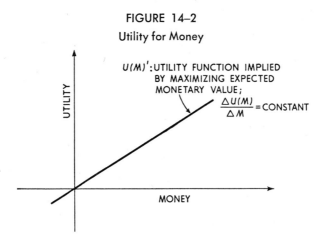

their utility function, and they experience a sense of success if they receive more (see Siegel [1957] and Simon [1957]). This amount of reward also might be related to the "satisficing" reward discussed by Simon and others. The amount of money associated with an individual's level of aspiration is not a constant over time; rather, it varies with the individual's experience. If he enjoys a series of successful initial experiences, he will increase his level of aspiration (i.e., the point of inflection of his utility function will shift to the right with the passage of time); if his initial experiences are unfavorable, he will tend to be frustrated and search for satisfactory alternatives to his present position. If he cannot find such alternatives, he will tend to lower his level of aspiration.

It is quite consistent for an individual with a utility function of this shape [$U(M)$ in Figure 14–3] to (1) pay small premium to insure against large losses, even when the premiums include a "load-

---

[6] The original conjecture was by Friedman and Savage (1948), supported by empirical observations that many people were willing to accept long-shot risky ventures (e.g., lotteries) at the same time that they insured against large losses. Since then, there has been some experimental support of this view.

FIGURE 14–3

Utility Function for Money

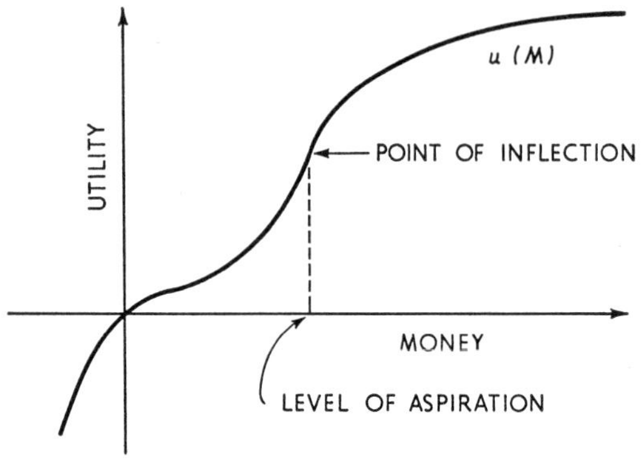

ing" charge above the actuarial cost of bearing the risk; and (2) simultaneously accept risky propositions which promise a chance at relatively large gains in return for modest investments, even though the mathematical expectation may make the gamble an unfair one.

Example 1

Consider the entrepreneur whose utility table contains the pairs shown in Table 14–5. Say that he is faced with two decisions:
(a) Should he pay a $100 premium to insure against a potential $10,-000 fire loss when he knows that the insurance company has calculated the probability of fire on his class of property to be one out of

TABLE 14–5

$U(M)$	M
−800	−$10,000
−2	−200
−1	−100
0	0
250	10,000

200? (b) Should he invest $100 in an oil-drilling venture where the geologist has said there is only one chance in 200 of striking oil (with the expectation of $10,000 profit) and a 199/200 chance of losing the $100 investment? Let us analyze these decisions in terms of expectations calculated from the utility measures. The decision to insure or not may be represented as in Table 14–6.

The expected utility of act 1 is less than the expected utility of act 2; the entrepreneur maximizes his utility by taking act 2 (insuring).

The decision to invest or not may be analyzed in the same manner. The utility table shown in Table 14–7 may be constructed on the

TABLE 14–6

Conditional and Expected Utility

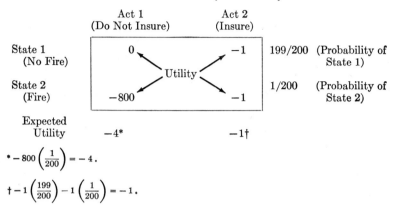

	Act 1 (Do Not Insure)	Act 2 (Insure)		
State 1 (No Fire)	0	−1	199/200	(Probability of State 1)
State 2 (Fire)	−800	−1	1/200	(Probability of State 2)
Expected Utility	−4*	−1†		

$$* - 800 \left(\frac{1}{200} \right) = -4.$$

$$\dagger - 1 \left(\frac{199}{200} \right) - 1 \left(\frac{1}{200} \right) = -1.$$

TABLE 14–7

Conditional and Expected Utility

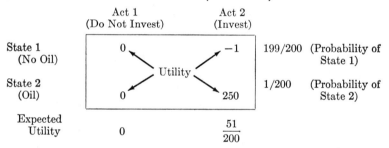

	Act 1 (Do Not Invest)	Act 2 (Invest)		
State 1 (No Oil)	0	−1	199/200	(Probability of State 1)
State 2 (Oil)	0	250	1/200	(Probability of State 2)
Expected Utility	0	$\frac{51}{200}$		

basis of the available information. It follows that the expected utility of act 1 is less than the expected utility of act 2. It is seen that the entrepreneur maximizes utility by taking act 2 (investing). The risky venture would be accepted at the same time the entrepreneur was insuring against a loss, contrary to the decisions indicated by expected monetary value.

Example 2

Determine which lottery is to be preferred.

Lottery A:

$$I_1 = \$1,000$$
$$I_2 = \$2,000$$
$$p_1 = 0.25$$
$$p_2 = 0.75$$

Lottery B:

$$I_0 = \$1,750 \text{ for certain}$$

The utility function is shown in Table 14–8.

The expected monetary value of lottery A is:

$$I(A) = 1{,}000 \times 0.25 + 2{,}000 \times 0.75 = \$1{,}750.$$

Is the expected monetary value of \$1,750 of lottery A preferred over the \$1,750 of lottery B for certain? We solve this problem by the use of expected utility.

TABLE 14–8

Income	Utility
\$1,000................	100
1,400................	130
1,500................	132
1,750................	140
1,900................	145
2,000................	160

The utility of lottery A is:

$$\begin{aligned} U(A) &= U(1{,}000) \times 0.25 + U(2{,}000) \times 0.75 \\ &= 100 \times 0.25 + 160 \times 0.75 \\ &= 145. \end{aligned}$$

The utility of lottery B is:

$$U(B) = U(I_0) = U(\$1{,}750) = 140.$$

Lottery A is preferred.

We have computed the expected monetary value of A to be \$1,750, and the expected utility of A is 145. The certainty equivalent of A is \$1,900, i.e.:

$$U(\$1{,}900) = U(A) = 145.$$

The person considering the investment attaches a value of up to \$150 to the privilege of gambling and takes lottery A instead of Lottery B:

$$I^* - I(A) = 1{,}900 - 1{,}750 = \$150.$$

While this means that B would have to be at least as large as \$1,900 to accept B, it does not mean that the investor would pay \$150 to play A instead of B.

Instead of the utility function as previously given, assume that $U(\$1{,}000) = 48$. The utility of lottery A is now:

$$U(A) = 48 \times 0.25 + 160 \times 0.75 = 132$$

and A has a utility equivalent of \$1,500 for certain.

The discount for risk is:

$$I(A) - I^* = 1{,}750 - 1{,}500 = \$250.$$

In this case the subject would accept a certain amount of $1,500 to avoid lottery A with its monetary expectation of $1,750. Since lottery B has a certainty payment of $1,750, it would be preferred to lottery A.

RISK PREFERENCE AND RISK AVERSION

We assume that many individuals may be characterized by a utility function such as $U(I)$ in Figure 14–4. In this example the utility function has an inflection point associated with income I_3. We would identify the individual's level of aspiration for income as I_3. Any level of income less than I_3 will be unsatisfactory to him. He will be frustrated and will search for opportunities to increase his income. He would tend to be a risk taker and to accept risky alternatives. If fair gambles are available to him in this range of income, he would accept them; he would pay something of a premium to get some lotteries.

Any level of income equal to or greater than I_3 will be satisfactory to the individual. He would not be frustrated with such an income and would tend to avoid risk. He would pay an insurance premium to avoid some risky alternatives in this income range.

For example, assume that the individual whose utility function is shown in Figure 14–4 is confronted with the single choice of taking lottery A or lottery B. Let us define lottery A as:

$$p\text{—Probability of } I_1$$
$$(1 - p)\text{—Probability of } I_3.$$

Let alternative B consist of the certain sum of I_2, where I_2 is the mathematical expectation of lottery A. That is:

$$I_2 = pI_1 + (1 - p)I_3.$$

The choice is between the certain income I_2 or a lottery between incomes I_1 and I_3. To predict the choice, we would have to calculate the expected utilities of the alternatives. Thus:

$$U(B) = U(I_2)$$

and

$$U(A) = pU(I_1) + (1 - p)U(I_3).$$

It follows that $U(A) > U(B)$, and the individual would accept the lottery in this case. Indeed, he would prefer lottery A to any certain

FIGURE 14–4

Utility Function

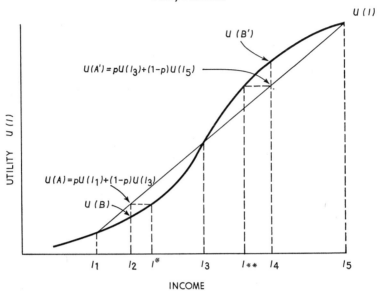

income up to the amount I^*, the certainty equivalent of the lottery in utility terms.[7]

Now, assume the individual had to choose between lotteries A' and B':

Lottery A':

$$p\text{—Probability of } I_3$$
$$(1 - p)\text{—Probability of } I_5.$$

Lottery B', the certain income I_4, where:

$$I_4 = pI_3 + (1 - p)I_5.$$

Again, we must determine the utility of the alternatives. The utility of the certain income I_4 is $U(B')$. The utility of lottery A' is

$$U(A') = pU(I_3) + (1 - p)U(I_5).$$

In this case, $U(B') > U(A')$, and the individual would not accept the lottery. He is a risk averter in this range of income. He would pay an insurance premium to avoid lottery A' if he could secure income I_4 for certain.

---

[7] This analysis is based on the assumption that lotteries A and B are the only choices available. If the individual has access to a market offering any fair gamble, and there are no cultural restrictions on using this market, then he can exchange any certain income for one of many fair gambles, and the utility of certain income would coincide with the highest linear tangent line between two points on $U(I)$. Generally, such an ideal market does not exist, and there are cultural constraints on such choices.

PROHIBITION ON INTERPERSONAL COMPARISON OF UTILITY

The scale of the utility function, and its zero point, are arbitrary. For the entrepreneur who had to make the investment and insurance decisions, we could have selected a different zero point, or a different utility scale, and he would have made the same decisions. Indeed, we could add a constant to each utility index, or multiply each index by a positive constant, without changing the essential properties of the utility function.

For this reason, it is improper, and decidedly incorrect, to compare the utility schedule of one person with that of another. For example, if you derived your own utility function for money and selected a scale so that your index for $3,000 was $9\frac{1}{2}$, it would be quite wrong for you to present the argument to your employer (whose utility index for $3,000 you had just discovered to be one half) that he could increase the general welfare nine utility points by the simple expedient of giving you a $3,000 raise. He could counter with equal justification that he had just multiplied his scale by a large constant and could improve the social estate only by reducing your salary.

BIBLIOGRAPHY

CHERNOFF, H., and MOSES, L. E. *Elementary Decision Theory.* New York: John Wiley & Sons, Inc., 1959.

DORFMAN, R.; SAMUELSON, P. A.; and SOLOW, R. M. *Linear Programming and Economic Analysis.* New York: McGraw-Hill Book Co., Inc., 1958.

FRIEDMAN, M., and SAVAGE, L. J. "The Utility Analysis of Choices Involving Risk," *Journal of Political Economy,* August, 1948.

LUCE, R. D., and RAIFFA, H. *Games and Decisions.* New York: John Wiley & Sons, Inc., 1957.

SAVAGE, L. J. *The Foundations of Statistics.* New York: John Wiley & Sons, Inc., 1954.

SCHLAIFER, R. *Probability and Statistics for Business Decisions.* New York: McGraw-Hill Book Co., Inc., 1959.

SHUBIK, M. *Strategy and Market Structure.* New York: John Wiley & Sons, Inc., 1959.

SIEGEL, S. "Level of Aspiration and Decision Making," *Psychological Review,* 1957.

SIEGEL, S., and FOURAKER, L. E. *Bargaining and Group Decision-Making: Experiments in Bilateral Monopoly.* New York: McGraw-Hill Book Co., Inc., 1960.

SIMON, H. A. *Models of Man.* New York: John Wiley & Sons, Inc., 1957.

VON NEUMANN, J., and MORGENSTERN, O. *Theory of Games and Economic Behavior.* Princeton: Princeton University Press, 1944.

PROBLEMS

14-1. Entrepreneur W has a utility index of five for a loss of $1,000, and 12 for a profit of $3,000. He says that he is indifferent between $10 for certain and a 0.4 chance at a $1,000 loss and a 0.6 chance at a $3,000 profit. What is his utility index for $10?

14-2. Entrepreneur X has a utility index for −$2.00 of 50; his index for $500 is 60. He maintains that he is indifferent between $500 for certain and a lottery of a 0.8 chance at −$2.00 and a 0.2 chance at $20,000. What is his utility index for $20,000?

14-3. Entrepreneur Y has a utility index of −108 for $11,000, and −275 for zero dollars. He is indifferent between a 0.5 chance at $11,000 plus a 0.5 chance at a $20,000 loss and a certainty of zero. What is his utility index for a loss of $20,000?

14-4. Entrepreneur Z has a utility index of 10 for $18,750, six for $11,200, and zero for zero dollars. What probability combination of zero dollars and $18,750 would make him indifferent to $11,200 for certain?

14-5. Entrepreneur W has a utility index of five for a loss of $1,000 and a utility index of six for a loss of $500. What is the slope of his utility function between these points?

14-6. Two economists, Alfred M. Noxie and J. Maynard K. Bampton, are arguing about the relative merits of their respective decision rules. Noxie says he always takes that act with the greatest expected monetary value; Bampton says he always takes the act with the greatest expected utility, and his utility function for money is $U = 10 + 0.2M$. For decisions involving monetary pay-offs, who will make the better choices?

14-7. You are a fire insurance salesman confronted by a balky mathematician who argues that he should not insure his house against fire because of the small loading charge which provides the overhead for the insurance company. If his analysis is correct, what does this imply about the shape of his utility function?

14-8. You have a date for the quantitative analysis ball; the admission is $10, which you do not have. On the day of the dance, your psychology instructor offers you either $8.00 for certain or a 50–50 chance at nothing or $12. Which choice would you make, assuming you had no other source of funds or credit? Why? If the utility of $8.00 is 20, and the utility of zero dollars is zero, what does this imply about the utility of $12?

14-9. You are the plant manager for a small manufacturing concern. The parking lot next to the factory must be repaved. A large contractor has told you that he will submit a bid at any time consisting of the expected full cost plus 10 per cent profit. The only uncertainty in the cost calculation on this job is the weather. If it is clear, the incremental cost of the job will be $40,000. If it rains, the incremental cost will be $55,000. The Weather Bureau has informed you that the chance of rain for the relevant period is one out of ten, and that all contractors know and accept this information.

You know you will get two other bids on the job. Two small local contractors, Willie and Joe, have been engaged in a bitter rivalry ever since World War II. In recent years the object of their rivalry has been to see who would be the first to enter the "Six-Figure Club." Requirements for admission consist of making a profit of $100,000 or more for one year. You know that Willie has made profits this year of $109,500, and Joe has made profits of $95,000. There is so little time left in the year that your job will be the last possible job for each of them. Also, they both have excess capacity and can undertake the job. What bids would you expect? How would you explain the bids?

14-10. Suppose that Smith has a utility function $u(x) = x^{2/3}$, where x is in dollars ($0 \leq x \leq 1,000$). Smith is offered the following choices:
A—$8.00 for sure
B—A lottery with a one-half chance for zero dollars and a one-half chance for $64.
Which lottery would you predict Smith will choose?

14-11. The Iota Engineering Company does subcontracting on government contracts. Iota is a small company with limited capital. The utility function is described as follows:
$$u(x) = -x/100 - x^2/5,000 \, , \, x < -1,000$$
$$u(x) = x/100 - 170 \, , \, -1,000 < x < 10,000$$
$$u(x) = \sqrt{x} \, , \, x > 10,000.$$

a) Suppose Iota is considering bidding on a given contract. It will cost $2,000 to prepare the bid. If the bid is lost, the $2,000 cost is also lost. If Iota wins the bid, it will make $40,000 and recover the $2,000 bid preparation cost. If Iota feels that the odds are 50–50 of winning the contract if a bid is submitted, what should it do?

b) What would the probability of winning have to be before Iota would submit a bid?

Chapter 15

COMPETITION AND
GROUP DECISIONS

GROUP DECISIONS

MOST OF the decisions described in this book take the form of a businessman choosing an act in the face of an uncertain, but inanimate, set of environmental factors. The decision maker must take a position with respect to nature, and there is no reason to believe that the forces of nature will conspire to chasten a particular executive.

There is an important set of business problems where the decision maker is confronted with one or more animate opponents. The orderly analysis of choice in this situation becomes quite complex.

In this chapter and the next, we shall present some problems of this type, and propose solutions for them. We shall call problems of this type group decision problems.

TWO-PERSON GROUPS

The simplest group consists of two individuals. The essence of the group problem is found when:

1. It is in the interest of both individuals to come to an agreement regarding a range of issues subject to their mutual concern.
2. Given that an agreement will be reached, the interests of the individuals are generally in opposition.

A classic example of the two-person group problem is that of the single buyer of a commodity being confronted by a single seller of the commodity. Economists have proposed a variety of solutions for this situation over the years. One will be sketched here, following the treatment of William Fellner (1949).

Let us assume that the buyer of the commodity has a linear demand function of the form $r = a - bq$, where:

$r =$ Average revenue, or value of the commodity to the buyer
$a =$ The Y-axis intercept of the revenue function
$-b =$ The slope of the revenue function
$q =$ The quantity exchanged.

Any price-quantity contract that satisfies the demand equation (i.e., the purchase price is equal to r, the average revenue) will yield zero profits to the buyer. Assume that the buyer is motivated solely by a desire to maximize his own profit.

Let the seller's supply function be represented by the linear equation

$$c = a' + b'q$$

where

$c =$ The minimum price required by the seller to bring forth q units of product
$a' =$ The Y-axis intercept of the supply function
$b' =$ The slope of the supply curve
$q =$ The quantity exchanged.

Any price-quantity contract which satisfies the supply function will yield zero profits to the seller if c is equal to the average cost of the seller. Assume the seller is motivated solely by his own profits, and c is equal to average cost.

If the situation affords no structural advantage to either buyer or seller, contracts negotiated between the parties will have a central tendency at the quantity which maximizes the joint profits of the two individuals (Siegel and Fouraker [1960]). That quantity may be identified as follows.

The buyer's profit would be:

$$\pi_b = rq - pq = aq - bq^2 - pq$$

where p is the agreed-upon exchange price and q is the exchanged quantity.

The seller's profit would be:

$$\pi_s = pq - cq = pq - a'q - b'q^2.$$

The joint profits of the buyer and seller would be:

$$\pi_b + \pi_s = aq - bq^2 - a'q - b'q^2.$$

This function will be maximized by that value of q which makes the first derivative zero, provided the second derivative is negative.

$$\frac{d(\pi_b + \pi_s)}{dq} = a - 2bq - a' - 2b'q = 0$$

$$q = \frac{a - a'}{2b + 2b'}$$

$$\frac{d^2(\pi_b + \pi_s)}{dq^2} = -2b - 2b' < 0$$

The same result may be obtained by equating marginal revenue, which is $(a - 2bq)$, with marginal cost, which is $(a' + 2b'q)$.

FIGURE 15–1

Bilateral Monopoly

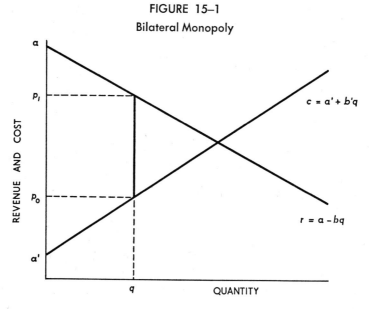

This situation is shown in Figure 15–1. The price at which the exchange will take place is indeterminate, but will lie somewhere between p_0, the *status quo* (or minimum price for the seller) and p_1 (the *status quo* or maximum price for the buyer). The set of prices between p_0 and p_1, coupled with the quantity q which maximizes joint profits, is defined as the Pareto set of contracts in this situation. A Pareto contract has this property: If the parties have arrived (tentatively) at such a contract, a movement to any other feasible adjustment will involve a sacrifice on the part of at least one of the individuals. A non-Pareto contract has this property: There will be a subset of contracts on the Pareto set to which the parties can move with mutual benefit. That is, the profits of both buyer and seller can be increased by moving from a non-Pareto contract to certain Pareto contracts.[1]

The exchange price may be below the r which would result from inserting the value of q in the equation $r = a - bq$ and above the c which would result from inserting q in the equation $q = a' + b'q$. Thus, we reach a solution where supply is not equal to demand (using our definitions of supply and demand).[2] It should be remembered that the value of r is the maximum price for the buyer, and he will be agreeable to paying less than r for q units. In like manner, the seller will be agreeable to accepting more than c for the q units. If they move from the Pareto optimum, one or the other, or both, will be worse off; thus, it pays the bilateral monopolists to buy and sell q units.

The negotiated price in such situations has a central tendency toward the mid-point of the Pareto set, regardless of the relative slopes of the supply and demand functions (Siegel and Fouraker [1960]). However, there is considerable dispersion of such prices. We now turn to the possible causes of such dispersion.

TWO-PERSON DECISIONS AND UTILITY FUNCTIONS

Say that two individuals, I and II, are considering an issue of mutual concern, not necessarily an economic transaction as discussed above, and they have reduced the alternatives to a Pareto set of possible agreements. Assume that individual I has ordered these agreements according to his preferences, and has constructed a von Neumann–Morgenstern utility function over this ordered Pareto set. Let the agreements range from a_1 to a_n, so that I's utility function increases monotonically over this range. Then, if II constructed a utility function over the same set of agreements, it would have to fall monotonically from a_1 to a_n. This requirement follows from the identification of the set $a_1, \ldots, a_n$ as a Pareto set. There are several models which suggest a specific agreement, or a subset of agreements, as being more likely than others in this situation.

---

[1] If the structure of the bargaining situation is not symmetrical, i.e., if one party has an advantage, the expected adjustment may not be an element of the Pareto set. For example, if either buyer or seller can set the price, while the other must be content to select the quantity, the resulting exchange will generally fail to maximize joint profits. The expected quantity will fall short of that which identifies the Pareto set. See Bowley (1928).

[2] We could express the demand equation as an inequality $r \leq a - b_q$ and redefine r to be an acceptable price of the product to the buyer.

When first confronted with this problem, many suggest the agreement which maximizes the sum of the utilities of I and II. However, since a von Neumann–Morgenstern utility function is unique only to a linear transformation, the agreement which maximizes the sum of the utilities is arbitrary. The prohibition against interpersonal comparison of utilities is the great obstacle in the analysis of group decisions. We shall consider, in this chapter and the next, a few of the suggested paths around the obstacle.

Nash (1950) suggested one route. Assume a_1 and a_n are the *status quo* boundary solutions for I and II, respectively, and assign zero utility to a_1 for I and zero utility to a_n for II. Then the Nash solution is that agreement, or set of agreements, for which the product of the two utility functions is maximized.[3] Under the specified conditions the identification of the Nash solution is invariant with respect to the permitted linear transformations of the utility functions. For example, if the agreements can be arranged on a cardinal scale, and if the utility functions are linear, the Nash solution would be the agreement halfway between a_1 and a_n. This would correspond to a 50–50 split of a fixed sum which was to be divided between I and II.

An alternative approach may be derived from level-of-aspiration considerations. Let $a(\mathrm{I})$ represent I's level of aspiration (the minimum agreement in the set of agreements acceptable to I), so that any agreement a_i

$$a_1 \leq a_i < a(\mathrm{I})$$

will be unsatisfactory to I, and will cause him to continue the negotiations or search for some other means of reaching a satisfactory agreement (Simon [1957]). If an agreement a_j is acceptable to I, it is defined as satisfactory:

$$a(\mathrm{I}) \leq a_j \leq a_n$$

There are similar concepts for II. His level of aspiration, $a(\mathrm{II})$, is the least attractive agreement of that group of agreements which II considers acceptable. Therefore, any agreement a_j

$$a_1 \leq a_j \leq a(\mathrm{II})$$

would be satisfactory to person II. An agreement a_i

$$a(\mathrm{II}) < a_i \leq a_n$$

would be frustrating to person II, and would induce search activity.

---

[3] This coincides, under certain conditions, with the solution proposed by Raiffa (1953) and Zeuthen (1930). See Harsanyi (1956).

There are two possibilities:

1. $a(\text{II}) < a(\text{I})$
2. $a(\text{II}) \geq a(\text{I})$.

The first situation indicates that there is no mutually acceptable agreement. It is unlikely that the parties can resolve a conflict of this sort with dispatch. Nor can a third party suggest, or impose, a workable solution while this condition holds. However, the psychological

FIGURE 15–2

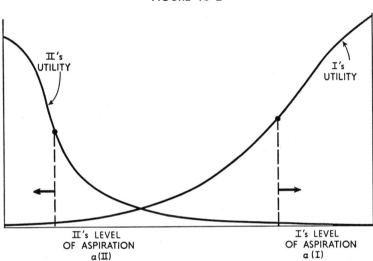

model indicates that people tend to lower their aspiration levels in response to a series of failure experiences (Simon [1957]). Society has developed a number of institutional processes to depress aspirations in this situation. The legal process itself is the best example; but formal requirements for bargaining, cooling off, etc., serve the same purpose.

In the second case, there is at least one mutually acceptable agreement. If $a(\text{II}) > a(\text{I})$, there may be a number of agreements satisfactory to both parties. This condition, if suspected by one or both members of the group, may have the same effect as a successful experience: It may cause an increase in one or both levels of aspiration. The dynamics of bargaining may force the parties toward the condition where $a(\text{I}) = a(\text{II})$ and a unique agreement is indicated.[4]

For the moment, assume that the agreements can be measured on

---

[4] This solution would probably correspond to the value of a two person zero sum game, as described in the next chapter.

FIGURE 15–3

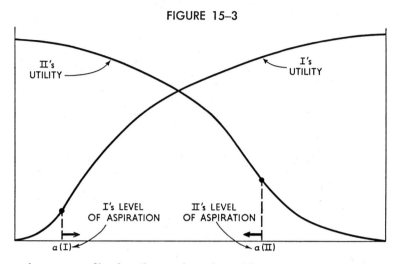

a continuous cardinal scale, so that the utility function is continuous. The level of aspiration is now associated with the inflection point on a utility function U, where $\dfrac{dU}{da}$ is a maximum and $\dfrac{dU^2}{da^2} = 0$. Since an inflection point is invariant with respect to linear transformations, the aspiration level can be defined unambiguously for the individual. This permits an interpersonal comparison of aspirations. The case of no acceptable agreement is shown in Figure 15–2; that of several acceptable agreements is shown in Figure 15–3; and a unique acceptable agreement is identified in Figure 15–4.

FIGURE 15–4

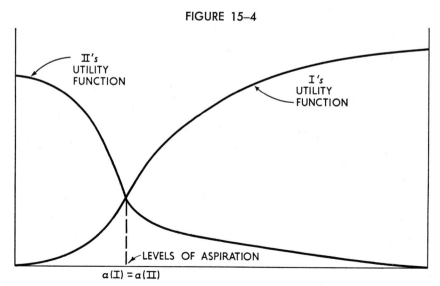

Another model of the two-person group decision is presented in the next chapter.

THREE-PERSON GROUPS

We have seen that a rather radical change in method of analysis occurs when the analyst moves from the single decision maker to the two-person group. Even though they are more complex than individual decisions, bilateral relationships are remarkably stable, a condition attested to by the institution of marriage. The next step, from two-person groups to three-person groups, again involves a great in-

TABLE 15–1

Rank	I	II	III
1.	A	B	C
2.	B	C	A
3.	C	A	B

crease in complexity of analysis. With three-person groups, coalitions can form and control the decision process in some situations. This possibility makes the three-person group less stable in the decision process than the two-person group. Again, the marital analogy holds: Triangles are notoriously unstable.

The complexity of the three-person group decision problem might be indicated by a classical problem. Say that three people, I, II, and III, consider three alternatives, A, B, and C. The group is to choose one of the alternatives by a process of paired comparisons and majority rule. The preferences of the three individuals are as shown in Table 15–1, the most preferred alternative receiving the first rank, and so on.

Say that alternative A is first contrasted with alternative B. Since both I and III prefer A to B, A will win, and B will be eliminated. The remaining contest pits A against C. Alternative C will survive as the group's choice, for II and III prefer C to A.

However, assume C is matched against A in the initial trial. Again, C would win, eliminating alternative A. However, C would now have to withstand comparison with B, which it could not do successfully. Players I and II prefer B to C, so B would emerge as the group's final choice, unless, of course, the first trial was between B and C, for this would yield B, and we have seen that A dominates B. The cyclic nature of this group decision was studied by Condorcet (1785) and later by Dodgson (1958). Considerations of this sort led Arrow (1951) to the investigation and proof of his general possibility theorem (page 59): "If we exclude the possibility of interpersonal comparisons of utility, then the only methods of passing from individual tastes to social preferences which will be satisfactory and which will be defined for a wide range of sets of individual orderings are either imposed or dictatorial."

If individual preferences vary widely, then there is only one way for a group of such individuals to reach a joint decision (consistent with the very reasonable set of axioms developed by Arrow): dictatorship, or the imposition of a set of values unrelated to those of any member of the group. Since human groups have not at all times been plagued with dictators, there must be ways of avoiding Arrow's formulation of the problem. He suggests several. For example, there is the idealist's position: There exists some unique "true" or objectively moral ordering (Kant's moral imperative) which holds for all persons. If there is only one moral ordering of outcomes for each member of society, that ordering will be the decision of the group. The ordering will be invariant with respect to the form of the decision process: It could be by majority rule, by dictatorship, or by consensus. But this does not resolve the conflict: It shifts the discussion to the question of how the true moral ordering will be discovered, and by whom. Some argue this can be accomplished by a set of philosopher kings; or by general discussion and exchange of views of the group, with eventual majority rule accepted, as a matter of faith, as the means of identifying the true ordering; or by silent prayer and consensus; or by a religious leader; and so on. These proposals have been challenged at various times as suggestions for benevolent dictatorship.

Alternatively, it may be argued that the group can solve its decision problem by having a preference for the means by which the decision is reached. If we all agree that majority rule is preferred over all other decision rules, and prefer what appear to be poor results derived by that method over better results derived by a competing method, then the conflict is resolved. But if there is conflict about the means as well as the ends of group activity, we are back with Arrow's conclusion.

Another approach is to attack the interpersonal comparison problem. For the two-person case, we saw that this was possible in some limited sense, through the development of conflict models. The question at hand concerns the extension of the model to groups of three or more persons.

The Nash model, for n independent players with identifiable *status quo* points, is directly transferrable. Assuming the players do not form coalitions, the optimal solution according to this model is that choice which maximizes the product of the utilities of the participants.

Game theory, as we shall see in the next chapter, can also be extended to conflict situations involving more than two people. However, the recommended solutions are not very specific.

Another possibility is provided by the level-of-aspiration model, which also may be extended to three or more participants. Let us start by considering a simple conflict situation where three people, I, II, and III, must divide a constant-sum reward, R, among themselves. Let the decision rule be that a majority can determine the division of R among the three participants, so that a coalition of two can impose a solution. One approach, derived from n-person game theory, would be to identify all possible coalitions and the related pay-off to those coalitions. The best defensive act of members not in the coalition is to form an opposing coalition, which also may have a reward associated with it. In our conflict situation, we would have a table as shown in Table 15–2, which would identify the characteristic function of the three-person game.

TABLE 15–2

Coalition	Reward	Opposing Coalition	Reward
I, II.....................	R	III	0
I, III....................	R	II	0
II, III...................	R	I	0
I, II, III................	R	0	0

This is a useful device for identifying the coalitions which could form, and their rewards. But it is not very useful in predicting which coalition will form. Aspiration considerations may be of value in this connection. Say the three members of our conflict group have aspirations of a_1, a_2, and a_3, ranked as follows: $a_1 < a_2 < a_3$. The first player aspires to share a_1, such that any reward less than a_1 will frustrate him, and any reward equal to or greater than a_1 will satisfy him. It seems reasonable to suppose that the two low-aspiration players will form a coalition against the high-aspiration player. The question remains as to how the members of the winning coalition would divide the reward between them. A possible sequence is as follows:

1. Let one of the members of the coalition (say I, but it could be II) assume the role of leader, who will propose a division of R among the three players. He could propose this schedule:

$a_3 - \Delta$ for himself (where Δ is a small amount) provided $a_3 - \Delta \geq a_1$

$R - a_3 + \Delta$ for II, provided $R - a_3 + \Delta \geq a_2$

0 for III.

2. The best counterproposal that III can make (that contains a minimal satisfactory share for him) will be a_3 for III and $R - a_3$ for the other coalition member. If player I interprets his role of leader as one which precludes entertaining a counteroffer from III, then the counteroffer must be extended to player II.

3. However, player II will probably refuse III's counteroffer, since he was offered $R - a_3 + \Delta$ initially, which exceeds by a small amount the most favorable counteroffer the high-aspiration player can make. Therefore, this will tend to be a stable solution to the problem of dividing R among the three players.[5]

For three players the only condition on the size of R is that $R - a_3 + \Delta \geq a_2$, or $a_3 - \Delta \geq a_1$. An interesting feature of the level-of-aspiration solution is that although player III does not share in the rewards, it is his level of aspiration which determines the division of R between the members of the winning coalition.

This approach may be readily extended to larger groups than three, although the stability restrictions on R become more specific. In general the prediction is that a minimal coalition of low aspiration players will form.

TABLE 15–3

Rank	I	II	III
1	A	B	C
2	B	C	A
3	C	A	B

Level-of-aspiration considerations may indicate a determinate solution in some instances of the cyclic voting problem. For example, let three participants, I, II, and III, have the preference order-

---

[5] A similar example is found in von Neumann and Morgenstern (1947), p. 226.

ings for the three alternatives A, B, and C shown in Table 15–3. Say that person I prefers a 0.5 chance at B plus a 0.5 chance at nothing to alternative C for certain. Further, he prefers the lottery 0.5 chance at A plus a 0.5 chance at C to the certainty of alternative B. We could then identify A as the level of aspiration for I. If person II also responded by choosing the comparable lottery in each case, i.e.,

$$0.5C + 0.5(\text{Nothing}) > A$$
$$0.5B + 0.5A > C$$

we would identify B as his level of aspiration. Suppose III chose the $0.5A + 0.5(\text{Nothing})$ over B for certain, but preferred A for certain to the lottery $0.5C + 0.5B$. We would conclude that III's level of aspiration was alternative A. If the group decision was by majority rule, it would seem probable that I and III would form a coalition and choose alternative A, since this is the only alternative that is satisfactory to two persons. Of course, every such conflict situation does not have a unique solution. There may be no consistent aspiration (if, for example, III aspired to C), or there may be several consistent aspirations (if, for example, II aspired to C).[6]

BIBLIOGRAPHY

ARROW, K. J. *Social Choice and Individual Values*. New York: John Wiley & Sons, Inc., 1951.

BOWLEY, A. L. "On Bilateral Monopoly," *Economic Journal*, Vol. XXXVIII (1928), pp. 651–59.

BUCHANAN, J. M., AND TULLOCK, G. *The Calculus of Consent*. Ann Arbor: University of Michigan, 1962.

CONDORCET. *Essai sur l'application de l'analyse á la probabilité des décisions rendues á la pluralité des voix*. Paris, 1785.

DODGSON, C. L., in BLACK, D. (ed.) *The Theory of Committees and Elections*. Cambridge: Harvard University Press, 1958.

FELLNER, W. *Competition among the Few*. New York: Alfred A. Knopf, Inc., 1949.

HARSANYI, J. C. "Approaches to the Bargaining Problem before and after the theory of Games," *Econometrica*, Vol. XXIV, 1956, pp. 144–57.

NASH, J. F. "The Bargaining Problem," *Econometrica*, Vol. XVIII (1950), pp. 155–62.

---

[6] Donald Harnett has conducted experimental investigations of situations where there is no unique, obvious solution. He observed the decisions actually reached by groups in situations similar to the above and compared these decisions with the predictions of decisions offered by models based on aspirations and on majority rule. See his doctoral dissertation, "A level of Aspiration Model for Group Decision Making" Cornell University, 1964. Also see Buchanan and Tullock (1962). We assume an interval scale for the above alternatives.

RAIFFA, H. "Arbitration Schemes for Generalized Two-Person Games," in KUHN, H. W., and TUCKER, A. W. (eds.). *Contributions to the Theory of Games*, Vol. II. Annals of Mathematical Studies, No. 28. Princeton: Princeton University Press, 1953.

SIEGEL, S., and FOURAKER, L. E. *Bargaining and Group Decision-Making, Experiments in Bilateral Monopoly*. New York: McGraw-Hill Book Co., Inc., 1960.

SIMON, H. A. *Models of Man*. New York: John Wiley & Sons, Inc., 1957.

ZEUTHEN, F. *Problems of Monopoly and Economic Warfare*. London: Rutledge, 1930.

PROBLEMS

15–1. Explain why a buyer and a seller of a product may not arrive at an equilibrium solution where the supply curve is equal to the demand curve for the amount of product exchanged. Assume there is one buyer and one seller.

15–3. The ABC Company has a demand curve:

$$r = 120 - 10q.$$

The XYZ Company has a supply curve:

$$c = 15 + 5q.$$

Define the symbols as in the body of the chapter.

a) What value of q equates the supply and demand functions?

b) If the supply and demand functions are equated, what will ABC pay in total to XYZ for the product? What will be the price? What is the sum of the profits of the firms?

c) At what output is the sum of the profits of both firms maximized?

d) At the output obtained in part *c*, what is the maximum price ABC would pay? What would be the minimum price acceptable to XYZ? At what price will the exchange take place?

15–3. Assume two adjoining countries, one highly industrial and one highly agricultural, have very high tariffs and do almost no across-boundary trading. One has a surplus of agricultural products, and the other has excess industrial capacity. Is this "no trading" a Pareto solution? Explain.

15–4. Two parties are bargaining. It is suggested that they should maximize the sum of their utilities. One has a utility function $F(x)$, and the second has a utility function $G(x)$. Show that maximizing the sum of the utility functions does not lead to a unique solution.

15–5. Assume three persons have the following three preference arrangements:

Rank	I	II	III
1.....................	A^*	B^*	C
2.....................	B	C	A^*
3.....................	C	A	B

The levels of aspirations of the three individuals are marked with asterisks. I's aspirations can be met only by A, II's aspirations can be met only by B, and III's aspirations can be met by either C or A.

a) Using majority rule without considering aspirations, what choice would be made?

b) Using the level-of-aspiration approach, indicate what choice would be made. (Assume more than one ballot is allowed.)

15-6. Show a typical utility function of a union and a management which have arrived at a strike situation. Describe what happens to the utility functions to come to a settlement.

Chapter 16

GAME THEORY

WE SHALL now develop a mathematical model which has its primary application to the relationships among two independent competing entities (i.e., individuals or organizations). This analysis is derived from the monumental work of von Neumann and Morgenstern, *Theory of Games and Economic Behavior*.

GAMES

In the context of this chapter the word "games" is a generic term, incorporating conflict situations of a particular sort. In these situations the motives of the participants are dichotomized: The success of one party tends to be at the expense of the others, so they are in a conflict, or rivalrous relationship. However, any one of a wide range of agreements is preferable to no agreement, from the standpoint of all concerned, so it is in their mutual interest to co-operate to the extent of participating in the process and reaching some decision. Most parlor games are characterized by this condition, and have some advantages for analytical purposes (the objectives usually are unambiguous and known to all parties; the rules and procedures are specified; there is a terminal point for play; etc.). However, the essential characteristics are shared by most instances of social or business conflict, so the mathematics of games is of general interest.

We shall introduce a two-person zero-sum game and a two-person nonconstant-sum game in this chapter. Since the mathematics becomes difficult very quickly in response to minor modifications of the problem, we shall investigate relatively simple situations.

TWO-PERSON ZERO-SUM GAMES

In a two-person zero-sum game the interests of the two opponents are opposed in such a manner that the sum of their utilities add to zero for every outcome of the game. An example of a zero-sum game would be two persons with linear utility functions with respect to money matching pennies. The sum of money (utility) won by one is the sum of money (utility) lost by the other. Both participants know the pay-off matrix in game theory.

It is a characteristic of two-person zero-sum games that there is a unique minimax solution. The prime advantage of a minimax solution in this situation is that it is the best choice of the decision maker if the other participant has chosen a minimax strategy. Unlike a game against nature, where the sole advantage of a minimax strategy is a form of conservatism, in a game against a thinking opponent, minimax is likely to be a desirable procedure. Minimax may not lead to the best possible outcome if one of the opponents does not use a minimax strategy.

We shall use a pay-off matrix which shows the profits of the party whose strategies are listed down the left side of the matrix. The profits of the opponent (his strategies are listed across the top of the matrix) are not listed, since they are the negative values of the pay-offs shown. In Table 16–1 the pay-offs shown are for firm I.

TABLE 16–1

I \ II	Strategy 1	Strategy 2	Minimum of Row
Strategy 1..................	10	14	10
Strategy 2..................	7	12	7
Maximum of column.......	10	14	

In the margins of the pay-off matrix are the row minimums and column maximums. The minimax strategy attempts to maximize a security level for the players (minimize the maximum possible loss, or maximize the minimum gain).

For each strategy of I, we find the minimum gain we would make if faced by the best strategy of II (these are the row minimums). For each strategy of II, we find the maximum gain of I (this is also the maximum loss of II). These are the column maximums. I will choose the largest of the row minimums (in this case strategy 1), and II will choose the smallest of the column maximums (in this case strategy 1). Since the maximin equals the minimax (both have values of ten), we have an equilibrium. The values are called an "equilibrium" pair. If one of the parties tried to move from this equilibrium while the other maintained his position, the mover would not improve his position. A pure strategy leads to a strictly determined game when the maximum of the minimum values of a row is equal to the minimum of the maximum values of the columns.[1]

It should be noted that the margins give the guaranteed minimum profits of I or the guaranteed maximum costs of II. Since the values listed in the matrix may be expectations, these may be guaranteed expected values.

MIXED STRATEGIES

In the above example involving a zero-sum game, there was some pure strategy (i.e., one of the listed strategies) which was an equilibrium strategy. In some situations an equilibrium does not exist for a pure strategy. We shall offer an example where there is no pure

TABLE 16–2
Firm I's Market Share

I \ II	No Advertising	Medium Advertising	Large Advertising	Row Minimum
No advertising......	60	50	40	40
Medium advertising.	70	70	50	50
Large advertising...	80	60	75	75
Column maximums.....	80	70	75	

strategy solution. Let the pay-offs be utilities to firm I for various market shares. (See Table 16–2.)

Now, the maximum of the minimum of the rows is 75, and this is not equal to the minimum of the maximum of the columns, which is 70. If firm I chooses the strategy "Large advertising" and firm II chooses "Medium advertising," we are not at equilibrium. For example, I can improve his position by shifting to a medium advertising campaign. But then II could improve his position by shifting to a large advertising campaign, and so on.

The method of finding the equilibrium solution is as follows: First, we shall eliminate the strategies which are dominated by other strategies. II would not use the strategy "No advertising," since

---

[1] This statement is valid as long as the decision maker whose positive gains are described in the pay-off matrix has his strategies listed down the side of the matrix; otherwise, we would have to modify the description of a strictly determined game with pure strategies.

that strategy is inferior to the other two strategies, no matter what strategy I follows. Also, I would not use "No advertising" for the same reason. Thus, the choice is between medium and large advertising. Rather than making a choice between the two, we shall adopt a mixed strategy which will consist of choosing one with a predetermined probability, p, and the other with probability $(1 - p)$. Assuming a correct p, this procedure will lead to a minimax equilibrium. The mixed strategy allows the opponents to increase their security

TABLE 16–3

II I	Medium	Large	Probability
Medium......................	70	50	p
Large........................	60	75	$1 - p$

$$U_1 = 70p + 60(1 - p)$$
$$U_2 = 50p + 75(1 - p)$$
$$p = \frac{3}{7}$$
$$1 - p = \frac{4}{7}$$
$$U_1 = U_2 = \frac{450}{7}$$

level (for I the minimum expected pay-off and for II the maximum expected pay-off).

We shall solve for the p to be used by I. We want to choose "medium" with probability p, so that the expected utilities resulting from II choosing either decision are equal. We shall let U_1 be the expected utility if II chooses "Medium"; U_2 will be the expected utility if II chooses "Large." We want to find the p which equates the two expected utilities.

The strategy of I will be to set up a random process which will lead to a choice of "Medium" three sevenths of the time and a choice of "Large" four sevenths of the time. This will lead to an expected utility of $\frac{450}{7}$, which is a higher security level than the minimum utility which would be encountered with a pure strategy of "medium" (the gain could be as low as 50) or if a strategy of "Large" was used (the gain could be as low as 60). The mixed strategy has raised the security level of I.

A similar analysis would be made for II:

$$U_1 = 70p + 50(1 - p)$$
$$U_2 = 60p + 75(1 - p)$$
$$p = \frac{5}{7}$$
$$1 - p = \frac{2}{7}$$
$$U_1 = U_2 = \frac{450}{7}.$$

The expected utility of I is equal to the expected utility of II if both follow their indicated mixed strategies. The mixed strategies of the rivals lead to an equilibrium, for they maximize the security level of each player.

A more elaborate example of pure and mixed strategies in a zero-sum game follows, with a more detailed explanation of why mixed strategies, as described above, will maximize a player's security level.

A ZERO-SUM GAME—AN EXAMPLE: COMPANY VERSUS UNION

The labor contract between your company and the union will terminate in the near future. A new contract must be negotiated, preferably before the old one expires. You are a member of a management group charged with selecting the company representatives and a strategy for them to follow during the coming negotiations. After a consideration of past experience, the group agrees that the feasible strategies for the company are as follows:

C_1 = All-out attack; hard, aggressive bargaining
C_2 = A reasoning, logical approach
C_3 = A legalistic strategy
C_4 = An agreeable, conciliatory approach.

Which strategy is best for the company? That depends on the strategy adopted by the union, and that knowledge is not available. However, assume the history of the union suggests that it is considering one of the following set of approaches:

U_1 = All-out attack; hard, aggressive bargaining
U_2 = A reasoning, logical approach
U_3 = A legalistic strategy
U_4 = An agreeable, conciliatory approach.

We now must consider the consequences of each of our lines of action, conditional upon the union adopting any one of its available strategies. With the aid of an outside mediator, we construct Table 16–4.

If the company adopts strategy C_1 and the union adopts strategy U_1, the final contract will involve a 20-cent-per-hour increase in wages and benefits to the average worker. If the union adopts strategy U_2 in response to C_1, it will secure a 25-cent-per-hour increase; strategy U_3 is even better for the union against the company's C_1—it yields a 40-cent-per-hour raise. However, if the union

TABLE 16–4

Conditional Costs to Company
(Gains of Union)

Union Strategies	Company Strategies			
	C_1	C_2	C_3	C_4
U_1..............	+20¢	+15¢	+12¢	+35¢
U_2..............	+25	+14	+ 8	+10
U_3..............	+40	+ 2	+10	+ 5
U_4..............	− 5	+ 4	+11	0

adopts U_4 against C_1, it will end up with a 5-cent cut in wages. The other entries have a similar connotation. Both union and company must decide on the over-all strategy before negotiations begin; an attitude cannot be taken and then changed when the other party commits itself. Assume the company's utility function is approximately linear in money, so these figures may serve as the utility index for the company.[2] The mediator informs the management group that he has been in touch with the union; it has also been considering alternative strategies and possible results of these lines of action. The mediator indicates that the union has constructed a table that does not vary significantly from Table 16–4, and he has provided the union with comparable information. Assume the union also has a linear utility function.

THE SELECTION OF OPTIMUM STRATEGIES

Given these conditions, what will the bargainers do? The company would prefer the union to be conciliatory (U_4) in response to

---

[2] In general, this will not be the case unless the wage costs are a relatively unimportant part of the firm's total costs and the negotiations do not have strong emotional or symbolic significance. Where the union and the company are both large and strong, this is not likely to be the situation and the possible wage changes should be converted to utility terms.

its aggressive attack (C_1), with the result of a 5-cent reduction in wages. But if the company adopts C_1, it is quite possible the union will select a legalistic approach (U_3) and "sock" the firm for a 40-cent wage boost. The second best solution from the company's viewpoint would result from both the company and the union being agreeable (C_4, U_4). But if the company chooses C_4, the union might select an aggressive strategy (U_1) and win a 35-cent wage increase.

The union experiences the same difficulty: If it adopts U_3 in the hope of a 40-cent raise, the company may select a reasoning approach (C_2) which yields only 2 cents to the union. It is clear, however, that the union will never follow a conciliatory strategy (U_4), for it can gain more from U_1 no matter what strategy the company adopts. We may say that strategy U_1 dominates strategy U_4.

One rule the participants might adopt in such a situation is the minimax strategy. The company might adopt that strategy which minimizes the maximum wage increase it would have to grant, regardless of the action of the union. If the union adopted this rule, it would choose that strategy which maximized the minimum wage increase. In the case at hand, the minimax strategy for the company is C_3, with a maximum wage increase of 12 cents; the maximum strategy for the union is U_1, with a minimum wage increase of 12 cents. Since, in Table 16–4, +12 cents is both the maximum of its C_3 column and the minimum of its U_1 row, it is the equilibrium solution of this situation. In game theory, 12 is designated as the value of the game. The pure strategies U_1, C_3 provide equilibrium in this case, for if the company follows C_3, then U_1 is the union's best defense. If the union follows U_1, then C_3 is the company's best defense.[3]

MIXED STRATEGIES

Not every conflict situation will have a minimax equilibrium attainable by pure strategies. By changing one of the critical figures in Table 16–4, we can transform it into such a case. Say the intersection of C_3 and U_3 now is +19 cents rather than +10 cents, so that +12 cents is no longer the maximum of its column. This is shown in Table 16–5. Now C_2 is the strategy which minimizes the company's maximum loss; the union's maximum strategy remains U_1. The intersection of these strategies is not an equilibrium point, however,

---

[3] A zero-sum game may have more than one equilibrium pair; however, all of the equilibrium pairs will have the same value, so the players will be indifferent among them.

TABLE 16–5

Conditional Costs to Company
(*Gains of Union*)

Union Strategies	Company Strategies			
	C_1	C_2	C_3	C_4
U_1...............	+20¢	+15¢	+12¢	+35¢
U_2...............	+25	+14	+ 8	+10
U_3...............	+40	+ 2	+19	+ 5
U_4...............	− 5	+ 4	+11	+ 0

because + 15 cents is not the maximum of its column *and* the minimum of its row. If the union adopted strategy U_1, the company would prefer to have strategy C_3, not C_2. But if the company had strategy C_3, the union would like U_3 better than U_1. If the union had U_3, the company's optimum strategy would be C_2. Yet C_2 is the strategy against which the union would take U_1, as indicated initially. We have completed the full circle. The pure strategies U_1, C_2 are not an equilibrium pair; they are not best against each other.

Let us reduce Table 16–5 to the relevant strategies shown in Table 16–6. This is done by successive elimination of dominated

TABLE 16–6

Union Strategies	Company Strategies	
	C_2	C_3
U_1.........	+15¢	+12¢
U_3.........	+ 2	+19

strategies. Union strategy U_4 is dominated by U_1, so U_4 may be dropped. Then, company strategy C_1 is dominated by either C_2 or C_3; thus, C_1 may be dropped. This leaves union strategy U_2 dominated by U_1, so that the only remaining union strategies are U_1 and U_3. At this point the company strategy C_4 is dominated by C_2, so the only pertinent strategies for the company are C_2 and C_3. Our objective now is to derive some mixture of the strategies which will improve the position of both parties with respect to the available pure strategies. For example, assume that it is possible for the company to use strategy C_2, at random, one half of the time, and strategy C_3, at random, the other half. Then, if the union used strategy U_1, the expected wage increase would be

$$\tfrac{1}{2}(+15¢) + \tfrac{1}{2}(+12¢) = +13\tfrac{1}{2}¢$$

If the union used U_3, the expected wage increase would be

$$\tfrac{1}{2}(+2\cancel{c}) + \tfrac{1}{2}(+19\cancel{c}) = +10\tfrac{1}{2}\cancel{c}.$$

Either of these is preferable from the company viewpoint to the $+15$ cents indicated by the minimax rule. The union, of course, also may adopt such a mixed strategy. One of von Neumann's great contributions was to prove that every two-person zero-sum game, regardless of the number of strategies available to the participants, has a unique equilibrium value. As a special case, the solution may involve pure

FIGURE 16–1

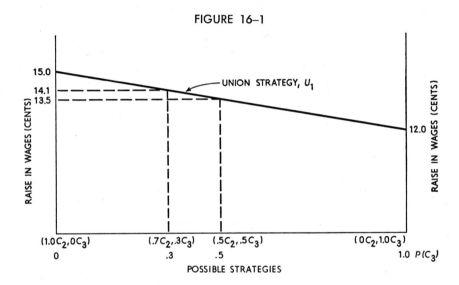

strategies, as shown initially. If this is not the case, we still know that for some pair of *mixed* strategies an equilibrium exists.

A simple and instructive way to find the solution for the two-person, two-strategy case is the geometric method suggested by Luce and Raiffa (1957). First, we shall derive the optimum mixed strategy for the company. Consider Figure 16–1, where possible mixed company strategies may be evaluated against the union's strategy U_1. On the vertical axes the possible raises are plotted. The horizontal axis is scaled in terms of mixed strategies for the company from the limit of $(1.0C_2, 0C_3)$—the pure strategy C_2—to the limit $(0C_2, 1.0C_3)$, the pure strategy C_3. At the extremes the pay-offs are $+15$ cents and $+12$ cents, as shown in Table 16–6. The device of the mixed strategy enables us to select any point on the line connecting $+15$ cents and $+12$ cents as a pay-off to the union's strategy, U_1. For example, if we wanted to choose $+13.5$ cents in response to U_1, we would select the mixed strategy $(0.5C_2, 0.5C_3)$. If we chose the mixed strategy $(0.7C_2, 0.3C_3)$, the pay-off would be $+14.1$ cents. Any point on the straight line in Figure 16–1 is a feasible payment to the union if it follows strategy U_1.

Now, in Figure 16–2, we construct the appropriate mixed strategies pay-off line for U_3, and consider it in conjunction with the U_1 line developed in Figure 16–1. The new line indicates the returns to the union for strategy U_3, assuming the company selects a mixed

FIGURE 16–2

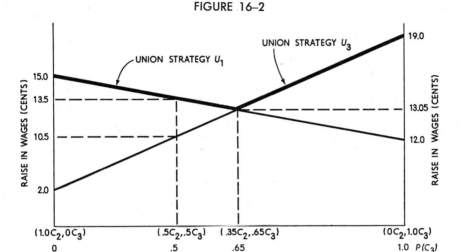

strategy between $(1.0C_2, 0C_3)$ and $(0C_2, 1.0C_3)$. For example, if the company adopts $(0.5C_2, 0.5C_3)$, the raise is 13.5 cents if the union adopts strategy U_1 and 10.5 cents if the union adopts U_3. From the company's standpoint the maximum pay-off for this strategy is 13.5 cents. For mixed strategies between $(1.0C_2, 0C_3)$ and $(0.35C_2, 0.65C_3)$, the maximum raise to the union is obtained if the union follows strategy U_1; for mixed strategies between $(0.35C_2, 0.65C_3)$ and $(0C_2, 1.0C_3)$, the maximum raise to the union is associated with union strategy U_3. The heavy line in Figure 16–2 defines the set of maximum raises the company would have to provide, assuming the union always adopted the most favorable strategy available to it in response to any mixed strategy adopted by the company. If the company follows the rule of minimizing the maximum raise it would have to pay, it would adopt the mixed strategy $(0.35C_2, 0.65C_3)$ and give the union a raise of $0.35(15\cent) + 0.65(12\cent) = 13.05\cent$ if it adopts strategy U_1, or $0.35(2\cent) + 0.65(19\cent) = 13.05\cent$ if the union adopts strategy U_3. Regardless of the union's action, it cannot get more than 13.05 cents per hour of expected wage increase (i.e., its best average increase is 13.05).

What strategy could we expect the union to follow? The minimax philosophy dictates that the union assume the company will erect the stoutest defense against any strategy it selects. We have sketched in Figure 16-3 the strategies available to the union and the set of minimum wage increases associated with those strategies. If the com-

FIGURE 16-3

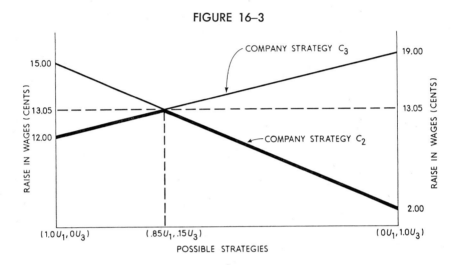

pany adopts strategy C_3, the wage increases to the union in return for various mixed strategies are indicated by the line joining 12 cents and 19 cents. This line would indicate the minimum raise for strategies between $(1.0U_1, 0U_3)$ and $(0.85U_1, 0.15U_3)$. The line joining 15 cents and 2 cents defines the wage increases in response to various union mixed strategies if the company follows strategy C_2. This strategy provides the minimum wage boost for union action in the range $(0.85U_1, 0.15U_3)$ to $(0U_1, 1.0U_3)$. If the union wishes to maximize the minimum wage increase, it will adopt the strategy $(0.85U_1, 0.15U_3)$. This provides an expected increase of

$$0.85(15¢) + 0.15(2¢) = 13.05¢$$

if the company adopts strategy C_2, and

$$0.85(12¢) + 0.15(19¢) = 13.05¢$$

if the company adopts strategy C_3. The sum 13.05 cents is a saddle point in this game and provides the equilibrium solution.

It should be remembered that the example assumes that the monetary measures are also utility measures. The 13.05 is the utility of the cost to the company of following the mixed strategy, and it is also the utility of the wage increase to the union. If we fail to recognize that the 13.05 measures utility (as well as money), then we may fall into the trap of thinking that the mixed strategy is not a minimax strategy because one possible event is a wage increase of 19.00 following the mixed strategy, but the maximum wage increase following C_2 is only 15.00. The mixed strategy is logical; for example, the utility of the cost to the company of U_3 is equal to $0.35U(2¢) + 0.65U(19¢) = 0.35(2) + 0.65(19) = 13.05$. The 13.05 is a utility measure and, as such, leads us to conclude that the mixed strategy results in minimum maximum cost for the company and maximum minimum wage increase to the union (in terms of utility or, equivalently in this example, expected monetary values).

MINIMAX

In games against nature, minimax strategy is very conservative, and minimax is not a very desirable criterion. However, in a two-person constant-sum game against a thinking opponent, it is reasonable, since it provides a participant with maximum security. It insures a certain outcome, regardless of the behavior of the opponent. No matter how cunning, how clever, how unscrupulous he may be, his best outcome is determined by your actions. You are indifferent to the strategy he selects, for you are prepared for all contingencies.

Minimax has a particular appeal to students on academic scholarships preparing for exams, football coaches, and most credit officers and bankers. It is not a good strategy for those who think they can outguess their opponents and are willing to accept the risk of going on the offensive. In our example the union group might learn by the grapevine that management has hired a labor law expert to head its bargaining contingent and conclude that management would follow the legalistic strategy C_3. On the basis of this estimate of management's intentions, the union might adopt the pure strategy U_3, in the hope of a 19-cent increase. It might be right and gain nearly 6 cents more than the conservative minimax strategy would provide for it. Or management might follow minimax, in which case it would have an expected cost of 13.05 cents, even with U_3. But the lawyer might be nothing but window dressing for a true C_2 strategy, and the union would have to settle for 2 cents.

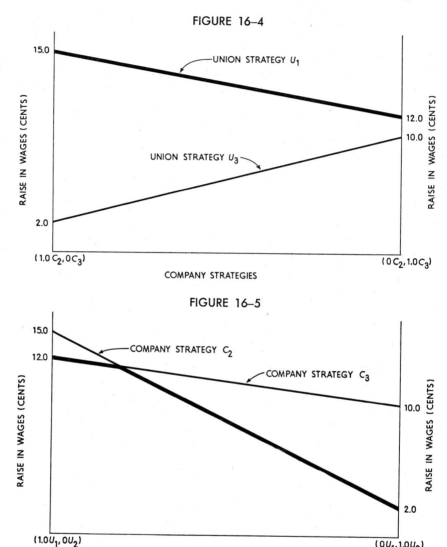

FIGURE 16–4

FIGURE 16–5

	U_1	U_3
C_2	15¢	2¢
C_3	12	10

All graphs of strategies do not have the same characteristics as Figures 16–3, of course. For example, we have plotted the *original* strategies (Table 16–4) in Figures 16–4 and 16–5. Figure 16–4 indicates that the company minimizes the maximum raise by adopting

$(0C_2, 1.0C_3)$, the pure strategy C_3, yielding 12 cents. Figure 16–5 indicates that 12 cents is the largest raise the union can get with assurance, obtained by following the pure strategy U_1.

The change of the intercept (C_2, U_3) from 10 cents to 19 cents enabled the union to increase its maximum wage increase from 12.00 cents to 13.05 cents. If it were in its power to do so, the union should be willing to yield up to 1.05 cents per hour to get the change in the intercept.

NONZERO-SUM GAMES

For most two-person conflict situations the utilities of the participants will not sum to a constant for all outcomes of the game. Some solutions will yield more joint satisfaction to the participants than

TABLE 16–7

I \ II	No Advertising	Advertise
No advertising........	+2 + 2	−15 + 5
Advertise...........	+5 −15	−10 −10

others. These games are called nonzero-sum games. A famous example, originally called the "prisoner's dilemma," is given here.

Assume two firms are faced with a decision relative to whether or not they will advertise. They each have two possible decisions—no advertising, or avertising. The matrix of pay-offs is as shown in Table 16–7.

The symbols in the matrix refer to the utilities of the two firms for each pair of decisions: I's utility and II's utility. For example, if I advertises and II does not, I will have a utility of five and II a utility of −15.

The pay-off matrix for firm II is shown in Table 16–8.

No matter what I's decision is, II is better off if it advertises. That is, if I does not advertise, II will, for it prefers a pay-off of five

TABLE 16–8

I \ II	No Advertising	Advertise
No advertising........	+ 2	+ 5
Advertise...........	−15	−10

rather than a pay-off of two. If I advertises, so will II, for it prefers a pay-off of -10 to one of -15. Thus the advertising strategy dominates the no-advertising strategy for II, and II is led to the decision to advertise. Exactly the same analysis holds for I, since the decision it faces is exactly the same as that of II. I and II are both led by a rational decision process to advertise and incur a loss of -10 each. If they were not so rational, they might each follow the dominated strategy of no advertising and receive a pay-off of $+2$ each.

Of course, the above analysis assumes the two parties cannot co-operate (i.e., communicate their intentions), since this would change the nature of the game. It also assumes a one-shot playing of the game, with no learning by the parties concerned. It is possible that I and II would learn by the unhappy experience of their first try at this game and co-operate during a later playing of the game, even without actually communicating.

The above is an example of a two-person nonzero-sum game. While there is a type of solution because the advertising decision dominates the no-advertising decision, it is not a completely satisfactory solution. A pair of nonrational players may arrive at the more desirable solution where both parties do not advertise. Nonzero-sum games frequently do not have easily determined satisfactory solutions.

UNCERTAIN PAY-OFFS

In the above example the pay-offs were certain amounts. It is possible for the pay-offs of a game to be subject to probability distributions. For example, instead of II knowing that his loss will be two if both firms advertise, he can be told that the pay-off will be either a loss of eight with a 0.5 probability or a gain of four with a probability of 0.5. The expected loss is:

$$-8 \times 0.5 = -4$$
$$4 \times 0.5 = \frac{2}{-2}$$

When the pay-offs are the result of a stochastic process, it necessitates an additional computation. Before we analyze the possible decisions, the expected utility of each pair of decisions is computed and inserted into the matrix. It should be remembered that we are using expectations of utility and not expected monetary values.

MERCHANDISING DECISIONS: ANOTHER NONZERO-SUM GAME EXAMPLE

Given two firms, r and y, the choice of an optimum level of merchandising by y depends to some extent upon the merchandising decision of r. In the same sense, r's selection of an optimum merchandising strategy depends upon the level of expenditures by firm y. Once either party commits itself to a program of action, the decision problem is relatively simple for the remaining competitor. What if the managers of firms y and r must choose their merchandising strategies simultaneously? Further, if this situation is to be repeated over time, each manager knows that his choice of a merchandising strategy will influence subsequent merchandising decisions by his opponent.

SIZE-OF-MARKET DECISION

Let us first consider a case where the share of market is fixed and the problem is to determine how much each firm will allocate to increasing the size of the market. Assume a general relationship between sales and total merchandising outlays of the form:

$$Q = Q_1 + \left(\sum_{i=1}^{n} b_i A_i \right)^{\frac{1}{K}}$$

where Q is total sales of the product; Q_1, sales with no merchandising activity; n, the number of firms; b_i, an index of the effectiveness of the merchandising outlays for the ith firm; A_i, the amount of those outlays for the ith firm; and K, an index of consumer resistance to merchandising.

As an example, assume there are two firms, y and r, each possessing half the market, a profit margin of $8.00 per unit sold, and linear utility functions for money. For the other parameters, let $Q_1 = 0$, $K = 2$, $b_1 = b_2 = 1$. Then, y's profit function is

$$\pi_y = 4(A_y + A_r)^{\frac{1}{2}} - A_y,$$

and r's profit function is

$$\pi_r = 4(A_y + A_r)^{\frac{1}{2}} - A_r.$$

The problem is for y and r to choose merchandising outlays A_y and A_r so as to maximize profits. The inherent difficulty of the problem may be seen in Table 16–9, where y's merchandising strategies are

TABLE 16–9

(In each cell the upper-right entry is y's profit, π_y; the lower-left entry is r's profit, π_r.)

r's Expenditures (A_r):	\multicolumn{7}{c}{y's Expenditures (A_y)}
	0	**1**	**2**	**3**	**4**	**8**	**16**
0	0.0 ╲ 0.0	3.0 ╲ 4.0	3.6 ╲ 5.6	3.8 ╲ 6.8	4.0 ╲ 8.0	3.2 ╲ 11.2	0.0 ╲ 16.0
1	4.0 ╲ 3.0	4.6 ╲ 4.6	4.8 ╲ 5.8	5.0 ╲ 7.0	4.8 ╲ 7.8	4.0 ╲ 11.0	0.4 ╲ 15.4
2	5.6 ╲ 3.6	5.8 ╲ 4.8	6.0 ╲ 6.0	5.8 ╲ 6.8	5.6 ╲ 7.6	4.8 ╲ 10.8	0.8 ╲ 14.8
3	6.8 ╲ 3.8	7.0 ╲ 5.0	6.8 ╲ 5.8	6.6 ╲ 6.6	6.4 ╲ 7.4	5.2 ╲ 10.2	1.6 ╲ 14.6
4	8.0 ╲ 4.0	7.8 ╲ 4.8	7.6 ╲ 5.6	7.4 ╲ 6.4	7.2 ╲ 7.2	6.0 ╲ 10.0	2.0 ╲ 14.0
8	11.2 ╲ 3.2	11.0 ╲ 4.0	10.8 ╲ 4.8	10.2 ╲ 5.2	10.0 ╲ 6.0	8.0 ╲ 8.0	3.6 ╲ 11.6
16	16.0 ╲ 0.0	15.4 ╲ 0.4	14.8 ╲ 0.8	14.6 ╲ 1.6	14.0 ╲ 2.0	11.6 ╲ 3.6	6.8 ╲ 6.8

arrayed across the top, and r's along the side. The resulting profits are shown in the body of the table, the entry in the upper right side of the square representing y's profits, π_y, and the one in the lower left of the square representing r's profits, π_r. If each firm spends nothing, each will receive zero profits; if y spends \$4.00 and r spends nothing, y will make \$4.00, and r will make \$8.00; and so forth. The first row indicates that as y increases his expenditures, y's profits will rise to a maximum of \$4.00 and then will fall, while r's profits continue to rise. It might seem, then, that y's best strategy would be to spend \$4.00, regardless of r's action. If y does, r's best counteraction, on the assumption that y will continue to spend \$4.00, will be to spend nothing, for the maximum profit r could obtain under these circumstances is \$8.00.[4] It might seem that $A_y = \$4.00$, $A_r = 0$

---

[4] If y assumes r will spend nothing, y's maximum π_y is when

$$\frac{d\pi_y}{dA_y} = \frac{4}{2}(A_y)^{-\frac{1}{2}} - 1 = 0$$

or $A_y = 4$ and

$$\frac{d^2\pi_y}{dA_y{}^2} = -(A_y)^{-\frac{3}{2}} < 0$$

If r assumes $A_y = 4$, r maximizes π_r when

$$\frac{d\pi_r}{dA_r} = \frac{4}{2}(A_r + 4)^{-\frac{1}{2}} - 1 = 0$$

or $A_r = 0$, since

$$\frac{d^2\pi_r}{dA_r{}^2} < 0.$$

would be a solution for the game; indeed, this pair is defined as an equilibrium pair in game theory, for each strategy is optimum, given the action of the other player.

But why should y settle for a $4.00 profit when r makes $8.00, especially since r has not contributed anything to the merchandising campaign? For instance, if y spent only $1.00 on merchandising and made it known to r that this was his plan, would r stop "free-loading"? The answer is yes—r maximizes his profits by spending $3.00, where $\pi_r = \$5.00$, and y's profits are $7.00. This again is an equilibrium pair (best against each other), so it is apparent that an equilibrium pair is no guarantee of a stable solution!

Perhaps y should go to zero expenditures, forcing r to spend $4.00, and providing y with the $8.00 profit. But then r would be in a position to reason just as y has done, and they might find themselves stuck at 0/0, each waiting for the other to be the merchandising martyr. Another tactic might occur to y at this point: Firm y might increase expenditures slightly, and then fall back to zero if r did not match y's outlays. After a while, r probably would get the idea, so that y and r might arrive at a strategy pair such as $A_y = \$2.00$ and $A_r = \$2.00$. This might be considered a solution, for it is the best adjustment either y or r can make, assuming the other will continue his expenditures at $2.00 (again, it is an equilibrium pair); further, each firm enjoys the same profit level, $6.00. But why stop at $6.00? It appears that the firms have found the way out of their dilemma, so that they could continue to match expenditures out to the maximum joint profit position of $A_y = \$8.00$, $A_r = \$8.00$, $\pi_y = \$8.00$, $\pi_r = \$8.00$. This, then, should be the solution adjustment—indeed, it is what management would do if the two firms consolidated, for no higher profit sum is possible.

But if y commits itself to an expenditure level of $8.00 per period, what is to prevent r from suddenly cutting back to zero? It might seem attractive to r—he makes $11.20 rather than $8.00. One might argue that r would not reduce his expenditures for the same reason that y would not reduce his, since the ultimate sequence of events would be from $A_y = 8$ to $A_y = 4$ to $A_y = 0$, and then back out the diagonal once more.

But y might get in a financial pinch, and the present value of $3.20, i.e. $11.20 − \$8.00$, might be greater than r's good will plus the prospect of higher future earnings. Or y may delegate this re-sponsibility to his son, who has studied calculus but not game theory, and so would go to the \$11.20 position; or y may just make a mistake. In any event, there is no stable solution for this game situation.

SHARE-OF-MARKET DECISION

In this section, we shall assume that the size of the market is fixed but the share of the market going to a firm is a function of its relative merchandising expenditures, and share of the market measures the utility of the decision.

TABLE 16–10

Change in Percentage of Market Going to y

Strategies of y	Strategies of r			
	r_1	r_2	r_3	r_4
y_1.............	0.00	−0.15	−0.25	−0.28
y_2.............	0.16	0.00	−0.12	−0.20
y_3.............	0.27	0.11	0.00	−0.11
y_4.............	0.32	0.20	0.08	0.00

Returning to a two-firm example, for a given level of merchandising outlay by r, y's share of the market will increase as he increases his merchandising expenditure. What strategies should y and r follow under these conditions?

Table 16–10 may give an indication of the direction the solution will take. At the top of the table, r_i $(i = 1, \ldots, 4)$ represents the merchandising strategies available to firm r, reflecting increasing levels of expenditures; y_i $(i = 1, \ldots, 4)$ then represents increasing levels of merchandising expenditures by firm y. The entries in the body of Table 16–10 indicate the change in the share of market going to firm y.

If $y_i = r_i$, the market shares will not change; if firm y chooses strategy y_1 and firm r chooses strategy r_4, firm y will lose 0.28 of the market to firm r. If r chooses strategy r_2 and y selects strategy y_3, y will gain 0.11 of the market. This is set up as a zero-sum game (we have not considered the costs of the various strategies) that has an equilibrium point at y_4, r_4; that is, minimax strategy would lead each party to the largest merchandising level.[5]

---

[5] It is essential that it be understood that it is assumed that the two firms have utility functions which are linear with their share of the market. Minimax strategy refers to the minimization (or maximization) of a utility measure. Thus, for the above explanations to be correct, the changes in percentage of market must represent the utility of the strategy pairs.

Now, if we assign costs that rise with the increasing level of merchandising activity, we shall have a counterpart of the problem we were concerned with in the preceding section. The issue is: Will the parties continue to follow the counterpart of a minimax strategy and select y_4, r_4, or will they maximize joint profits and go back to y_1, r_1? There is no way to answer this question on an a priori ground.

SIZE-OF-MARKET AND SHARE-OF-MARKET MERCHANDISING DECISIONS

We have seen that when the firms must simultaneously select merchandising strategies, there is likely to be indeterminacy in both the size-of-market and the share-of-market cases. In the size-of-mar-

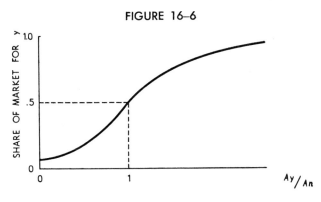

FIGURE 16–6

ket model, one firm desired to spend very little on merchandising and hoped its rival would spend a great deal; in the share-of-market model, one firm desired to spend a great deal on merchandising and hoped its rival would spend very little. In both of these cases, it was impossible to find a stable solution.

However, in most merchandising campaigns the management has both size-of-market and share-of-market objectives in mind. Since the tendencies in the separate cases seem to be contradictory, perhaps a joint analysis will provide a solution.

Assume that two firms have the same margin for a product, $4.00. Say the size of the market is determined by the equation

$$Q = (A_r + A_y)^{\frac{1}{2}}$$

and the share of the market is derived from some function such as shown in Figure 16–6. From the resulting profit equations, we construct Table 16–11, where several alternative levels of merchandising outlays are listed (in the margins) for each firm. The associated profits are in the body of the table, y's profit being that in the upper right-hand corner, and r's being that in the lower left-hand corner of an entry. If y spends four units on merchandising, for example, and r spends only two units, then y's profit will be 2.9 utility units, and r's will be 0.9 units. The maximum joint profits are four, which obtain when y and r each spend two units on merchandising.

It would appear reasonable to suppose, in this case, that the two

TABLE 16–11

A_r Strategies for r:	A_y Strategies for y					
	1	2	3	4	5	6
1 .... 1.8	π_y 1.8 / π_r 1.8	2.8 / 1.0	3.7 / 0.3	4.2 / −0.4	4.8 / −1.0	4.6 / −1.0
2 .... 2.8	1.0 / 2.0	2.0 / 2.0	2.3 / 1.5	2.9 / 0.9	4.5 / −0.9	4.4 / −1.2
3 .... 3.7	0.3 / 3.7	1.5 / 2.3	1.9 / 1.9	2.0 / 1.6	2.0 / 1.2	2.4 / 0.6
4 .... 4.2	−0.4 / 4.2	0.9 / 2.9	1.6 / 2.0	1.6 / 1.6	1.6 / 1.4	1.4 / 1.0
5 .... 4.8	−1.0 / 4.8	−0.9 / 4.5	1.2 / 2.0	1.4 / 1.6	1.2 / 1.2	1.0 / 1.1
6 .... 4.6	−1.0 / 4.6	−1.2 / 4.4	0.6 / 2.4	1.0 / 1.4	1.1 / 1.1	1.0 / 1.0

competitors will spend substantially more than a total of four units. Say r spends two units; y can increase his profit by spending more than two units, to a maximum of 4.5 profit for a merchandising outlay of five units. Further, if y does not spend the five units but spends only two in the hope that r will do the same, there is at least some chance that r will jump to an outlay of five, thus reducing y's profit from two to −0.9. The counterpart of the conservative minimax strategy in this case would be for both firms to spend five units, since this assures them of at least 1.1 return each. But if r is consistent in his outlay of five units, y can increase his profit from 1.2 to 1.4 by cutting his expenditures from five to four. This would not seem to be a very risky tactic, for it would be most unlikely that r would select strategy $A_r = 6$. The new adjustment increases r's profit as well, from 1.2 to 1.6. Perhaps this windfall might make him amenable to reducing his outlay from five to four, which would not reduce his profit but would increase y's from 1.4 to 1.6. But then, if such co-operation is possible, why not go to the adjustment which maximizes joint gain—two and two?

We have come full circle on the question of interdependence of decisions, without a solution. This is as it should be, for businessmen too have failed to find an easy equilibrium in this area of adjustment. If you understand why, the mission of this chapter is accomplished.

BIBLIOGRAPHY

DORFMAN, R., AND STEINER, P.   "Optimal Quality and Optimal Advertising," *American Economic Review,* May, 1954.

EVANS, F. B.   "Discussion of the Strategy of Market Segmentation," *Advancing Marketing Efficiency* (ed. Stockman). Chicago: American Marketing Association, 1959.

FRIEDMAN, L.   "Game Theory Models in the Allocation of Advertising Expenditures," *Operations Research,* September–October, 1958.

GILLMAN, L.   "Operations Analysis and the Theory of Games: An Advertising Example," *Journal of the American Statistical Association,* December, 1950.

LUCE, R. D., and RAIFFA, H.   *Games and Decisions.* New York: John Wiley & Sons, Inc., 1957.

SHUBIK, M.   *Strategy and Market Structure.* New York: John Wiley & Sons, Inc., 1959.

VON NEUMANN, J., and MORGENSTERN, O.   *Theory of Games and Economic Behavior.* Princeton: Princeton University Press, 1944.

WILLIAMS, J. D.   *The Compleat Strategyst.* New York: McGraw-Hill Book Co., Inc., 1954.

PROBLEMS

16–1. Prepare the pay-off matrix for matching pennies, player 1 saying he can match player 2. What does this assume about the utilities of players 1 and 2?

16–2. In matching pennies, is the minimax strategy a pure strategy?

16–3. If a player follows a pure strategy in matching pennies, what is the most he is liable to lose on a series of n plays?

16–4. Assume the following pay-off matrix for two opponents, A and B, the amounts being the utility gained by A and lost by B for any given intersection of strategies:

	B_1	B_2
A_1	10	6
A_2	8	2

a) What strategy will A follow?
b) What strategy will B follow?
c) What is the "value" of the game?
d) Plot these strategies from player A's standpoint.

16–5. Assume the following pay-off matrix for A and B, the amounts being the utilities gained by A and lost by B for any given intersection of strategies:

	B_1	B_2
A_1	10	6
A_2	8	12

a) What is the maximum minimum gain A can make for sure by following a pure strategy?
b) What is the minimum maximum loss B can incur for sure by following a pure strategy?
c) If A and B follow mixed strategies, what is the value of the game?
d) What is the mixed strategy for A?
e) Plot the mixed strategies for A and B.

16–6. Consider a set of pay-offs ranging from zero to X where party A has an increasing utility function over this range with a level of aspiration of $\frac{1}{2}X$ and party B has a diminishing utility function over this range with a level of aspiration at X.
a) Will the negotiations be long or short, if you had to predict?
b) Could you predict a range (less than zero to X) in which the settlement is likely to fall? What is it?

16–7. What type of conflict situation is more likely: a zero-sum game or a nonzero-sum game?

16–8. Say the following pay-off matrix is appropriate for the merchandising strategies of two opponents:

Strategies of a	Strategies of b	
	b_1	b_2
a_1	0 \ 0	2 \ 1
a_2	\ 1 4	\ 3 5

a) What strategy will a follow? Why?
b) What strategy will b follow? Why?
c) What outcome would you predict for this situation?

16–9. Two firms, f and g, face the following profit pay-off for alternative merchandising strategies:

| Strategies | Strategies of f | |
of g	f_1	f_2
g_1.........	$\begin{smallmatrix}&8\\8&\end{smallmatrix}$	$\begin{smallmatrix}&10\\1&\end{smallmatrix}$
g_2.........	$\begin{smallmatrix}&1\\10&\end{smallmatrix}$	$\begin{smallmatrix}&2\\2&\end{smallmatrix}$

a) What strategy will f follow? Why?
b) What strategy will g follow? Why?
c) What is the solution of the game?
d) Identify the equilibrium pair, if there is one.

16–10. If Problem 16–9 were repeated daily for n days, where n is large, do you think the players would continue to follow an equilibrium strategy? What does this suggest?

16–11. The ABC Company and the XYZ Company are both currently distributing, through a subsidiary, automobiles in the country of Afro. The profits per year of the two subsidiaries are currently as follows: ABC, $10 million; and XYZ, $20 million.

The ABC Company is considering establishing a manufacturing plant in Afro. An analyst has projected a profit of $38 million after the plant begins operations (this assumes the XYZ Company continues to distribute automobiles, but not to manufacture them, in the country).

An analyst for the XYZ Company has heard of the plans of the ABC Company. If the plant is built by ABC, he projects XYZ's profits to fall to $4 million. If the XYZ Company builds a plant and the ABC Company does not, he anticipates profits of $38 million and a decrease in the profits of ABC to $4 million.

If both companies build plants, it is expected that they would both earn $5 million per year.

Required:
What should the companies do?

Chapter 17

LINEAR PROGRAMMING—THE

SIMPLEX METHOD

LINEAR programming is a mathematical technique designed to assist organizations in planning certain of their activities. The originator of the technique was G. B. Dantzig (1951), who used it in response to various planning problems confronting the United States Air Force.

The problem for which linear programming provides a solution may be summarized as follows: Maximize (or minimize) some dependent variable which is a function of several independent variables when the independent variables are subject to various restraints. The dependent variable is usually some economic objective, such as profits, production, costs, work weeks, or tons shipped. More profits are generally preferred to less profits, and lower costs are preferred to higher costs, etc.; therefore, it is appropriate to represent one of the organization's objectives as a maximization or minimization of the dependent variable (other things being equal). The size of the dependent variable depends upon several critical factors in most situations; these factors are designated as the independent variables. We assume a linear relationship between the dependent variable and its determinants; that is, we assume that a linear equation of the form

$$f = A_1X_1 + A_2X_2 + \ldots + A_NX_N$$

may be written, where f is the dependent variable (say, profits) and $X_1, X_2, \ldots, X_N$ are the independent variables that affect f. This equation is often called the objective function. The coefficients $A_1, A_2, \ldots, A_N$ are constants. All the X's are of the first power, which is necessary to characterize the relationship as a linear equation. The assumption of linearity has two justifications: (1) For

250

many situations, it is a good approximation of reality, and (2) it simplifies the mathematics enormously. These reasons also explain the general practice of assuming that the restraints on the independent variables have the form of linear inequalities. Each of the variables X_1, X_2, . . . , X_N are subject to some restraint of the type

$$B_1X_1 + B_2X_2 + \ldots + B_NX_N \geq C_1$$

The B coefficients are constants. The constant C_1 restricts f, the objective function, as a result of restricting the independent variables, X_1, X_2, . . . , X_N (instead of $\geq$, we could have $\leq$ or an equality).

TABLE 17–1

Product	Capacity	Per Unit Profit	Total Incremental Profit per Day
A................100 units per day		$5.00	$ 500
B................600 units per day		2.00	1,200

The problem of maximizing f subject to the objective function and the various restraints is conceptually simple. When there are few independent variables, common sense and some arithmetic will yield a solution, and scientists had solved such problems for generations before Dantzig's contribution. However, as is often the case, intuition is of little use when the problem is more complex; when the number of independent variables is increased from three to four, from four to five, and so on, the problem defies rule-of-thumb procedures. Dantzig made it possible to handle a problem with any finite number of restraints in an orderly way.

This technique has exceptional power and generality. It is applicable to a variety of problems in a modern business organization, and may be handled in a routine way with the aid of digital computers. It is one of the quantitative techniques which has provided management with a remarkable leverage on a set of problems that defied efficient solutions a few years ago.

As a simple example, consider the following problem, which can be solved by the use of common sense or marginal analysis. Assume the incremental profit of product A is $5.00 per unit and the profit of product B is $2.00 per unit and we can sell all we make of both products; further, the products may be produced with the same equipment. We can compute which product we should produce once we find out the capacity of our facilities in terms of A and B (see Table 17–1).

In this simple example, product B is obviously a more desirable product than A. Now, assume a more complicated problem where the plant is capable of making twenty different products in fifteen different departments, and each product requires different production time in each department. If the difficulty of this problem is not impressive, assume that each department contains ten processes and each product requires different production time in each process. How do we determine the optimum product mix? A problem of this type is best solved by linear programming. The term "linear" is appropriate, since all profit and cost relationships are assumed to be linear, i.e., the highest degree of any variable is one and no variables are multiplied by any other variable.

There are several methods for solving linear programming problems. In this chapter, we shall introduce a graphical solution and then discuss the simplex method, which is a systematic method for deriving a solution. In the Appendix to this chapter, we shall consider some of the underlying mathematics of the simplex procedure, and shall offer some discussion of the logic and reason for the simplex method and present an algebraic technique for solving simple linear programming problems.

In some of the examples to follow, the answers will be obvious; this is because the examples were constructed to be as simple as possible. The reader should keep in mind that we are attempting to illustrate a technique that may be applied to extremely complex problems. We apply it to simple situations for expository purposes. The computations arising in most complex linear programming problems would be done on a computer; one of the important features of the simplex procedure is that it can be programmed on a computer.

A GRAPHIC SOLUTION

It is not usually possible to solve linear programming problems graphically because of our inability to graph a space of dimension greater than three. However, it is useful to see how a simple problem may be solved graphically.

Situation. One machine has twelve hours and a second machine has eight hours of excess capacity. The firm manufactures products A and B. Each unit of product A requires two hours of time on both machines. Each unit of product B requires three hours of time on the first machine and one hour on the second machine. The incremental

FIGURE 17–1

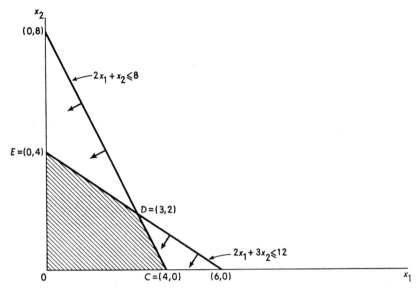

profit is \$6.00 per unit of A and \$7.00 per unit of B, and the firm can sell as many of either product as it can manufacture.

Problem. Assuming the objective is to maximize profit, how many units of product A and product B should be produced?

Solution. Let:

$X_1 = $ The number of units of product A to be produced
$X_2 = $ The number of units of product B to be produced
$P = $ The incremental profit.

We can express the situation and the objective (to maximize profit) using the equations below:

$$\text{Maximize:} \quad P = 6X_1 + 7X_2$$
$$\text{Subject to:} \quad 2X_1 + 3X_2 \leq 12$$
$$2X_1 + X_2 \leq 8$$
$$X_1, X_2 \geq 0.$$

In Figure 17–1 the two constraining equations are shown. The equation

$$2X_1 + 3X_2 \leq 12$$

is the constraint imposed by limitation of hours available (twelve) on the first machine, and all points to the left are possible (feasible) combinations of X_1 and X_2. Similarly:

$$2X_1 + X_2 \leq 8$$

is the constraint associated with the second machine, and points to the left are feasible. We also have constraints $X_1 \geq 0$ and $X_2 \geq 0$, since we cannot have negative output. The hatched region in Figure 17–1 is the set of points that are feasible under all the constraints. Clearly, not all of these points will maximize profit.

The area $OCDE$ is called a convex polygon. (Because we are dealing with linear equations, the set of solutions [feasible points] will always be a convex polygon for solvable linear programming prob-

FIGURE 17–2

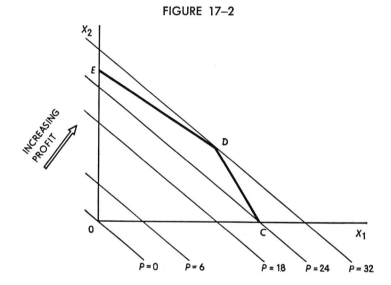

lems.) It can be shown mathematically that the optimum solution will always be at an extreme point (corner point) of the convex polygon.[1]

Let us see intuitively why this would be so for our example. In Figure 17–2 the profit function is graphed for various profit levels.

Consider the profit function for which $P = 18$. This line contains many feasible points (points within $OCDE$), all of which would give us \$18 profit. But the line $P = 24$ is better than $P = 18$, since it contains feasible points with profit of \$24. We continue considering lines parallel to line $P = 18$ until we reach the line $P = 32$. Here, there is only one point in the $OCDE$ polygon—namely, D itself. And D (which is $X_1 = 3$, $X_2 = 2$) is the optimal solution.

The fact that D is the optimal point is dependent upon the slope

---

[1] If there is more than one optimum solution, these solutions will comprise two or more corner points and all convex combinations of these points.

of the profit function,[2] that is, upon the relative profitability of products A and B. Had B been considerably more profitable than A (say, $8.00 per unit of B to $2.00 per unit of A), then our profit function would have much less slope, and the optimum point would be point E with $X_1 = 0$ and $X_2 = 4$ (that is, only product B would be produced). Similarly, if product A were sufficiently more profitable than B, the optimum solution would be point C.

Since we know the optimum solution must be on an *extremum* or corner point, one method of solving a linear programming problem is simply to list all extreme points and find the one (or more) that maximizes the profit function. However, for large problems, this is an impractical method. Instead, we rely upon a procedure called the simplex method, which examines extreme points in a methodical fashion to find the optimum.

THE SIMPLEX METHOD

Example 1—Maximization of Profits

Let us consider the same problem that we solved above by graphic methods. Recall that we had:

$$\begin{aligned}
\text{Maximize:} \quad & P = 6X_1 + 7X_2 \\
\text{Subject to:} \quad & 2X_1 + 3X_2 \leq 12 \\
& 2X_1 + X_2 \leq 8 \\
& X_1 \geq 0 \\
& X_2 \geq 0
\end{aligned}$$

where

$X_1 = $ The number of units of product A
$X_2 = $ The number of units of product B
$6 = $ The incremental profit per unit of product A
$7 = $ The incremental profit per unit of product B.

We wish to maximize the profit function, which is

$$P = 6X_1 + 7X_2$$

in this case. The function which is being maximized (or minimized) is called the objective function.

The first inequality indicates that the number of units of A times the two hours which A requires on machine 1, plus the number of

---

[2] The slope of the objective function is $-\frac{6}{7}$ ($P = 6x_1 + 7x_2$; $7x_2 = P - 6x_1$; $x_2 = P - 6x_1$; $x_2 = P - \frac{6}{7}x_1$; and $-\frac{6}{7}$ is the slope).

units of B times the three hours which B requires on machine 1, must be less than or equal to 12, where 12 is the amount of excess capacity of machine 1. The second inequality establishes the necessary conditions that must be met with respect to machine 2. Note that the best product mix may not use all of the capacity which is available.

The next step is to use the simplex method to find a solution to the restraint inequalities which simultaneously maximizes profits. The simplex method proceeds as follows:

a) Introduce slack variables X_3 and X_4 to convert the inequalities to equalities. It is always possible to convert the inequalities to equalities, since there must be some amount—say, X_3—which, when added to $2X_1$ and $3X_2$, will equal 12 ($2X_1$ plus $3X_2$ is less than or equal to 12; thus, X_3 may be zero or greater than zero). The inequalities rewritten as equalities are:

$$2X_1 + 3X_2 + X_3 = 12$$
$$2X_1 + 1X_2 + X_4 = 8.$$

So that all variables are represented in each equation, we add slack variables with zero coefficients to the equations which are lacking some variables. For example, $0X_4$ is added to the first equation, and $0X_3$ is added to the second:

$$2X_1 + 3X_2 + X_3 + 0X_4 = 12$$
$$2X_1 + X_2 + 0X_3 + X_4 = 8.$$

The profit equation becomes:

$$P = 6X_1 + 7X_2 + 0X_3 + 0X_4.$$

Note that the slack variables introduce no profit, and their coefficients in the profit equation are zero.

b) Construct the first simplex table (see Table 17–2). The first row and first column of the table are the C_j's, or the profit per unit (the coefficients of the variables in the profit equation) for each

TABLE 17–2

C_j			0	0	6	7
	Solution Mix	P_0	X_3	X_4	X_1	X_2
0	→X_3	12	1	0	2	3
0	X_4	8	0	1	2	1
	Z_j	0	0	0	0	0
	$C_j - Z_j$		0	0	6	7
						↑

variable, X_1, X_2, X_3, and X_4, which are column headings. The second column of the table is headed "Solution Mix," and under it will be found the "products" or the variables of the first-trial solution. These consist in the first instance of the slack variables. It is desirable that the coefficients of the chosen variables of the first solution, that is, the columns under the variables, consist of a one and the remainder zeros. The third column heading is labeled P_0, and under it will be found the amounts of the products of the solution mix. In

TABLE 17–3

Solution Mix	X_1	X_2	$\ldots X_n$
X_1	1	0	$\ldots$ 0
X_2	0	1	$\ldots$ 0
. .			$\ldots$.
. .			$\ldots$.
. .			$\ldots$.
X_n	0	0	$\ldots$ 1

Table 17–2, this will be the constant terms of the restraint inequalities 12 and eight. Thus, one possible solution is to have X_3 take a value of 12 and X_4 a value of eight. This satisfies the restraint equations but is undesirable, since the resulting profit is zero.

Several characteristics of the first solution should be noted. The number of terms in the solution is equal to the number of restraints (there are two restraints and two terms, X_3 and X_4, in the solution). We find the product mix of the initial solution by inspecting each column and choosing only those columns which have one component which is a positive one, and whose other terms are zero. Thus, column X_3 is $\binom{1}{0}$, and column X_4 is $\binom{0}{1}$. Secondly, the one must be in a different row than the one of any other column. Thus, X_3 has a one in the first row, and X_4 has a one in the second row. Having found the columns with the specified characteristics, we list the column headings in the Solution Mix column. The first column heading listed should be the column which has a one in the first row; the second listed should have a one in the second row; etc. Thus the first n columns, where n is the number of restraints, should appear as shown in Table 17–3.

Note that we have a diagonal of ones and the remainder of the numbers in the first n columns are zeros.

Under each column heading (such as X_3, X_4, X_1, or X_2) of Table

17–2 are written the coefficients from the restraint equations of the variables found in the heading. Thus, under X_1 is written $\binom{2}{2}$; under X_2 is written $\binom{3}{1}$; under X_3 is written $\binom{1}{0}$; and under X_4 is written $\binom{0}{1}$. It is convenient to write the columns containing the slack variables immediately after the solution column, P_0. Thus the column headings are P_0, X_3, X_4, X_1, and X_2.

What do the numbers in each of the columns of the body of the simplex table represent? These are the reductions in the variables in the solution which will result from introducing one unit of each variable. For example, in Table 17–2, $\binom{3}{1}$ is under column X_2. For every unit of product B (i.e., units of X_2) introduced into the solution, three units of slack variable X_3 and one unit of slack variable X_4 must be removed from the solution in order to stay within the required restraints. An inspection of our constraint equations confirms the reasonableness of this interpretation:

$$2X_1 + 3X_2 + X_3 + 0X_4 = 12.$$
$$2X_1 + 1X_2 + 0X_3 + X_4 = 8.$$

For every unit of X_1 introduced into the solution, two units of X_3 and two units of X_4 must be removed.

The numbers in the body of the simplex table may be called substitution coefficients.

Under each column of Table 17–2 is a Z_j total (where the j subscript refers to the specific column which is being totaled). The Z_j total of a column is the amount of gross profit which is given up by replacing some of the present solution mix with *one* unit of the item heading the column. It is found by multiplying the C_j of the row by the number in the row and jth column, and adding. The computations of the Z_j's of Table 17–2 are as follows:

$$Z_{P0} = 12(0) + 8(0) = 0.$$
$$Z_3 = 1(0) + 0(0) = 0.$$
$$Z_4 = 0(0) + 1(0) = 0.$$
$$Z_1 = 2(0) + 2(0) = 0.$$
$$Z_2 = 3(0) + 1(0) = 0.$$

Under the Z_j row is a row designated $C_j - Z_j$. Subtract the Z_j total from the C_j amount at the very top of the column to find the profit which is added by one unit of the product (if $C_j - Z_j$ is positive) or the amount of profit which will be lost (if $C_j - Z_j$ is negative). Thus, *if one unit of B is added to the solution* (replacing some amounts of X_3 and X_4), $7.00 of profit will be added.

We have found twelve units of X_3 and eight units of X_4 to be one possible solution; but since the profit resulting from this product mix is zero (Z_j for the P_0 column), we attempt to find a more desirable solution. The procedure to compute Table 17–4 (the second simplex solution) is as follows:

a) Determine the column (if any) of Table 17–2 which will contribute the greatest profit per unit (the column which has the great-

TABLE 17–4

C_i			0	0	6	7
	Solution Mix	P_0	X_3	X_4	X_1	X_2
7	X_2	4	$\frac{1}{3}$	0	$\frac{2}{3}$	1
0	$\rightarrow X_4$	4	$-\frac{1}{3}$	1	$\frac{4}{3}$	0
	Z_i	28	$\frac{7}{3}$	0	$14\frac{2}{3}$	7
	$C_i - Z_i$		$-\frac{7}{3}$	0	$\frac{4}{3}$	0

est positive $C_j - Z_j$). Product B contributes $7.00 per unit, which is greater than the contribution of any other product. This means that we want to replace some of X_3 or X_4 with one or more units of B (column X_2, the replacing column, is marked with an arrow). The significance of the three and the one in the X_2 column is that, to insert one unit of X_2 into the solution, we must remove three units of X_3 and one unit of X_4.

b) The next step is to determine which row (X_3 or X_4) is to be replaced by X_2. Divide each amount in the P_0 column by the amount *in the comparable row* of the X_2 column:

For X_3 row: $12\frac{2}{3} = 4$ For X_4 row: $8\frac{1}{1} = 8$

The smallest number obtained by this computation gives the maximum number of X_2 units, four, which may be injected into the solution. If any of the amounts are negative, they should be eliminated from consideration; otherwise, the smallest amount, as computed above, determines the row to be replaced. In this case the X_3 row should be replaced (this row is marked by an arrow).

c) The actual replacement is accomplished making use of two techniques.

The replacing row (X_2) is determined by dividing each amount presently in row X_3, the row being replaced, by the amount in the X_2 column in the same row:

$$1\tfrac{2}{3} = 4$$
$$\tfrac{1}{3} = \tfrac{1}{3}$$
$$\tfrac{0}{3} = 0$$
$$\tfrac{2}{3} = \tfrac{2}{3}$$
$$\tfrac{3}{3} = 1.$$

Thus the new top row should be $(4, \tfrac{1}{3}, 0, \tfrac{2}{3}, 1)$; and it is labeled X_2 (see Table 17–4).

The second technique is for computing the amounts in all other rows. The component of each row is determined by taking the present amount in a specified row and column (say, column P_0 and row X_4, i.e., the element eight) and subtracting the product of (a) the amount in the same row and the X_2 column (the element one is at the intersection of the row and the column of X_4 and X_2 in Table 17–2), and (b) the amount in the same column of the new replacing row (four is the element in the P_0 column of the new row). Thus the new element is $8 - (1 \cdot 4) = 4$. This is easier to illustrate than to describe (see Table 17–5).

TABLE 17–5

Old X_4 Row $-$	(Old X_4 Row X_2 Column	$\cdot$	New X_2 Row)	$=$	Values of New X_4 Row
8	$-$ (1)	$\cdot$	(4)	$=$	4
0	$-$ (1)	$\cdot$	$(\tfrac{1}{3})$	$=$	$-\tfrac{1}{3}$
1	$-$ (1)	$\cdot$	(0)	$=$	1
2	$-$ (1)	$\cdot$	$(\tfrac{2}{3})$	$=$	$1\tfrac{1}{3}$
1	$-$ (1)	$\cdot$	(1)	$=$	0

The new values of the X_4 row are $(4, -\tfrac{1}{3}, 1, 1\tfrac{1}{3}, 0)$.

These computations accomplish the substitution of as much of product B as is consistent with the restraints. It also accomplishes the removal of as much X_3 and X_4 as is necessary to provide for the insertion of the B units into the solution. The C_j value of X_2, \$7.00, is inserted in the C_j column, X_2 row.

The computation of the Z_j's of Table 17–4 is as follows:

$$Z_{P0} = 7 \cdot 4 + 0(4) = 28.$$
$$Z_3 = 7 \cdot \tfrac{1}{3} + 0(-\tfrac{1}{3}) = \tfrac{7}{3}.$$
$$Z_4 = 7 \cdot 0 + 0(1) = 0.$$
$$Z_1 = 7 \cdot \tfrac{2}{3} + 0(\tfrac{4}{3}) = 14\tfrac{2}{3}.$$
$$Z_2 = 7 \cdot 1 + 0(0) = 7.$$

The profit arising from this product mix is \$28, which is an improvement in comparison with the previous solution. However, Table 17–4 indicates that we can substitute some units of A; and \$1.33, or $\frac{4}{3}$ dollars of profit, will be added for each unit of A substituted into the solution. Thus, we can compute a new table, Table 17–6.

TABLE 17–6

C_j			0	0	6	7
	Solution Mix	P_0	X_3	X_4	X_1	X_2
7	X_2	2	$\frac{1}{2}$	$-\frac{1}{2}$	0	1
6	X_1	3	$-\frac{1}{4}$	$\frac{3}{4}$	1	0
	Z_j	32	2	1	6	7
	$C_j - Z_j$		-2	-1	0	0

a) The new replacing product or column is X_1 (it has the largest net profit per replacing unit).

b) The row which is replaced by X_1 is X_4, determined as follows:

$$\text{For } X_2 \text{ row: } \frac{4}{\frac{2}{3}} = 6.$$

$$\text{For } X_4 \text{ row: } \frac{4}{\frac{4}{3}} = 3.$$

Each amount in the P_0 column is divided by the amount in the comparable row of the X_1 column. The three is the smaller amount and is from the X_4 row; thus, X_4 should be replaced by X_1.

c) The new X_1 row (replacing row X_4) in Table 17–6 has the values:

$$\frac{4}{\frac{4}{3}} = 3$$

$$\frac{-\frac{1}{3}}{\frac{4}{3}} = -\frac{1}{4}$$

$$\frac{1}{\frac{4}{3}} = \frac{3}{4}$$

$$\frac{\frac{4}{3}}{\frac{4}{3}} = 1$$

$$\frac{0}{\frac{4}{3}} = 0$$

The replacing row is determined by dividing each amount presently in row X_4 by the amount in the X_1 column in row X_4.

TABLE 17–7

Old X_2 Row	$-$	$\left(\begin{array}{c}\text{Old } X_2 \text{ Row} \\ X_1 \text{ Col.}\end{array}\right.$	$\cdot$	$\text{New } X_1 \text{ Row}\Big)$	$=$	Values of New X_2 Row
4	$-$	$(\tfrac{2}{3})$	$\cdot$	(3)	$=$	2
$\tfrac{1}{3}$	$-$	$(\tfrac{2}{3})$	$\cdot$	$(-\tfrac{1}{4})$	$=$	$\tfrac{1}{2}$
0	$-$	$(\tfrac{2}{3})$	$\cdot$	$(\tfrac{3}{4})$	$=$	$-\tfrac{1}{2}$
$\tfrac{2}{3}$	$-$	$(\tfrac{2}{3})$	$\cdot$	(1)	$=$	0
1	$-$	$(\tfrac{2}{3})$	$\cdot$	(0)	$=$	1

The new X_1 row is $(3, -\tfrac{1}{4}, \tfrac{3}{4}, 1, 0)$.

d) The new values of the X_2 row are shown in Table 17–7.
The new X_2 row is $(2, \tfrac{1}{2}, -\tfrac{1}{2}, 0, 1)$.
The computation of the Z_j's of Table 17–6 is as follows:

$$Z_{P0} = 7 \cdot \quad 2 + 6 \cdot \quad 3 = 32$$
$$Z_3 = 7 \cdot \quad \tfrac{1}{2} + 6 \cdot (-\tfrac{1}{4}) = \quad 2$$
$$Z_4 = 7 \cdot (-\tfrac{1}{2}) + 6 \cdot \quad \tfrac{3}{4} = \quad 1$$
$$Z_1 = 7 \cdot \quad 0 + 6 \cdot \quad 1 = \quad 6$$
$$Z_2 = 7 \cdot \quad 1 + 6 \cdot \quad 0 = \quad 7.$$

All $C_j - Z_j$ values are negative or zero, indicating that any further substitution will not result in an increase in profit; thus an optimum solution has been obtained. The optimum strategy is to produce two units of B and three units of A (that is, $X_1 = 3$, $X_2 = 2$); this will result in $32 of profit. From the profit equation, we also obtain:

$$P = \$6.00X_1 + \$7.00X_2 + 0X_3 + 0X_4 = (\$6.00 \cdot 3) + (\$7.00 \cdot 2) = \$32.00.$$

The restraint equations are satisfied:

$$2X_1 + 3X_2 \leq 12$$
$$6 \quad + 6 \quad \leq 12$$
$$2X_1 + \quad X_2 \leq 8$$
$$6 \quad + 2 \quad \leq 8.$$

It should be noted that in this problem, we were maximizing an amount (profit) subject to restraints, all of which were in the form of a sum of variables equal to or less than a constant. This is important, since certain steps in the solution process will be modified as we change the description of the problem.

Example 2—Minimization of Costs

This example will differ from the previous example in several respects:

a) An amount is being minimized (rather than maximized).
b) There are three restraints: one equality and two inequalities.

Note that one of the inequalities is in the form of the variable being equal to *or greater than* a constant.

Situation. The final product has a specification that it must weigh 150 pounds. The two raw materials used are A, with a cost of \$2.00 per unit, and B, with a cost of \$8.00 per unit. At least 14 units of B and no more than 20 units of A must be used. Each unit of A weighs five pounds; each unit of B weighs 10 pounds.

Problem. How much of each type of raw material should be used for each unit of final product if we wish to minimize cost?

Solution. The first step is to establish the cost equation, that is, the objective function. In Example 1 the objective function was the profit equation. In this example, it is the cost equation

$$P = 2X_1 + 8X_2$$

where

$X_1 =$ The number of units of product A
$X_2 =$ The number of units of product B
$2 =$ The cost of a unit of product A
$8 =$ The cost of a unit of product B.

Instead of finding the combination of X_1 and X_2 which minimizes the function $2X_1 + 8X_2$, we could solve the problem of maximizing $P = -2X_1 - 8X_2$. Both solutions would be the same; but to illustrate the procedure, we shall solve the minimization problem.

We must set up the equations which establish the restraints. There are three:

	Interpretation
$5X_1 + 10X_2 = 150$	The total weight must be equal to 150 pounds.
$X_1 \le 20$	No more than 20 units of A may be used.
$X_2 \ge 14$	At least 14 units of B must be used.
$X_1 \ge 0$	The amount of A used cannot be negative.

Graphic Analysis. To strengthen our understanding of the problem, we shall briefly illustrate again the graphic approach (see Figure 17–3).

Since the equation $5X_1 + 10X_2 = 150$ must be satisfied exactly, the solution must lie on the line CDE. And since the solution must satisfy the constraints $X_1 \ge 0$ and $X_2 \ge 14$, we can eliminate all but the line segment CD. Actually, we need examine only the points C and D, since the optimum must be a corner point. Note that the constraint $X_1 \le 20$ is not binding; that is, it in no way influences our set of feasible solutions. The restrictions of the other constraints make the $X_1 \le 20$ constraint unnecessary.

FIGURE 17-3

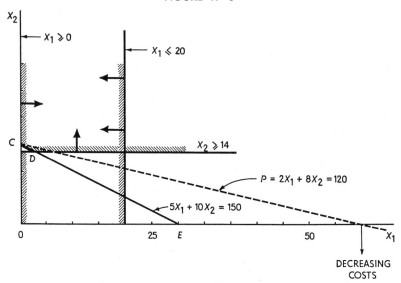

The profit function $P = 2X_1 + 8X_2 = 120$ is also shown in Figure 17–3. This is not the optimum, since we can move the $P = 120$ line down to the left and decrease cost. The least cost will be reached at $P = 116$, which goes through the optimum point D ($X_1 = 2$, $X_2 = 14$).

We shall now solve the same problem with the simplex procedure.

The Simplex Method. In the previous example, we introduced slack variables to establish equalities. To solve the present problem, we introduce "artificial" variables in the equalities, or where there is an inequality with the symbol $\geq$, indicating the sum of the variables is equal to or greater than a constant. In the equality an artificial variable, X_3, is introduced; but in the cost function (speaking more generally, the objective function) the coefficient of this variable will be made *large*, so that the X_3 will be driven out of the final solution. This is necessary, since there can be no X_3 in the final solution (X_3 must equal zero, so that $5X_1 + 10X_2 = 150$).

In a "greater than" inequality, two variables are introduced. One, a *negative* slack variable, here X_5, is used to convert the inequality to an equality (this will have a zero coefficient in the cost function). The second, here X_6, is an artificial variable which will be driven out of the final solution by a large coefficient in the cost function. The restraints may now be expressed in the following equations:

$$5X_1 + 10X_2 + X_3 = 150$$
$$X_1 + X_4 = 20$$
$$X_2 - X_5 + X_6 = 14.$$

The new cost function is:

$$P = 2X_1 + 8X_2 + MX_3 + 0X_4 + 0X_5 + MX_6$$

where M is a very large number.

To understand better the simplex table which follows (Table 17–8), we shall expand the restraint equations by adding X's with

TABLE 17–8

C_j			M	0	M	2	8	0
	Solution Mix	P_0	X_3	X_4	X_6	X_1	X_2	X_5
M	X_3	150	1	0	0	5	10	0
0	X_4	20	0	1	0	1	0	0
M	$\rightarrow X_6$	14	0	0	1	0	1	-1
	Z_j	$164M$	M	0	M	$5M$	$11M$	$-M$
	$C_j - Z_j$		0	0	0	$2 - 5M$	$8 - 11M$	M

zero coefficients to each restraint equation so that each equation has all the variables X_1 through X_6:

$$5X_1 + 10X_2 + 1X_3 + 0X_4 + 0X_5 + 0X_6 = 150$$
$$1X_1 + 0X_2 + 0X_3 + 1X_4 + 0X_5 + 0X_6 = 20$$
$$0X_1 + 1X_2 + 0X_3 + 0X_4 - 1X_5 + 1X_6 = 14$$

The first simplex table in this example (Table 17–8) is constructed from the coefficients of the variables of the restraint equations, the constant restraints (150, 20, 14 in the P_0 column), and the cost coefficients of the cost equation.

Note that the first solution consists of the slack variables or artificial variables which have *coefficients of one* in one row and zero in the other rows (check the X_3, X_4, and X_6 columns).

Since we are attempting to minimize costs, the column with the most negative $(C_j - Z_j)$ total will be chosen as the replacing column. Column X_2 wins this contest, since $8 - 11M$ (M is very large) is the most negative total.

The row to be replaced is the X_6 row, since $\dfrac{14}{1}$ is less than $\dfrac{150}{10}$, and $\dfrac{20}{0}$ is not mathematically defined.

TABLE 17-9

C_j			M	0	M	2	8	0
	Solution Mix	P_0	X_3	X_4	X_6	X_1	X_2	X_5
M	$\rightarrow X_3$	10	1	0	-10	5	0	10
0	X_4	20	0	1	0	1	0	0
8	X_2	14	0	0	1	0	1	-1
	Z_j	$112 + 10M$	M	0	$8 - 10M$	$5M$	8	$-8 + 10M$
	$C_j - Z_j$		0	0	$11M - 8$	$2 - 5M$	0	$-10M + 8$

Table 17–9 is the second simplex table of this example. A computation of the X_3 row and the X_4 row follows:

X_3 Row

$$150 - \quad 14 \cdot (10) = \quad 10$$
$$1 - \quad 0 \cdot (10) = \quad 1$$
$$0 - \quad 0 \cdot (10) = \quad 0$$
$$0 - \quad 1 \cdot (10) = -10$$
$$5 - \quad 0 \cdot (10) = \quad 5$$
$$10 - \quad 1 \cdot (10) = \quad 0$$
$$0 - (-1) \cdot (10) = \quad 10$$

X_4 Row

$$20 - \quad 14 \cdot (0) = 20$$
$$0 - \quad 0 \cdot (0) = \quad 0$$
$$1 - \quad 0 \cdot (0) = \quad 1$$
$$0 - \quad 1 \cdot (0) = \quad 0$$
$$1 - \quad 0 \cdot (0) = \quad 1$$
$$0 - \quad 1 \cdot (0) = \quad 0$$
$$0 - (-1) \cdot (0) = \quad 0$$

The largest negative $(C_j - Z_j)$ column of Table 17–9 is X_5 (the $-10M$ is very large), and the row to be replaced is X_3 $\left(\dfrac{10}{10}\right.$ is chosen, since $\dfrac{20}{0}$ is not mathematically defined, and $\dfrac{14}{-1}$ is not eligible, since the ratio is negative).[3]

TABLE 17-10

C_j			M	0	M	2	8	0
	Solution Mix	P_0	X_3	X_4	X_6	X_1	X_2	X_5
0	$\rightarrow X_5$	1	$\frac{1}{10}$	0	-1	$\frac{1}{2}$	0	1
0	X_4	20	0	1	0	1	0	0
8	X_2	15	$\frac{1}{10}$	0	0	$\frac{1}{2}$	1	0
	Z_j	120	$\frac{8}{10}$	0	0	4	8	0
	$C_j - Z_j$		$M - \frac{8}{10}$	0	M	-2	0	0

[3] At this point, it would save several steps if we replaced row X_3 with column X_1. The total saving from using X_1 is greater than the total saving from using X_5, but the simplex method bases its choice of replacing column on unit costs. Without working the problem, we do not know that X_1 is a better choice; thus the use of the simplex method leads to the correct solution, but not always via the shortest route.

Table 17–10 is the third simplex table of this example. A computation of the X_4 row and the X_2 row follows:

X_4 Row

$$20 - 1 \cdot (0) = 20$$
$$0 - \tfrac{1}{10} \cdot (0) = 0$$
$$1 - 0 \cdot (0) = 1$$
$$0 - (-1) \cdot (0) = 0$$
$$1 - \tfrac{1}{2} \cdot (0) = 1$$
$$0 - 0 \cdot (0) = 0$$
$$0 - 1 \cdot (0) = 0$$

X_2 Row

$$14 - 1 \cdot (-1) = 15$$
$$0 - \tfrac{1}{10} \cdot (-1) = \tfrac{1}{10}$$
$$0 - 0 \cdot (-1) = 0$$
$$1 - (-1) \cdot (-1) = 0$$
$$0 - \tfrac{1}{2} \cdot (-1) = \tfrac{1}{2}$$
$$1 - 0 \cdot (-1) = 1$$
$$-1 - 1 \cdot (-1) = 0$$

The largest negative $(C_i - Z_i)$ column of Table 17–10 is X_1 (X_3 is not negative, since M is very large). The row to be replaced is X_5.

TABLE 17–11

C_j			M	0	M	2	8	0
Solution Mix	P_0		X_3	X_4	X_6	X_1	X_2	X_5
2	X_1	2	$\tfrac{2}{10}$	0	-2	1	0	2
0	X_4	18	$-\tfrac{1}{5}$	1	$+2$	0	0	-2
8	X_2	14	0	0	1	0	1	-1
Z_j		116	$\tfrac{4}{10}$	0	4	2	8	-4
$C_j - Z_j$			$M - \tfrac{4}{10}$	0	$M - 4$	0	0	4

Table 17–11 is the fourth simplex table of this example. A computation of the X_4 row and the X_2 row follows:

X_4 Row

$$20 - 2 \cdot (1) = 18$$
$$0 - \tfrac{2}{10} \cdot (1) = -\tfrac{1}{5}$$
$$1 - 0 \cdot (1) = 1$$
$$0 - (-2) \cdot (1) = +2$$
$$1 - 1 \cdot (1) = 0$$
$$0 - 0 \cdot (1) = 0$$
$$0 - 2 \cdot (1) = -2$$

X_2 Row

$$15 - 2 \cdot (\tfrac{1}{2}) = 14$$
$$\tfrac{1}{10} - \tfrac{2}{10} \cdot (\tfrac{1}{2}) = 0$$
$$0 - 0 \cdot (\tfrac{1}{2}) = 0$$
$$0 - (-2) \cdot (\tfrac{1}{2}) = 1$$
$$\tfrac{1}{2} - 1 \cdot (\tfrac{1}{2}) = 0$$
$$1 - 0 \cdot (\tfrac{1}{2}) = 1$$
$$0 - 2 \cdot (\tfrac{1}{2}) = -1$$

With Table 17–11, we have reached an optimum solution. Exactly the same solution could have been reached by maximizing the objective function $P = -2X_1 - 8X_2$ (finding the smallest negative amount).

The optimum solution is to use two units (or 10 pounds) of A and 14 units (or 140 pounds) of B. This combination leads to a cost of $116, which is the least-cost combination of raw material consistent with the restraints. The end product weighs 150 pounds; there are two units of $X_1 \leq 20$, 14 units of $X_2 \geq 14$; thus the restraints are satisfied. While we easily solved this problem by graphic analysis, with a more complicated version of the problem (for example, 30 raw materials and 20 restraints), we would find the linear programming techniques more efficient for obtaining an optimum solution.

Example 3—A Problem without a Unique Solution

Under certain situations, it is possible that the linear programming problem does not have a unique solution. For example, assume that the third simplex table (Table 17–10), when developed in Example 2, appeared as shown in Table 17–12.

TABLE 17–12
Table 17–10 Modified

C_j			M	0	M	-16	8	0
	Solution Mix	P_0	X_3	X_4	X_6	X_1	X_2	X_5
0	X_5	1	$\frac{1}{10}$	0	-1	$-\frac{1}{2}$	0	1
0	X_4	20	0	1	0	-1	0	0
8	X_2	15	$\frac{1}{10}$	0	0	$-\frac{1}{2}$	1	0
	Z_j	120	$\frac{8}{10}$	0	0	-4	8	0
	$C_j - Z_j$		$M - \frac{8}{10}$	0	M	-12	0	0

Column X_1 has been changed so that not only is $(C_j - Z_j)$ negative (as it was in Table 17–10), but all coefficients in the X_1 column are negative. In this situation, there is no one optimum solution. If profit was being maximized, an analogous situation would occur if the $(C_j - Z_j)$ total were positive and all coefficients in the column were negative.

In modified Table 17–10 (Table 17–12) the negative $(C_j - Z_j)$ indicates that \$12 of costs are saved for every unit of X_1 injected into the solution. However, the negative coefficients of $-\frac{1}{2}$, -1, and $-\frac{1}{2}$ indicate that for every unit of X_1 injected into the solution, say, as a substitute for X_5, the ability to inject additional units will be increased. Thus the desirable action would be to keep adding units of X_1. The more X_1 we use, the higher the profits; the problem does not have a unique optimum solution, since it contains no restriction on X_1.

If the above situation develops, the cause will frequently be a misstated restraint. Business situations properly described will not usually result in a nonsolvable table as illustrated above.

Example 4—Degeneracy

A solution known as a degenerate solution may develop when one of the restraints is redundant, that is, when one of the restraints is not necessary for a solution. For example, if there are two restraints, $X_1 \geq 16$ and $X_1 \geq 30$, the former restraint is not necessary. The restraint stating that X_1 must be equal to or greater than 30 eliminates the need for the restraint that X_1 must be equal to or greater than 16. If X_1 is greater than or equal to 30, it will also be greater than or equal to 16. Most redundant restraints will not be as easily recognized as the above.

Only certain redundant restraints will lead to degeneracy; it is not always a simple matter to predict a degenerate situation. The following illustration shows how to recognize degeneracy and suggests a method of solution which will generally be effective.

Maximize profits, given the profit equation $P = 4X_1 + 3X_2$, and subject to the restraints:

$$4X_1 + \ 2X_2 \leq 10.0$$
$$2X_1 + \tfrac{8}{3}X_2 \leq \ 8.0$$
$$X_1 \geq \ 0.0$$
$$X_2 \geq \ 1.8$$

This can be interpreted as a problem of assigning two machines to two products, X_1 and X_2 (one machine has ten hours and the other eight hours of free time). At least 1.8 units of X_2 must be manufactured.

Written out in full and converted to equalities, the inequalities become:

$$4X_1 + \ 2X_2 + 1X_3 + 0X_4 + 0X_5 + 0X_6 = 10.0$$
$$2X_1 + \tfrac{8}{3}X_2 + 0X_3 + 1X_4 + 0X_5 + 0X_6 = \ 8.0$$
$$0X_1 + \ \ X_2 + 0X_3 + 0X_4 + 1X_5 - 1X_6 = \ 1.8$$

X_3, X_4, and X_6 are slack variables. X_5 is an artificial variable. The complete profit function becomes:

$$P = 4X_1 + 3X_2 + 0X_3 + 0X_4 - MX_5 + 0X_6$$

Note that the artificial variable X_5 has a profit factor coefficient of $-M$, where M is a very large number. This insures that X_5 will not appear in the final solution.

The first two simplex tables of this illustration are Tables 17–13 and 17–14.

In Table 17–13, column X_2 should replace row X_5.

TABLE 17–13

C_j			0	0	$-M$	0	4	3
	Solution Mix	P_0	X_3	X_4	X_5	X_6	X_1	X_2
0	X_3	10	1	0	0	0	4	2
0	X_4	8	0	1	0	0	2	$8/3$
$-M$	$\rightarrow X_5$	1.8	0	0	1	-1	0	1
	Z_j	$-1.8M$	0	0	$-M$	M	0	$-M$
	$C_j - Z_j$		0	0	0	$-M$	4	$3 + M$
								$\uparrow$

TABLE 17–14

C_j			0	0	$-M$	0	4	3
	Solution Mix	P_0	X_3	X_4	X_5	X_6	X_1	X_2
0	X_3	6.4	1	0	-2	$+2$	4	0
0	$\rightarrow X_4$	3.2	0	1	$-8/3$	$8/3$	2	0
3	X_2	1.8	0	0	1	-1	0	1
	Z_j	5.4	0	0	3	-3	0	3
	$C_j - Z_j$		0	0	$-M - 3$	$+3$	4	0
						$\uparrow$		

In Table 17–14, column X_1 is the next replacing column. What row should be replaced? Dividing the components of P_0 by the corresponding components of X_1, we obtain:

$$\text{For row } X_3: \quad \frac{6.4}{4} = 1.6$$

$$\text{For row } X_4: \quad \frac{3.2}{2} = 1.6$$

$$\text{For row } X_2: \quad \frac{1.8}{0} = \text{Undefined}$$

The choice of row to be replaced is complicated by the fact that both row X_3 and X_4 are equally acceptable according to the criterion we have established. This is the signal that degeneracy exists. Fortunately, the simplex procedure will generally give the correct answer, if we choose *either* of the two rows and later choose the other row if the first choice does not give a solution. Let us replace row X_4 with X_1.

In Table 17–15, all $C_j - Z_j$'s are zero or negative; thus the solution is $X_1 = 1.6$ and $X_2 = 1.8$.

If we had substituted column X_1 for row X_3, we would obtain that shown in Table 17–16.

TABLE 17–15

C_j			0	0	$-M$	0	4	3
	Solution Mix	P_0	X_3	X_4	X_5	X_6	X_1	X_2
0	X_3	0	1	-2	$10/3$	$-10/3$	0	0
4	X_1	1.6	0	$1/2$	$-4/3$	$4/3$	1	0
3	X_2	1.8	0	0	1	-1	0	1
	Z_j	11.8	0	2	$-7/3$	$7/3$	4	3
	$C_j - Z_j$		0	-2	$-M+7/3$	$-7/3$	0	0

TABLE 17–16

C_j			0	0	$-M$	0	4	3
	Solution Mix	P_0	X_3	X_4	X_5	X_6	X_1	X_2
4	X_1	1.6	$1/4$	0	$-1/2$	$1/2$	1	0
0	$\rightarrow X_4$	0	$-1/2$	1	$-5/3$	$5/3$	0	0
3	X_2	1.8	0	0	1	-1	0	1
	Z_j	11.8	1	0	1	-1	4	3
	$C_j - Z_j$		-1	0	$-M-1$	1	0	0

The column X_6 has a positive $C_j - Z_j$; thus, X_6 is the next replacing column. The row to be replaced is X_4 (zero divided by $5/3$ is the smallest nonnegative amount, i.e., smaller than 1.6 divided by $1/2$). The new simplex table is shown in Table 17–17. All the $C_j - Z_j$'s are negative, and a solution has been reached.

Thus, replacing either row X_4 or row X_3 leads to the same amount of X_1 and X_2, and a profit of 11.8.

To summarize, redundant restraints may lead to degeneracy. A situation of degeneracy will show up through the simplex procedure when two or more rows can equally well be replaced according to the

TABLE 17–17

C_j			0	0	$-M$	0	4	3
	Solution Mix	P_0	X_3	X_4	X_5	X_6	X_1	X_2
4	X_1	1.6	$4/10$	$-3/10$	0	0	1	0
0	X_6	0.0	$-3/10$	$3/5$	-1	1	0	0
3	X_2	1.8	$-3/10$	$9/10$	0	0	0	1
	Z_j	11.8	$7/10$	$6/10$	0	0	4	3
	$C_j - Z_j$		$-7/10$	$-6/10$	$-M$	0	0	0

simplex criterion. The solution is to replace either row arbitrarily. This leads to two of the rows being eliminated from the solution. Note that the amount of X_3 becomes zero in the first solution, and the amount of X_4 becomes zero in the second solution; thus, both X_3 and X_4 are eliminated from the solution by the substitution of X_1 for either X_3 or X_4.

If the choice of the row does not lead to a solution (the simplex tables begin to repeat themselves), then choose the other row at the point where the degeneracy was discovered.

FIGURE 17–4

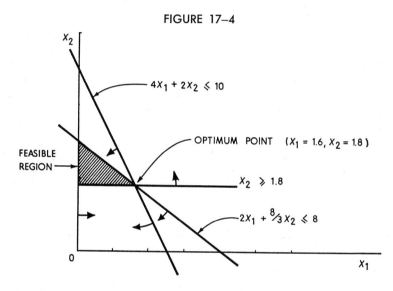

The degeneracy situation can also be identified by examining the graph of this problem, shown in Figure 17–4. Note that the optimum point occurs at the intersection of the three constraint equations. Since all the constraints are satisfied exactly, there is no slack in any constraint (that is, X_3, X_4, and X_6 all equal zero). In a nondegenerate case, at least one of these slack variables would be nonzero.[4]

Example 5—Extension to Many Dimensions

The previous four examples have involved only two dimensions. To illustrate the formulation of a linear programming problem in many dimensions, the following example is furnished.

A manufacturing firm makes equipment which utilizes many com-

---

[4] In general, the number of nonzero variables in the solution equals the number of constraints (other than the $X_j \geq 0$ constraints). Degeneracy results when the optimum solution contains a smaller number of nonzero variables than the number of constraints.

TABLE 17-18

Part Number	Variable Designation	Hours of Machining Required	Hours of Assembly Required	Hours of Test Required	Engineering Supervision Required	Working Capital Funds Required	Total Number of Units Needed	Price Quoted by Outside Manufacturer	Variable Cost of Materials, Direct Labor, etc.
182......	X_1	5	1	0	1	3	10	$100	$ 50
184......	X_2	2	1	0	1	5	5	150	50
193......	X_3	1	4	2	3	1	50	200	100
197......	X_4	3	0	3	2	1	25	100	50
284......	X_5	1	5	2	2	2	10	250	100
629......	X_6	0	2	2	3	2	5	200	100
845......	X_7	2	1	1	1	4	20	100	40

ponents. The assembly and testing of the complete unit are done by the firm; but it does not have enough capacity, technical personnel, or funds to produce all the components in its own plants. It therefore must purchase many components from outside suppliers. Seven such components and their requirements are shown in Table 17–18.

From Table 17–18, it can be seen that different parts require different amounts of resources and have different outside purchase costs. The question is: Which, if any, of these parts (and how many

TABLE 17–19

Hours of machining..............	90
Hours of assembly..............	97
Hours of testing................	200
Engineering supervisor hours.......	150
Discretionary cash..............	$250

of each part) should be manufactured internally, and which should be purchased from outside?

We can express this as a linear programming problem in which we maximize savings from internal manufacture, subject to constraints on capacity, personnel, and funds. Let us suppose we have available the amounts of resources shown in Table 17–19.

We can formulate the linear programming problem as follows:

Maximize:
$$P = 50X_1 + 100X_2 + 100X_3 + 50X_4 + 150X_5 + 100X_6 + 60X_7$$

where X_i is the amount of the ith part manufactured internally and the coefficients are the incremental per unit savings (purchase cost minus variable cost).

Subject to:
$$5X_1 + 2X_2 + X_3 + 3X_4 + X_5 + 0X_6 + 2X_7 \leq 90$$
$$X_1 + X_2 + 4X_3 + 0X_4 + 5X_5 + 2X_6 + X_7 \leq 97$$
$$0X_1 + 0X_2 + 2X_3 + 3X_4 + 2X_5 + 2X_6 + X_7 \leq 200$$
$$X_1 + X_2 + 3X_3 + 2X_4 + 2X_5 + 3X_6 + X_7 \leq 150$$
$$3X_1 + 5X_2 + X_3 + X_4 + 2X_5 + 2X_6 + 4X_7 \leq 250$$

and

$$X_1 \leq 10$$
$$X_2 \leq 5$$
$$X_3 \leq 50$$
$$X_4 \leq 25$$
$$X_5 \leq 10$$
$$X_6 \leq 5$$
$$X_7 \leq 20$$
$$\text{and all } X_j \geq 0, (j = 1, 2, \cdots, 7)$$

TABLE 17–20

C_i	Solution Mix	P_0	X_8	X_9	X_{10}	X_{11}	X_{12}	X_{13}	X_{14}	X_{15}	X_{16}	X_{17}	X_{18}	X_{19}	X_1	X_2	X_3	X_4	X_5	X_6	X_7
			0	**0**	**0**	**0**	**0**	**0**	**0**	**0**	**0**	**0**	**0**	**0**	**50**	**100**	**100**	**50**	**150**	**100**	**60**
0	X_8	90	1												5	2	1	3	1		2
0	→X_9	97		1											1	1	4		5	2	1
0	X_{10}	200			1										1	1	2	3	2	2	1
0	X_{11}	150				1									3	5	3	2	2	3	1
0	X_{12}	250					1								1		1	1	2	2	4
0	X_{13}	10						1									1				
0	X_{14}	5							1									1			
0	X_{15}	50								1									1		
0	X_{16}	25									1									1	
0	X_{17}	10										1			1						
0	X_{18}	5											1			1					
0	X_{19}	20												1							1
	Z_i	0	0	0	0	0	0	0	0	0	0	0	0	0	0	0	0	0	0	0	0
	$C_i - Z_i$	0	0	0	0	0	0	0	0	0	0	0	0	0	50	100	100	50	150 ↑	100	60

TABLE 17-21

C_j			0	0	0	0	0	0	0	0	0	0	0	0	50	100	100	50	150	100	60
C_i	Solution Mix	P_0	X_8	X_9	X_{10}	X_{11}	X_{12}	X_{13}	X_{14}	X_{15}	X_{16}	X_{17}	X_{18}	X_{19}	X_1	X_2	X_3	X_4	X_5	X_6	X_7
100	X_3	3	$\frac13$	$\frac14$					$-\frac14$			$-\frac54$	$-\frac12$	$-\frac14$	$\frac14$		1				
50	X_4	9	-1	$-1\frac12$					$-\frac{7}{12}$			$\frac{1}{12}$	$\frac16$	$-\frac{7}{12}$	$\frac{19}{12}$			1			
0	X_{10}	117	$-\frac23$	$-\frac14$	1				$\frac94$			$\frac14$	$-\frac32$	$\frac54$	$-2\frac14$						
0	X_{11}	63	$-\frac13$	$-\frac{7}{12}$		1			$\frac{11}{12}$			$\frac{19}{12}$	$-1\frac16$	$1\frac{1}{12}$	$-3\frac{5}{12}$						
0	X_{12}	103		$-\frac16$			1		$-2\frac56$			$-\frac56$	$-\frac53$	$-1\frac96$	$\frac76$						
0	X_{13}	10						1													
100	X_2	5							1							1					
0	X_{15}	47	$-\frac13$	$-\frac14$					$\frac14$	1		$\frac54$	$\frac12$	$\frac14$	$-\frac14$						
0	X_{16}	16		$\frac{1}{12}$					$\frac{7}{12}$		1	$-\frac{1}{12}$	$-\frac16$	$\frac{7}{12}$	$-\frac{19}{12}$						
150	X_5	10										1							1		
100	X_6	5											1							1	
60	X_7	20												1							1
Z_i		4,450	$5\frac53$	$20\frac56$	0	0	0	0	$45\frac56$	0	0	$29\frac16$	$58\frac13$	$5\frac56$	$104\frac16$	100	100	50	150	100	60
$C_j - Z_j$			$-5\frac53$	$-20\frac56$	0	0	0	0	$-45\frac56$	0	0	$-29\frac16$	$-58\frac13$	$-5\frac56$	$-54\frac16$	0	0	0	0	0	0

The initial tableau is given in Table 17–20, including the slack variables X_8 through X_{19}.

Note that there are twelve constraint equations, and so the main part of Table 17–20 has twelve rows. The initial solution is given by using the slack variables. The initial solution indicates that nothing is manufactured internally and all requirements are purchased from outside suppliers. This, of course, is not the optimum, and it gives a profit of zero.

The simplex method can now be applied to Table 17–20. The first column that should come into the solution is X_5, replacing row X_9. We do not intend to carry this problem through all the steps of the simplex procedure, since we wish merely to illustrate the formulation of the problem. However, the final simplex tableau is shown as Table 17–21. The solution gives a saving of $4,450. The meanings of the solution variables are shown in Table 17–22.

TABLE 17–22

Part Number	Requirement	Manufacture Variable Amount	Purchase Slack Variable Amount
182.........	10	$X_1 = 0$	$X_{13} = 10$
184.........	5	$X_2 = 5$	$X_{14} = 0$
193.........	50	$X_3 = 3$	$X_{15} = 47$
197.........	25	$X_4 = 9$	$X_{16} = 16$
284.........	10	$X_5 = 10$	$X_{17} = 0$
629.........	5	$X_6 = 5$	$X_{18} = 0$
845.........	20	$X_7 = 20$	$X_{19} = 0$

For the resource constraints, we have:

Variable Amount	Meaning
$X_8 = 0$	All machining hours are used (i.e., slack $= 0$).
$X_9 = 0$	All assembly hours are used.
$X_{10} = 117$	117 hours of test are not used.
$X_{11} = 63$	63 hours of engineering supervision are not used.
$X_{12} = 103$	$103 of working capital is not used.

Example 6—No Feasible Solution

It is possible for the restraint equations to be inconsistent with a feasible solution. For example, suppose we had

$$4X_1 + 2X_2 \leq 10$$
$$X_2 \geq 6$$
$$X_1 \geq 0.$$

There are no values of X_1 and X_2 which will satisfy these three conditions. There would be no solution to such a linear programming problem.

CONCLUSIONS

In this chapter, we considered the solutions of a certain class of problems, namely, problems in which we are seeking a maximum of a linear function which is constrained by a set of linear equations. We examined such problems graphically (for very simple cases) and introduced the simplex method as a computational device for large problems.

While emphasis has been placed upon understanding the simplex method, the actual computations in a business problem would probably be done on a computer. Linear programming routines based upon the simplex method are available for most electronic computers.

The Appendix to this chapter introduces mathematical notation and methods which will aid in understanding the logic of the simplex method.

APPENDIX

LINEAR PROGRAMMING—ALGEBRAIC METHODS

Chapter 17 described the simplex method of solving linear programming problems. In this Appendix, we shall discuss very briefly some concepts of linear algebra and show the applications of these concepts to the linear programming problem and its solution.

VECTORS

Vectors are lines with direction and length, and can be described by an ordered set of numbers. For example, given the X axis, one number describes the end point of any line from the origin. Thus, (4) describes the vector $\underline{a}$, and (-2) describes the vector $\underline{b}$ of Figure 17–5. In this Appendix a line under a letter indicates that the letter represents a vector.

FIGURE 17–5

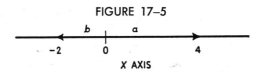

X AXIS

We can add the Y axis, which is drawn at right angles to the X axis and has a common origin. Then the end point of any line from the origin can be described by two numbers. The first number indicates the distance one moves along the X axis (positive to the right, negative to the left); the second number indicates the distance one moves up or down parallel to the Y axis (positive up, negative down). We can describe any point in a plane by the use of two ordered numbers which measure distances from the origin along

FIGURE 17–6

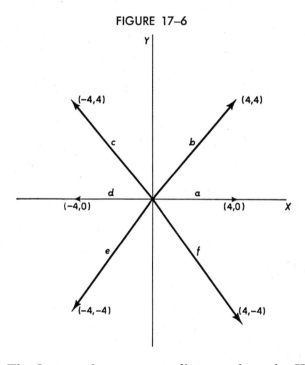

two axes. The first number measures distance along the X axis; the second number measures distance along the Y axis.

In Figure 17–6, vector a is described by $(4, 0)$, b by $(4, 4)$, c by $(-4, 4)$, d by $(-4, 0)$, e by $(-4, -4)$, and f by $(4, -4)$.

We can find the negative of a vector by multiplying its components by minus one.

Thus, $e = -b$, i.e., $(-4, -4) = -(4, 4)$; and $c = -f$, i.e., $(-4, 4) = -(4, -4)$.

We have assumed that the tail of all the vectors is at the origin. This is not a necessary requirement, but it simplifies the analysis, so we shall continue the assumption throughout this chapter. Also, the axes do not have to be perpendicular, but we shall utilize perpendicular axes, since they also simplify the analysis. To this point, we have limited the discussion to two dimensions (each vector has two components in a plane; thus, this is two-dimensional space, or two-space). We may be interested in a third dimension, which may be represented by a third component of the vector. The vector r of Figure 17–7 has three ordered components (4, 5, 8); it is a three-dimensional vector (we say vector r is in three-space).

The three axes are X, Y, and Z. We move four units along the X axis, five units along the Y axis, and eight units up the Z axis.

FIGURE 17–7

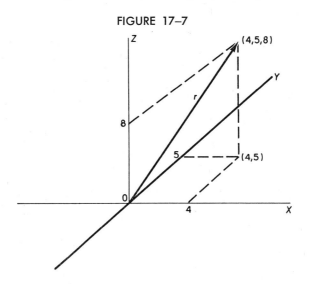

Actually, there is no limit to the number of components, or the dimension of a vector, though there is a limit to our ability to graph an interpretation when there are more than three components. A vector of four dimensions is (4, 5, 8, 7). A vector x of n dimensions is $(x_1, x_2, x_3, \ldots, x_n)$.

Instead of listing the components of a vector horizontally, they are frequently listed vertically. Thus, r may be represented as $\begin{pmatrix} 4 \\ 5 \\ 8 \end{pmatrix}$.

A vector represented horizontally is a *row* vector; a vertical vector is a *column* vector.

ADDING VECTORS

Vectors with the same number of components (the same dimension) may be added or subtracted (subtraction may be thought of as adding a negative vector). In Figure 17–8, a minus d is the same as a plus c, since $c = -d$.

To add vectors, we add the components of each vector. Graphically, the sum of two vectors (for example, $a + b$) is the diagonal of

FIGURE 17–8

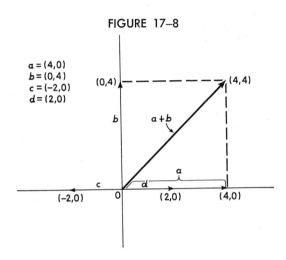

the parallelogram formed by the two vectors being added and the two vectors parallel to the two vectors being added. The diagonal originates at the mutual origin of the vectors:

$$a + b = \text{Vector } a + \text{Vector } b = (4, 0) + (0, 4)$$
$$= (4 + 0, 0 + 4) = (4, 4).$$

Examples

1. From Figure 17–8:
$$a - (d) = (4, 0) - (2, 0) = (2, 0)$$
$$a + (c) = (4, 0) + (-2, 0) = (2, 0)$$
$$a + (-d) = (4, 0) + (-2, 0) = (2, 0)$$

2.   Vector $r = (3, 5, 6, 4, 8)$

        Vector $s = (2, 1, 7, 8, 9)$

Vector $r + s = (5, 6, 13, 12, 17)$ Add each component.

Vector $r - s = (1, 4, -1, -4, -1)$ Subtract each component.

SCALAR MULTIPLICATION

Vectors may be multiplied by scalars (real numbers) to form scalar multiples of the vectors. In Figure 17–9, if a is the vector $(4, 3)$, then ka is the vector $k(4, 3)$ or $(k4, k3)$. If $k = 2$, then ka is

FIGURE 17–9

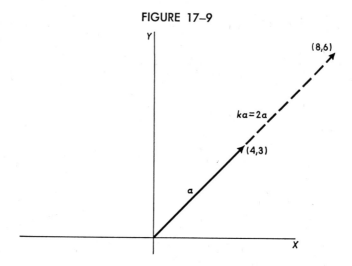

equal to 2(4, 3), or (8, 6). The vector (8, 6) is thus a scalar multiple of the vector (4, 3).

Let us assume we are dealing with one-dimensional vectors, i.e., all vectors that lie on a line—say, the X axis. If vector a is of some size—say, one unit—then *any vector* in that one-dimensional space may be described as a scalar multiple of a. The vector (8) is $8a$ or $8(1)$; vector (-5) is $-5(a)$ or $-5(1)$. If the scalar is greater than one, the original vector, a, will be stretched by scalar multiplication. If the scalar is less than one, scalar multiplication will contract the original vector (see Figure 17–10).

FIGURE 17–10

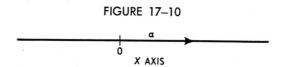

If we have two vectors (not scalar multiples of each other) in two-dimensional space, then any vector in the two-dimensional plane may be described as a sum of scalar multiples of those two vectors, which we shall call *basis vectors*. For example, assume we have two vectors:

$$a = (1, 0).$$
$$b = (0, 1).$$

Any specific vector in two-space may be described as one (and only one) scalar multiple of vector a plus a scalar multiple of b.

FIGURE 17–11

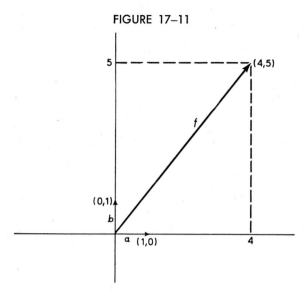

Figure 17–11 shows an example. Let vector $\underline{f}$ = (4, 5):

$$\text{Vector } \underline{f} = 4\underline{a} + 5\underline{b}$$

or

$$
\begin{aligned}
\underline{f} &= 4(1,\,0) + 5(0,\,1) \\
&= (4,\,0) + (0,\,5) \\
&= (4,\,5).
\end{aligned}
$$

Vector $\underline{f}$ = (4, 5) may be described as the sum of four times vector $\underline{a}$ plus five times vector $\underline{b}$. The vector f is said to be a *linear combination* of $\underline{a}$ and $\underline{b}$. The relationship may be written:

$$4\underline{a} + 5\underline{b} = \underline{f}$$

$$4\binom{1}{0} + 5\binom{0}{1} = \binom{4}{5}$$

$$\binom{4}{0} + \binom{0}{5} = \binom{4}{5}.$$

To say that $\underline{f}$ is a linear combination of $\underline{a}$ and $\underline{b}$ means that some scalar times $\underline{a}$, plus some scalar times $\underline{b}$, is equal to $\underline{f}$. The scalar may be any real number, including zero.

Let us assume that we do not know what scalars should be used to multiply vectors $\underline{a}$ and $\underline{b}$. The relationship may then be written:

$$x\binom{1}{0} + y\binom{0}{1} = \binom{4}{5}$$

or

$$\binom{x}{0} + \binom{0}{y} = \binom{4}{5}.$$

The sum of the first components of xa and yb must equal four; thus the scalar $x = 4$. The sum of the second components must equal five; thus the scalar $y = 5$.

In the above example the two basis vectors were of unit length and were perpendicular to each other. This simplified our computations, but these conditions are not necessary. Take two vectors $r = \begin{pmatrix} 2 \\ 6 \end{pmatrix}$ and $s = \begin{pmatrix} 7 \\ 5 \end{pmatrix}$ which are not perpendicular to each other.[5]

What linear combination of r and s will form the vector $t = \begin{pmatrix} 4 \\ 5 \end{pmatrix}$?

$$x\begin{pmatrix} 2 \\ 6 \end{pmatrix} + y\begin{pmatrix} 7 \\ 5 \end{pmatrix} = \begin{pmatrix} 4 \\ 5 \end{pmatrix}$$
$$\begin{pmatrix} 2x \\ 6x \end{pmatrix} + \begin{pmatrix} 7y \\ 5y \end{pmatrix} = \begin{pmatrix} 4 \\ 5 \end{pmatrix}.$$

To solve for x and y, we establish the following two equations:

$$2x + 7y = 4$$
$$6x + 5y = 5.$$

The coefficients of x are the components $\begin{pmatrix} 2 \\ 6 \end{pmatrix}$ of the vector a, and the coefficients of y are the components $\begin{pmatrix} 7 \\ 5 \end{pmatrix}$ of the vector b. The constants of the equations are the components $\begin{pmatrix} 4 \\ 5 \end{pmatrix}$ of the vector f.

Solving the two equations gives the solution $x = {}^{15}\!/_{32}$ and $y = {}^{7}\!/_{16}$:

I.	$2x + 7y =$	4
II.	$6x + 5y =$	5

Multiply I by -3 and add to II.

$$-16y = -7$$
$$y = {}^{7}\!/_{16}$$

I. $2x + 7y = 4$

$$2x + 7({}^{7}\!/_{16}) = 4 \qquad \text{Substitute } {}^{7}\!/_{16} \text{ for } y.$$
$$x = {}^{15}\!/_{32}$$

Substituting back in the original vector equations:

$${}^{15}\!/_{32}\begin{pmatrix} 2 \\ 6 \end{pmatrix} + {}^{7}\!/_{16}\begin{pmatrix} 7 \\ 5 \end{pmatrix} = \begin{pmatrix} 4 \\ 5 \end{pmatrix}$$
$$\begin{pmatrix} {}^{15}\!/_{16} \\ {}^{45}\!/_{16} \end{pmatrix} + \begin{pmatrix} {}^{49}\!/_{16} \\ {}^{35}\!/_{16} \end{pmatrix} = \begin{pmatrix} {}^{64}\!/_{16} \\ {}^{80}\!/_{16} \end{pmatrix} = \begin{pmatrix} 4 \\ 5 \end{pmatrix}.$$

[5] The two vectors are independent; i.e., one vector cannot be formed by taking linear combinations of the other vector (or vectors) in the set. There is no scalar k which will make kr equal to s. Basis vectors must be independent vectors.

By taking appropriate linear combinations of the basis vectors, *any* vector in two-space (the vector has two components and is said to be in two-space) can be formed. The appropriate scalars may be found by solving simultaneous equations, as they were in the example above.

As we have seen, *equations* may be formed from vector relationships. In the above example, two equations were formed:

$$2x + 7y = 4$$
$$6x + 5y = 5.$$

We may reverse the procedure and interpret equations as linear combinations of vectors. The above equations can be written as follows:

$$x\binom{2}{6} + y\binom{7}{5} = \binom{4}{5}.$$

The concept of vectors is closely related to the solution of simultaneous equations. The significance of this relationship becomes more evident if we attempt to find the solution to the following equations:

$$\text{I. } 2x_1 + 3x_2 + 2x_3 = 12$$
$$\text{II. } 2x_1 + x_2 + x_3 = 8.$$

There are two equations and three unknowns. Attempting to solve these equations simultaneously results in the following:

$$\text{I. } 2x_1 + 3x_2 + 2x_3 = 12$$
$$\text{II. } 2x_1 + x_2 + x_3 = 8$$
$$\text{III. } 2x_2 + x_3 = 4 \text{ (subtracting I from II)}$$
$$\text{IV. } -2x_1 + x_2 = -4 \text{ (subtracting two times II from I)}$$
$$x_2 = \frac{4 - x_3}{2} \text{ (from III)}$$
$$x_1 = \frac{4 + x_2}{2} \text{ (from IV)}$$

Since there are more unknowns than equations, this is as far as we can go. There are an infinite number of solutions, depending on the initial value of the x_3 (or x_1, or x_2) chosen. The vector interpretation of the equations is important:

$$\binom{2}{2}x_1 + \binom{3}{1}x_2 + \binom{2}{1}x_3 = \binom{12}{8}.$$

We have indicated that any vector in two-space can be formed from two basis vectors (in two-space a basis is two independent vectors). There is a theorem in linear algebra that a vector may be formed by one and only one linear combination of a set of *basis* vectors. In the above example, we have written the vector $\begin{pmatrix} 12 \\ 8 \end{pmatrix}$ as a linear combination of three vectors. Since we have one more vector than we need for a basis of the space (in this case, two-space), there is an infinite number of linear combinations which are possible. Each linear combination represents a solution, and there is an infinite number of solutions to the set of equations.

The same relationship between equations and vector equations in two-space carries over to three-dimensional space. In three-space, three independent vectors are required to span the space (i.e., be a basis for the space). It is easiest to illustrate this using unit perpendicular basis vectors, each with one component of one and the remainder of the components zero. For example:

$$\begin{pmatrix} 1 \\ 0 \\ 0 \end{pmatrix} x_1 + \begin{pmatrix} 0 \\ 1 \\ 0 \end{pmatrix} x_2 + \begin{pmatrix} 0 \\ 0 \\ 1 \end{pmatrix} x_3 = \begin{pmatrix} 12 \\ 14 \\ 8 \end{pmatrix}.$$

The three scalars which are a solution to this equation are $x_1 = 12$, $x_2 = 14$, and $x_3 = 8$. The comparable equations are:

$$\begin{array}{l} 1x_1 + 0x_2 + 0x_3 = 12 \\ 0x_1 + 1x_2 + 0x_3 = 14 \\ 0x_1 + 0x_2 + 1x_3 = 8. \end{array}$$

It can be seen that $x_1 = 12$, $x_2 = 14$, and $x_3 = 8$. These are the only amounts which satisfy the three equations, and the solution is unique.

SUBSTITUTION OF VECTORS

Assume the following two equations:

$$\begin{array}{l} 2x_1 + 3x_2 + 1x_3 + 0x_4 = 12 \\ 2x_1 + 1x_2 + 0x_3 + 1x_4 = 8. \end{array}$$

The comparable vector equation is:

$$\begin{pmatrix} 2 \\ 2 \end{pmatrix} x_1 + \begin{pmatrix} 3 \\ 1 \end{pmatrix} x_2 + \begin{pmatrix} 1 \\ 0 \end{pmatrix} x_3 + \begin{pmatrix} 0 \\ 1 \end{pmatrix} x_4 = \begin{pmatrix} 12 \\ 8 \end{pmatrix}.$$

The four vectors $\begin{pmatrix} 2 \\ 2 \end{pmatrix}$, $\begin{pmatrix} 3 \\ 1 \end{pmatrix}$, $\begin{pmatrix} 1 \\ 0 \end{pmatrix}$, and $\begin{pmatrix} 0 \\ 1 \end{pmatrix}$, and the constant vector $\begin{pmatrix} 12 \\ 8 \end{pmatrix}$, may be designated $\underline{P}_1, \underline{P}_2, \underline{P}_3, \underline{P}_4$, and $\underline{P}_0$, respectively, and the vector equation may be written:

$$x_1 \underline{P}_1 + x_2 \underline{P}_2 + x_3 \underline{P}_3 + x_4 \underline{P}_4 = \underline{P}_0.$$

It should be noted that the x's are scalars (i.e., numbers) and the P's are vectors. Since each vector contains two components, they are said to be in two-space. Any one of the above vectors can be written as a linear combination of any two basis vectors. For simplicity, we shall choose P_3 and P_4 as basis vectors and offer the following solution to the set of equations:

$$x_1 P_1 + x_2 P_2 + x_3 P_3 + x_4 P_4 = P_0 \qquad x_1 = 0$$
$$0P_1 + 0P_2 + 12P_3 + 8P_4 = P_0 \qquad x_2 = 0$$
$$0\binom{2}{2} + 0\binom{3}{1} + 12\binom{1}{0} + 8\binom{0}{1} = \binom{12}{8} \qquad \begin{array}{l} x_3 = 12 \\ x_4 = 8 \end{array}$$

Since we have four vectors in two-space, this is not a unique solution. We could substitute four units of P_2 for the twelve units of P_3 and four units of P_4:

$$0P_1 + 4P_2 + 0P_3 + 4P_4 = P_0 \qquad x_1 = 0$$
$$0\binom{2}{2} + 4\binom{3}{1} + 0\binom{1}{0} + 4\binom{0}{1} = \binom{12}{8} \qquad \begin{array}{l} x_2 = 4 \\ x_3 = 0 \end{array}$$
$$\binom{12}{4} + \binom{0}{4} = \binom{12}{8} \qquad x_4 = 4$$

Another possibility is to have a solution consisting of four units of P_1 and four units of P_3:

$$4P_1 + 0P_2 + 4P_3 + 0P_4 = P_0 \qquad x_1 = 4$$
$$4\binom{2}{2} + 0\binom{3}{1} + 4\binom{1}{0} + 0\binom{0}{1} = \binom{12}{8} \qquad \begin{array}{l} x_2 = 0 \\ x_3 = 4 \end{array}$$
$$\binom{8}{8} + \binom{4}{0} = \binom{12}{8} \qquad x_4 = 0$$

APPLICATION OF LINEAR ALGEBRA TO LINEAR PROGRAMMING

We have indicated that there may be an infinite number of solutions to a set of equations when there are more unknowns than equations. This has been explained in terms of vectors by suggesting that if there are more than the necessary number of vectors to form the basis of a space (two in two-space, three in three-space, etc.), then a vector in the space may be written in an infinite number of different linear combinations. Thus the scalars (x_1, x_2, x_3, x_4) may take on an infinite number of values in the last example of the previous section.

How do we reduce the number of solutions? In linear programming the objective function accomplishes this by giving us an equation which we are attempting either to maximize or to minimize, subject to certain restraints.

Let us return to the examples of the previous section and add an objective function, $f = 6x_1 + 7x_2$, which is to be maximized.

Our linear programming problem is:

$$\text{Maximize:} \quad f = 6x_1 + 7x_2 + 0x_3 + 0x_4$$
$$\text{Subject to:} \quad 2x_1 + 3x_2 + x_3 + 0x_4 = 12$$
$$2x_1 + x_2 + 0x_3 + x_4 = 8.$$

The requirement common to most linear programming problems, that all x's in the solution be positive, applies here. The restraint equations can be rewritten in vector form as follows:

$$x_1\begin{pmatrix}2\\2\end{pmatrix} + x_2\begin{pmatrix}3\\1\end{pmatrix} + x_3\begin{pmatrix}1\\0\end{pmatrix} + x_4\begin{pmatrix}0\\1\end{pmatrix} = \begin{pmatrix}12\\8\end{pmatrix}$$
$$x_1\underline{P}_1 + x_2\underline{P}_2 + x_3\underline{P}_3 + x_4\underline{P}_4 = \underline{P}_0.$$

In order to solve this problem, we can express the vector $\underline{P}_0$ as a linear combination of vectors $\underline{P}_1$, $\underline{P}_2$, $\underline{P}_3$, and $\underline{P}_4$. Each linear combination will give us the value for x_1, x_2, x_3, and x_4. These values can then be substituted in the objective function, f, and the value of f can then be computed. Since there are many linear combinations possible, there are many values of f. However, we can compute a value of f for each linear combination and choose that linear combination which makes f the largest. A reasonable place to start the solution is to let $x_3 = 12$, $x_4 = 8$, x_1 and $x_2 = 0$. Then:

(17–1) $$\underline{P}_0 = 0\underline{P}_1 + 0\underline{P}_2 + 12\underline{P}_3 + 8\underline{P}_4.$$

The value of f is:

$$f = 6(0) + 7(0) + 0(12) + 0(8) = 0.$$

Are there any values of x_i which will result in a larger f? We could guess at a new solution, as we did in the previous section; but here, we shall proceed more systematically. Let us inject some of vector $\underline{P}_2$ into the solution. We now have to solve for the number of units of $\underline{P}_3$ and $\underline{P}_4$ to be replaced by *one* unit of $\underline{P}_2$.

$$\underline{P}_2 = a\underline{P}_3 + b\underline{P}_4$$

where a and b are scalars to be determined.

The vector equation may be written as two equalities:

$$(3) = a(1) + b(0)$$
$$(1) = a(0) + b(1).$$

It can be seen that $a = 3$ and $b = 1$; thus, $\underline{P}_2 = 3\underline{P}_3 + 1\underline{P}_4$.

What scalar multiple of P_2 (what value of x_2) should be injected? Let us assume the correct amount is t.

Multiplying $\underline{P}_2 = 3\underline{P}_3 + \underline{P}_4$ by t gives:

$$tP_2 = 3tP_3 + tP_4$$

or

(17–2) $$t\underline{P}_2 - 3t\underline{P}_3 - t\underline{P}_4 = 0.$$

Return to equation 17–1 and add equation 17–2 to the right-hand side of that equation (which we may do, since the amount added is zero):

$$\underline{P}_0 = 0\underline{P}_1 + 0\underline{P}_2 + 12\underline{P}_3 + 8\underline{P}_4 + (t\underline{P}_2 - 3t\underline{P}_3 - t\underline{P}_4).$$

Arrange terms:

$$\underline{P}_0 = 0\underline{P}_1 + (0 + t)\underline{P}_2 + (12 - 3t)\underline{P}_3 + (8 - t)\underline{P}_4.$$

What is the maximum value of t which we can substitute and still not make the scalar of any vector negative? Below, we see that it can be as large as four:

$$12 - 3t = 0$$
$$t = 4$$
$$8 - t = 0$$
$$t = 8$$

Setting $t = 4$:

(17–3) $$\underline{P}_0 = 0\underline{P}_1 + 4\underline{P}_2 + 0\underline{P}_3 + 4\underline{P}_4.$$

Thus, $x_1 = 0$, $x_2 = 4$, $x_3 = 0$, and $x_4 = 4$ for this solution. The value of the objective function is:

$$f = 6(0) + 7(4) + 0(0) + 0(4) = 28.$$

This is an improvement over the zero value of f obtained previously, but it is not a maximum. Let us attempt to inject vector $\underline{P}_1$ into the solution. We shall have to substitute $\underline{P}_1$ for $\underline{P}_2$ and $\underline{P}_4$. The relationship of the three vectors is:

$$\underline{P}_1 = a\underline{P}_2 + b\underline{P}_4$$

$$\begin{pmatrix} 2 \\ 2 \end{pmatrix} = a\begin{pmatrix} 3 \\ 1 \end{pmatrix} + b\begin{pmatrix} 0 \\ 1 \end{pmatrix}.$$

Or rewriting as equations:

$$\begin{aligned} 2 &= 3a + 0b \\ 2 &= a + b \\ \hline a &= \tfrac{2}{3} \\ b &= \tfrac{4}{3} \\ \underline{P}_1 &= \tfrac{2}{3}\underline{P}_2 + \tfrac{4}{3}\underline{P}_4 \end{aligned}$$

We can check this linear combination as follows:

$$\binom{2}{2} = \tfrac{2}{3}\binom{3}{1} + \tfrac{4}{3}\binom{0}{1} \quad \text{or} \quad \binom{2}{2} = \binom{2}{\frac{2}{3}} + \binom{0}{\frac{4}{3}}$$
$$2 = 2 + 0$$
$$2 = \tfrac{2}{3} + \tfrac{4}{3}.$$

How many units of $\underline{P}_1$ shall we substitute for P_2 and P_4? Again, assume t units, and solve for t:

(17–4)
$$tP_1 = \tfrac{2}{3}tP_2 + \tfrac{4}{3}tP_4$$
$$\underline{t}P_1 - \tfrac{2}{3}tP_2 - \tfrac{4}{3}t\underline{P}_4 = 0.$$

Add equation 17–4 to the right-hand side of equation 17–3:

$$\underline{P}_0 = 0\underline{P}_1 + 4\underline{P}_2 + 0\underline{P}_3 + 4\underline{P}_4 + (t\underline{P}_1 - \tfrac{2}{3}t\underline{P}_2 - \tfrac{4}{3}t\underline{P}_4).$$

Arrange terms:

$$\underline{P}_0 = t\underline{P}_1 + (4 - \tfrac{2}{3}t)\underline{P}_2 + 0\underline{P}_3 + (4 - \tfrac{4}{3}t)\underline{P}_4.$$

Solve for the maximum t:

$$4 - \tfrac{2}{3}t = 0$$
$$t = 6$$
$$4 - \tfrac{4}{3}t = 0$$
$$t = 3.$$

The maximum t which is allowable is three.

(17–5)
$$\underline{P}_0 = 3\underline{P}_1 + 2\underline{P}_2 + 0\underline{P}_3 + 0\underline{P}_4.$$

Another possible solution is $x_1 = 3$, $x_2 = 2$, $x_3 = 0$, $x_4 = 0$. The objective function is:

$$f = 6(3) + 7(2) + 0(0) + 0(0) = 32.$$

Again, we have improved the value of the objective function by substituting a scalar multiple of one vector for two other vectors.

If we attempt further substitution, we shall find that it will result in a decrease in the function we are attempting to maximize. We have obtained an optimum solution ($x_1 = 3$ and $x_2 = 2$).

VECTOR ANALYSIS AND THE SIMPLEX METHOD

In Chapter 17 the simplex procedure was described as a method of solving linear programming problems. In this Appendix the same problem (see Example 1) has been solved using vector analysis. By comparing the simplex solution of Example 1 with the algebraic solution of this Appendix, it is possible to gain an understanding for each step of the simplex solution.

The equations

$$2x_1 + 3x_2 + 1x_3 + 0x_4 = 12$$

and

$$2x_1 + 1x_2 + 0x_3 + 1x_4 = 8$$

are the restraint inequalities

$$2x_1 + 3x_2 \leq 12$$

and

$$2x_1 + x_2 \leq 8$$

with the slack variables added.

Making use of our knowledge of vectors, the first simplex table could be written as shown in Table 17–23.

TABLE 17–23

C_i	Solution Mix	$\underline{P}_0$	0 $\underline{P}_3$	0 $\underline{P}_4$	6 $\underline{P}_1$	7 $\underline{P}_2$
0	$\underline{P}_3$	12	1	0	2	3
0	$\underline{P}_4$	8	0	1	2	1
	Z_i	0	0	0	0	0
	$C_i - Z_i$				6	7

Previously, we headed the columns with the variables (such as x_1 and x_2) and described the table as containing the coefficients of each variable. Table 17–23 modifies this interpretation. The columns now have vector headings (such as $\underline{P}_1$ and $\underline{P}_2$). The body of Table 17–23 contains the components of the vectors $\underline{P}_3$, $\underline{P}_4$, $\underline{P}_1$, and $\underline{P}_2$, in that order:

$$\underline{P}_0 = x_3\underline{P}_3 + x_4\underline{P}_4 + x_1\underline{P}_1 + x_2\underline{P}_2$$

$$\begin{pmatrix} 12 \\ 8 \end{pmatrix} = x_3\begin{pmatrix} 1 \\ 0 \end{pmatrix} + x_4\begin{pmatrix} 0 \\ 1 \end{pmatrix} + x_1\begin{pmatrix} 2 \\ 2 \end{pmatrix} + x_2\begin{pmatrix} 3 \\ 1 \end{pmatrix}.$$

The first solution mix is the *basis vectors* $\underline{P}_3$ and $\underline{P}_4$; the scalars of these vectors are twelve (which is x_3) and eight (which is x_4). All the column vectors are linear combinations of the basis vectors $\underline{P}_3$ and $\underline{P}_4$. The first number in each column is the amount by which $\underline{P}_3$ should be multiplied, and the second number is the amount by which

P_4 should be multiplied in order to obtain the vector which heads each column:

$$P_0 = 12P_3 + 8P_4 + 0P_1 + 0P_2$$
$$P_3 = 1P_3 + 0P_4 + 0P_1 + 0P_2$$
$$P_4 = 0P_3 + 1P_4 + 0P_1 + 0P_2$$
$$P_1 = 2P_3 + 2P_4 + 0P_1 + 0P_2$$
$$P_2 = 3P_3 + 1P_4 + 0P_1 + 0P_2.$$

Each simplex table gives the scalars by which the chosen basis vectors must be multiplied to obtain the linear combination which represents the vector at the head of the column.

Since P_0 is the solution vector, the first solution is:

$P_0 = 12P_3 + 8P_4 + 0P_1 + 0P_2$ (see equation 17–1 of the algebraic solution).

From the simplex table (Table 17–23), we see that the vector P_2 should be injected into the solution (the $C_j - Z_j = 7$ is the largest positive amount) and should replace P_3. How many units of P_2 can be injected? The simplex procedure is as follows:

$$\text{For } P_3: \quad 12/3 = 4$$
$$\text{For } P_4: \quad 8/1 = 8.$$

The calculation indicates that row P_3 (or basis vector P_3) should be replaced. Actually, the four computed above indicates the number of units of P_2 which should be substituted. The four is the value of t which was computed in the algebraic solution to accomplish the same objective.

Substituting P_2 for P_3 creates a new basis; it is necessary to change row P_4. After having completed the substitution, the computation of Z_j for the P_0 column is analogous to computing the objective function of the algebraic solution.

We want to rewrite the five equations listed above with the new basis P_2 and P_4. That is, we want to express P_0, P_3, P_4, P_1, and P_2 in terms of linear combinations of P_2 and P_4:

$$P_0 = 12P_3 + 8P_4$$

but

$$P_2 = 3P_3 + 1P_4.$$

Thus:

$$P_3 = \tfrac{1}{3}(P_2 - P_4).$$

Substituting in $P_0 = 12P_3 + 8P_4$ and the other equations gives:

$$
\begin{aligned}
P_0 &= 12 \times \tfrac{1}{3}(P_2 - P_4) + 8P_4 = 4P_2 + 4P_4 \\
P_3 &= 1 \times \tfrac{1}{3}(P_2 - P_4) + 0P_4 = \tfrac{1}{3}P_2 - \tfrac{1}{3}P_4 \\
P_4 &= 0 \times \tfrac{1}{3}(P_2 - P_4) + 1P_4 = 0P_2 + 1P_4 \\
P_1 &= 2 \times \tfrac{1}{3}(P_2 - P_4) + 2P_4 = \tfrac{2}{3}P_2 + \tfrac{4}{3}P_4 \\
P_2 &= 3 \times \tfrac{1}{3}(P_2 - P_4) + 1P_4 = 1P_2 + 0P_4.
\end{aligned}
$$

Referring to Table 17–2 on page 256, each number in row X_3 is being divided by three, the number in the X_2 column and X_3 row. These are the coefficients of $(P_2 - P_4)$ in the above equations. They are also the coefficients of P_2 in the simplified equations below. These coefficients are the new first row in the second simplex. Referring to Table 17–4 on page 259, we find the first row is 4, $\tfrac{1}{3}$, 0, $\tfrac{2}{3}$, 1. The second row is the coefficients of P_4 in the simplified equations. Rearranging the coefficients of P_4 in the equation for P_0, we have:

$$
\begin{aligned}
P_0 &= 12 \times \tfrac{1}{3}(P_2 - P_4) + 8P_4 \\
&= 4P_2 + 8P_4 - 12 \times \tfrac{1}{3}P_4 \\
&= 4P_2 + (8 - 12 \times \tfrac{1}{3})P_4
\end{aligned}
$$

The $(8 - 12 \times \tfrac{1}{3})$ is the number of units of P_4 in the new solution. It is the same computation which was previously made mechanistically in solving the simplex. The main advantage of the simplex method is that it systematically accomplishes the algebraic computations necessary to solve linear programming problems; also, this facilitates the solution, since the problem may then be programmed on an electronic computer.

BIBLIOGRAPHY

BENNION, E. G. *Elementary Mathematics of Linear Programming and Game Theory.* East Lansing: Michigan State University Press, 1960.

BOWMAN, E. H., and FETTER, R. B. *Analysis for Production Management.* Homewood, Ill.: Richard D. Irwin, Inc., 1960.

CHARNES, A., and COOPER, W. W. *Management Models and Industrial Applications of Linear Programming.* 2 vols. New York: John Wiley & Sons, Inc., 1963.

CHURCHMAN, C. W.; ACKOFF, R. L.; and ARNOFF, E. L. *Introduction to Operations Research.* New York: John Wiley & Sons, Inc., 1957.

DANTZIG, G. B. *Linear Programming and Extensions.* Princeton: Princeton University Press, 1963.

——, "Maximization of a Linear Function of Variables Subject to Linear Inequalities," in T. C. Koopmans (ed.) *Activity Analysis of Production and Allocation.* (see below).

Dartmouth College Writing Group. *Modern Mathematical Methods and Models*, Vol. I. Ann Arbor: Mathematical Association of America, 1959.

Dorfman, R.; Samuelson, P. A.; and Solow, R. M. *Linear Programming and Economic Analysis*. New York: McGraw-Hill Book Co., Inc., 1958.

Gass, S. I. *Linear Programming: Methods and Applications*. New York: McGraw-Hill Book Co., Inc., 1959.

Henderson, A., and Schlaifer, R. "Mathematical Programming: Better Information for Better Decision Making," *Harvard Business Review*, May-June, 1954.

Koopmans, T. C. (ed.). *Activity Analysis of Production and Allocation*. New York: John Wiley & Sons, Inc., 1951.

Vajda, S. *Readings in Linear Programming*. New York: John Wiley & Sons, Inc., 1958.

Problems

17–1. Given:
$$5X_1 + 10X_2 = 150$$
$$0 \leq X_1 \leq 20$$
$$0 \leq X_2 \geq 14.$$
Use the simplex method to find the values of X_1 and X_2 which maximize the function $P = -2X_1 - 8X_2$.

17–2. Given:
$$4X_1 + 2X_2 \leq 10$$
$$2X_1 + 8/3X_2 \leq 8$$
$$0 \leq X_1 \leq 6$$
$$X_2 \geq 0.$$
Use the simplex method to find the values of X_1 and X_2 which maximize the function $P = 4X_1 + 3X_2$.

17–3. Given:
$$4X_1 + 2X_2 \leq 10$$
$$2X_1 + 8/3X_2 \leq 8$$
$$0 \leq X_2 \leq 6$$
$$X_1 \geq 0.$$
Use the simplex method to find the values of X_1 and X_2 which maximize the function $P = 4X_1 + 3X_2$.

17–4. Given:
$$3X_1 + 2X_2 \geq 12$$
$$1/2X_1 + X_2 \geq 4$$
$$X_1 \geq 0$$
$$X_2 \geq 0.$$
Use the simplex method to find the values of X_1 and X_2 which minimize the function $P = 6X_1 + 4X_2$.

17–5. The ABC Company has the option of producing two products during periods of slack activity. For the next week, production has been scheduled so that the milling machine is free ten hours and skilled labor will have eight hours of available time.

Product A requires four hours of machine time and two hours of skilled labor per unit. Product B requires two hours of machine time and two hours of skilled labor per unit.

Product A contributes $5.00 per unit to profit, and product B contributes $3.00 per unit to profit (not including skilled labor or machine time cost).

Use the simplex method to find the amounts of product A and product B which should be produced.

17–6. The XYZ Company combines factors A and B to form a product which must weigh 50 pounds. At least 20 pounds of A and no more than 40 pounds of B can be used. The cost of A is $10 per pound; of B, $25 per pound.

Use the simplex method to find the amounts of factor A and factor B which should be used.

17–7. The Z Company combines factors A and B to form a product which must weigh 50 pounds. At least 20 pounds of A and no more than 40 pounds of B can be used. A costs $25 per pound, and B costs $10 per pound.

Use the simplex method to find the amounts of factor A and factor B which should be used.

17–8. A company sells two different products, A and B. The selling price and incremental cost information is as follows:

	Product A	Product B
Selling price......................	$60	$40
Incremental cost..................	30	10
Incremental Profit............	$30	$30

The two products are produced in a common production process and are sold in two different markets. The production process has a capacity of 30,000 man-hours. It takes three hours to produce a unit of A and one hour to produce a unit of B. The market has been surveyed, and company officials feel that the maximum number of units of A that can be sold is 8,000; the maximum for B is 12,000 units. Subject to these limitations, the products can be sold in any combination.

a) Formulate the above problem as a linear programming problem; i.e., write the appropriate equations.

b) Solve this problem by graphic methods.

17–9. The Ajax Nut Company sells mixed nuts of two quality levels. The more expensive mix has a higher proportion of cashews, while the cheaper mix contains more peanuts.

The prices of nuts purchased by Ajax are: cashews, 50 cents a pound; peanuts, 20 cents a pound. The two mixes sold by Ajax and their prices are: mixture A, 80 cents a pound; mixture B, 40 cents a pound. Ajax can sell any amount of each of these mixtures but, due to a shortage of nuts, can obtain no more than 200 pounds of cashews and 400 pounds of peanuts.

Management has decided that mixture A should not contain more than 25 per cent peanuts nor less than 40 per cent cashews. Mixture B should have no more than 60 per cent peanuts and no less than 20 per cent cashews.

How should Ajax mix its nuts? That is, how many pounds of mixture A should be produced (and what should be its composition), and how many pounds of mixture B (and its composition)? Formulate the simplex table and solve.

17-10. The advertising department of a certain firm wishes to plan its advertising strategy to reach certain minimum percentages of high- and low-income groups. Two alternatives are considered: television and magazines. Magazine advertising has an exposure for the high-income group of 2 per cent per page, but only a 1 per cent per page exposure for the low-income group. Television, on the other hand, exposes 3 per cent of the low-income group per show and only 1 per cent of the high-income group per show.

Magazine advertising costs $1,000 per page; television, $4,000 per show. If the firm wants a minimal exposure of 50 per cent of the high-income group and 30 per cent of the low-income group, what strategy should it use to minimize advertising cost? (NOTE: If a person views a show twice, or reads an advertisement twice, or views a show and reads an advertisement, this counts as double exposure. Exposure greater than 100 per cent is thus possible.)

Chapter 18

LINEAR PROGRAMMING—THE
DUAL PROBLEM

EVERY linear programming problem that we have solved has been of the type designated as "primal," the primal being the first problem to which our attention is generally directed. Each primal problem has a companion problem which is called the "dual." The dual has the same optimum solution as the primal, but it is derived by an alternative procedure, and the analysis of this procedure may be instructive for several types of decision problems.

Example—The Primal

Assume that two products, X_1 and X_2, are manufactured on two machines, 1 and 2.

Product X_1 requires three hours on machine 1 and one-half hour on machine 2.

Product X_2 requires two hours on machine 1 and one hour on machine 2.

There are six hours of excess capacity on machine 1 and four hours on machine 2.

Each unit of X_1 produces a net increase in profit of \$12, and each unit of X_2 an incremental profit of \$4.00.

The objective function (or profit function) to be maximized is:

$$P = 12X_1 + 4X_2$$

or, after including the slack variables:

$$P = 12X_1 + 4X_2 + 0X_3 + 0X_4.$$

The restraints are:

$3X_1 + 2X_2 \leq 6$. There are six hours available on machine 1. Each unit of X_1 requires three hours; X_2 requires two hours.

$\frac{1}{2}X_1 + X_2 \leq 4$.   There are four hours available on machine 2. Each
unit of X_1 requires one-half hour; X_2 requires one
hour.

$X_1 \geq 0$, $X_2 \geq 0$.   The X's cannot be negative. (We cannot produce a
negative amount of product.)

After slack variables are introduced to convert the inequalities
into equalities, we have:

$$3X_1 + 2X_2 + X_3 + 0X_4 = 6$$
$$\frac{1}{2}X_1 + X_2 + 0X_3 + X_4 = 4.$$

The successive simplex tables are shown in Tables 18–1 and 18–2.

TABLE 18–1

C_j			0	0	12	4
	Solution Mix	P_0	X_3	X_4	X_1	X_2
0	$\rightarrow X_3$	6	1	0	3	2
0	X_4	4	0	1	$\frac{1}{2}$	1
	Z_j	0	0	0	0	0
	$C_j - Z_j$		0	0	12	4

TABLE 18–2

C_j			0	0	12	4
	Solution Mix	P_0	X_3	X_4	X_1	X_2
12	X_1	2	$\frac{1}{3}$	0	1	$\frac{2}{3}$
0	X_4	3	$-\frac{1}{6}$	1	0	$\frac{2}{3}$
	Z_j	24	4	0	12	8
	$C_j - Z_j$		-4	0	0	-4

All the $C_j - Z_j$'s are ≤ 0; thus a solution has been reached. Two
units of X_1 should be produced, and this will result in a profit of $24.
No other combination of products will result in as high a profit. For
example, producing one unit of X_1 and one unit of X_2 results in a
profit of $12 \cdot 1 + $4.00 \cdot 1$, or $16. We cannot produce one unit of
X_1 and two units of X_2, since this would require more hours than are
available on machine 1.

The inclusion of three units of X_4 in the solution indicates that
machine 2 will be idle for three hours a period.

Example—The Dual

Continuing the example, we shall examine the dual problem. The following characterizes the dual:

1. If the objective function is *maximized* in the primal, the objective function of the dual is *minimized*. In this example the objective function is a cost equation.

2. The coefficients of the variables of the cost equation (the dual objective function) are the constants of the primal restraints. In this example, they are six and four, and represent the hours of each machine available. The variables U_1 and U_2 of the cost equation of the dual are the respective costs per hour of using machine 1 and machine 2.[1] The cost equation (or objective function) is:

$$C = 6U_1 + 4U_2 + 0U_3 + 0U_4 + MU_5 + MU_6.$$

3. The restraints are formed by transposing the coefficients used in the primal. In the primal the equations and coefficients were:

Equation	Coefficients	
$3X_1 + 2X_2 \leq 6$	3	2
$\frac{1}{2}X_1 + X_2 \leq 4$	$\frac{1}{2}$	1

The transposition is as follows (A^T indicates that A has been transposed):

$$A = \begin{pmatrix} 3 & 2 \\ \frac{1}{2} & 1 \end{pmatrix}$$
$$A^T = \begin{pmatrix} 3 & \frac{1}{2} \\ 2 & 1 \end{pmatrix}.$$

The first column of A is regarded as the first row of A^T, and the second column of A is regarded as the second row of A^T.

The constants for the dual restraints are obtained from the profit function (the objective function) of the primal. Thus the constants will be twelve and four.

4. If we are maximizing a primal objective function, and if the restraints of the primal are "less than or equal to," the restraints of the dual will be "greater than or equal to." Thus the restraints are:

$$3U_1 + \frac{1}{2}U_2 \geq 12$$
$$2U_1 + U_2 \geq 4.$$

---

[1] The U_1 and U_2 are opportunity cost measures and are not related to conventional accounting costs.

The interpretation of these restraints should illuminate the relationship between the primal and dual problems. The first inequality states that the time to produce product X_1 on machine 1 (three hours) times the cost per hour of using machine 1 (U_1) plus the time to produce product X_1 on machine 2 (one-half hour) times the cost per hour of using machine 2 (U_2) is greater than or equal to \$12. The \$12 is the net profit of a unit of X_1 (see the profit function of the primal). Thus the cost of producing X_1 is going to be either equal to the net profit (in which case X_1 will be produced) or greater than the net profit (in which case no units of X_1 will be produced).

TABLE 18–3

C_j			M	M	0	0	6	4
	Solution Mix	P_0	U_5	U_6	U_3	U_4	U_1	U_2
M	U_5	12	1	0	-1	0	3	$\frac{1}{2}$
M	$\rightarrow U_6$	4	0	1	0	-1	2	1
	Z_j	$16M$	M	M	$-M$	$-M$	$5M$	$\frac{3}{2}M$
	$C_j - Z_j$		0	0	M	M	$6 - 5M$	$4 - \frac{3}{2}M$

The interpretation of the second restraint is similar. The total cost per unit of producing product X_2 is $2U_1$ (cost of using machine 1) plus U_2 (cost of using machine 2). The total cost per unit is equal to or greater than \$4.00, where \$4.00 is the net increase in profit per unit of product X_2. Thus the cost of producing X_2 is going to be either equal to the net profit per unit of X_2 (in which case X_2 will be produced) or greater than the net profit (in which case no units of X_2 will be produced).

It should be noted that the form of solution does not allow for the costs of producing either product to be less than the incremental profit of the product. This is reasonable, since the value of the machine hours is measured by the profit they can produce. To have the total costs less than the profit would imply that we should produce more units of the product; but if the product is produced to the limit of productive capacity, the costs of the last unit will be equal to the profit. The only time the costs will be greater than the incremental profit will be when it is not desirable to produce any units of the product. Remember that these are opportunity, not accounting, costs.

The restraint equations, complete with slack variables and artificial variables, are:

$$3U_1 + \tfrac{1}{2}U_2 - U_3 + 0U_4 + U_5 + 0U_6 = 12$$
$$2U_1 + U_2 + 0U_3 - U_4 + 0U_5 + U_6 = 4.$$

The large coefficient M is assigned to U_5 and U_6 in the cost equation to drive these two variables from the solution; this is done because U_5 and U_6 are artificial variables.

Since we are minimizing a cost function, the replacing column of the simplex tables of this example (Tables 18–3, 18–4, and 18–5) will be the column with the largest negative $C_j - Z_j$.

TABLE 18–4

C_j			M	M	0	0	6	4
	Solution Mix	P_0	U_5	U_6	U_3	U_4	U_1	U_2
M	→U_5	6	1	$-\tfrac{3}{2}$	-1	$\tfrac{3}{2}$	0	-1
0.6	U_1	2	0	$\tfrac{1}{2}$	0	$-\tfrac{1}{2}$	1	$\tfrac{1}{2}$
	Z_j	$12 + 6M$	M	$3 - \tfrac{3}{2}M$	$-M$	$-3 + \tfrac{3}{2}M$	6	$3 - M$
	$C_j - Z_j$		0	$\tfrac{5}{2}M - 3$	M	$3 - \tfrac{3}{2}M$	0	$1 + M$

TABLE 18–5

C_j			M	M	0	0	6	4
	Solution Mix	P_0	U_5	U_6	U_3	U_4	U_1	U_2
0	U_4	4	$\tfrac{2}{3}$	-1	$-\tfrac{2}{3}$	1	0	$-\tfrac{2}{3}$
6	U_1	4	$\tfrac{1}{3}$	0	$-\tfrac{1}{3}$	0	1	$\tfrac{1}{6}$
	Z_j	24	2	0	-2	0	6	1
	$C_j - Z_j$		$M - 2$	M	2	0	0	3

The minimum of the cost equation is $24 (see Z_j of Table 18–5 of the dual). This is equal to the maximum of the profit equation (see Z_j of Table 18–2 of the primal).

Table 18–5 gives a solution, since all columns have positive $(C_j - Z_j)$ totals. U_1 has a value of $4.00, which means an hour of time of machine 1 has a value of $4.00. U_4 also has a value of $4.00.[2] The value of U_2 is zero, which means the "cost" of an hour of time on

---

[2] U_4 is the cost of inserting one unit of X_2 into the solution. See Table 18–2, and note that $C_2 - Z_2 = -4$.

machine 2 is zero. This is consistent with the fact that machine 2 has idle hours following the optimum schedule of production, and profit would not be increased by making more time on machine 2 available.

SHADOW PRICES

Note that the values of four for U_1 and U_4 are the same (except for the sign) as the $C_j - Z_j$ values for X_1 and X_4 in Table 18–2. This is not a coincidence. The U values of the dual solution are uniquely the $C_j - Z_j$ values of the primal solution. And similarly, the $C_j - Z_j$ values of the dual give the primal solution. The economic interpretation of the dual values (whether from the dual solution or from the $C_j - Z_j$'s of the primal) is of considerable value.

In the above example, we know that injecting one more unit of X_2 will have a cost of $4.00 in terms of lost opportunities. Also, we could place costs on the resources being used. The foreman could be told of the current alternative cost of each machine. Jobs must have an incremental profit of $4.00 per hour or more to be placed on machine 1. Jobs which have an incremental profit of less than $4.00 per hour (theoretically anything in excess of zero) can be assigned to machine 2. This procedure could be used to evaluate common costs, i.e., the value of production factors which are used in producing two or more products. The cost information evolved, using the dual of the linear programming primal problem, is sometimes referred to as a "shadow price" or an "accounting" price.

Shadow prices can be interpreted as the "cost" of a constraint. We can say that a unit of slack of machine 1, which has only six hours available, "costs" at a rate of $4.00 per hour ($U_1$ has a value of $4.00 per unit). It would be worth $4.00 per hour in increased profitability to obtain an additional hour on machine 1 (e.g., use a second shift). Thus the shadow price measures the value or worth of relaxing a constraint.

Another Example

Example 5 of Chapter 17 was a somewhat complex linear programming problem. It would be helpful to return to this example and interpret the economic information in the solution. The final solution of this example is reproduced as Table 18–6.

The last row ($C_j - Z_j$) lists the shadow prices. The variables X_8 through X_{12} are the slack variables associated with the constraints on resources (hours of capacity, personnel, and funds). When such slack

TABLE 18-6

C_j	Solution Mix	P_0	X_8 (0)	X_9 (0)	X_{10} (0)	X_{11} (0)	X_{12} (0)	X_{13} (0)	X_{14} (0)	X_{15} (0)	X_{16} (0)	X_{17} (0)	X_{18} (0)	X_{19} (0)	X_1 (50)	X_2 (100)	X_3 (100)	X_4 (50)	X_5 (150)	X_6 (100)	X_7 (60)
100	X_3	3		$\frac{1}{4}$					$-\frac{1}{4}$			$-\frac{5}{4}$	$-\frac{1}{2}$	$-\frac{1}{4}$	$\frac{1}{4}$		1				
50	X_4	9	$\frac{1}{3}$	$-\frac{1}{12}$					$-\frac{7}{12}$			$\frac{1}{12}$	$\frac{1}{6}$	$-\frac{7}{12}$	$\frac{19}{12}$			1			
0	X_{10}	117	1	$\frac{1}{4}$	1				$\frac{9}{4}$			1	$\frac{3}{2}$	$\frac{5}{4}$	$\frac{21}{4}$						
0	X_{11}	63	$-\frac{2}{3}$	$-\frac{7}{12}$		1			$\frac{11}{12}$			$\frac{19}{12}$	$-1\frac{1}{6}$	$\frac{11}{12}$	$\frac{35}{12}$						
0	X_{12}	103	$-\frac{1}{3}$	$\frac{1}{6}$			1		$-2\frac{5}{6}$			$\frac{5}{6}$	$\frac{5}{3}$	$-\frac{19}{6}$	$\frac{7}{6}$						
0	X_{13}	10						1							1						
100	X_2	5														1					
0	X_{15}	47	$-\frac{1}{3}$	$-\frac{1}{4}$					$\frac{1}{4}$	1		$-\frac{5}{4}$	$\frac{1}{2}$	$\frac{1}{4}$	$-\frac{1}{4}$						
0	X_{16}	16		$\frac{1}{12}$					$\frac{7}{12}$		1	$-\frac{1}{12}$	$\frac{1}{6}$	$\frac{7}{12}$	$-\frac{19}{12}$						
150	X_5	10											1						1		
100	X_6	5												1						1	
60	X_7	20																			1
	Z_j	4,450	$5\frac{2}{3}$	$20\frac{5}{6}$	0	0	0	0	$45\frac{5}{6}$	0	0	$29\frac{1}{6}$	$58\frac{1}{3}$	$5\frac{5}{6}$	$104\frac{1}{6}$	100	100	50	150	100	60
	$C_j - Z_j$		$-5\frac{2}{3}$	$-20\frac{5}{6}$	0	0	0	0	$-45\frac{5}{6}$	0	0	$-29\frac{1}{6}$	$-58\frac{1}{3}$	$-5\frac{5}{6}$	$-54\frac{1}{6}$	0	0	0	0	0	0

variables have a zero shadow price (as do X_{10}, X_{11}, and X_{12}), we cannot increase profits by making more of the resources available. The resources are not fully utilized in the optimum solution (e.g., there are $X_{10} = 117$ hours of test unused). On the other hand, the shadow prices associated with X_8 and X_9 give the increased profit associated with making one more unit of these resources available. For example, we could increase profits nearly \$21 by making one more hour of assembly time available (i.e., $C_9 - Z_9 = -20\frac{5}{6}$). Profits would be decreased \$21 by taking away one unit of time.

The variables X_{13} through X_{19} are the slack variables associated with requirements. The shadow prices refer to additional costs if these slack variables are increased. If, for example, one less part No. 284 (X_5) were produced, it would increase X_{17} by one at a cost of \$29 (the slack variable for requirements of part No. 284 is X_{17} and $C_{17} - Z_{17} = -29\frac{1}{6}$). Each unit of X_{17} which is produced saves \$29. If all requirements for a part are not manufactured internally, then if the needs for this part were increased, this would merely increase the number of units purchased outside the firm, without the profit (or costs) being affected. In like manner, the needs for the part could decrease without the change affecting the profit (the number purchased outside the firm would decrease). In the example, X_4, part No. 197, has a requirement of twenty-five units; and of these, nine units are to be produced internally, and $C_{16} - Z_{16} = 0$. Profit, as measured by the linear programming model, would not be affected by a change in the needs for X_4.

The shadow prices for X_1 through X_7 indicate the loss in profitability if some of a given part must be included in the solution. For X_2 through X_7 the prices are zero, and each of these variables is in the solution. $C_1 - Z_1 = -54\frac{1}{6}$ indicates that management would reduce its profit by this much if it required that at least one unit of X_1 (part No. 182) must be produced.

LIMITATIONS OF THE EXAMPLES

The above examples are typical of a large classification of economic problems, but it is important to note the limitations of the procedures described.

The significant characteristics of the problem from the viewpoint of the present discussion were:

1. The objective function of the primal was being maximized.
2. The sense of the primal restraints was "equal to or less than."

With these characteristics, we proceeded to make the sense of the dual restraints opposite to those of the primal. Unfortunately, different combinations of the above characteristics require different procedures in the dual. Two possibilities are shown in Table 18–7.

We may have a primal with an objective function which we are directed to maximize, but the sense of the restraint equations is "equal to or greater than." We can use the above directions by mul-

TABLE 18–7

If Primal Has—		Then Set Up Dual—	
Objective Function	Sense of Restraint Equation	Objective Function	Sense of Restraint Equation
Maximize	$\leq$	Minimize	$\geq$ (Opposite Sense)
Minimize	$\geq$	Maximize	$\leq$ (Opposite Sense)

tiplying the objective function by -1 and changing it from a maximizing to a minimizing problem. For example, maximize

$$f = 2X_1 - 3X_2$$

is equivalent to minimize $g = -2X_1 + 3X_2$, but the change would enable us to construct the dual from the primal.

The analyst may prefer to by-pass solving the dual as a by-product of the primal. He may initially solve the problem which might be thought of as the dual. The facts of the situation should indicate how the restraints are to be set up.

BIBLIOGRAPHY

See the Bibliography of Chapter 17.

PROBLEMS

18–1. There are two products, X_1 and X_2:

Product	Hours of Machine Time per Unit	Incremental Profit per Unit
X_1..................	4	$2.00
X_2..................	2	4.00

The machine has four hours of free time.

a) Using the *simplex method*, solve the primal and the dual.

b) Interpret the primal and the dual.

18–2. Assume two products, X_1 and X_2, are manufactured on two machines, 1 and 2. Product X_1 requires four hours on machine 1 and two hours on machine 2. Product X_2 requires two hours on machine 1 and $\frac{8}{3}$ hours on machine 2. There are ten hours of excess capacity on machine 1 and eight hours on machine 2. Each unit of X_1 produces a net increase in profit of $4.00, and each unit of X_2 an incremental profit of $3.00.

a) Determine the maximum profit and the product mix which results in the profit, using the simplex method.

b) Determine the value of each hour of machine time, solving the dual.

18–3. The XYZ Company has the option of producing two products during periods of slack activity. For the next period, production has been scheduled so that the milling machine is free ten hours and skilled labor will have eight hours of time available:

Product	Machine Time per Unit	Skilled Labor per Unit	Profit Contribution per Unit
A...............	4	2	$5.00
B...............	2	2	3.00

a) Solve the primal problem (the number of units of A and B which should be produced).

b) Solve the dual problem (the cost of an hour of machine time and an hour of skilled labor).

For Problems 18–4 to 18–8, solve the primal and the dual graphically. For each problem the primal is described.

18–4. Maximize the objective function:

$$f = 2x_1 + 4x_2$$

Subject to restraints:

$$4x_1 + 2x_2 \leq 4$$
$$x_1, x_2 \geq 0.$$

18–5. Maximize the objective function:

$$f = 2x_1 - 4x_2.$$

Subject to restraints:

$$4x_1 + 2x_2 \leq 4$$
$$x_1, x_2 \geq 0.$$

18–6. Minimize the objective function:

$$f = 2x_1 + 4x_2.$$

Subject to restraints:

$$4x_1 + 2x_2 \leq 4$$
$$x_1, \, x_2 \geq 0.$$

18–7. Minimize the objective function:

$$f = 2x_1 - 4x_2.$$

Subject to restraints:

$$4x_1 + 2x_2 \geq 4$$
$$x_1, \, x_2 \geq 0.$$

18–8. Give a possible economic interpretation of the primal and dual of Problem 18–4.

18–9. Same for Problem 18–5.

18–10. Same for Problem 18–6.

18–11. Same for Problem 18–7.

Chapter 19

LINEAR PROGRAMMING—THE
TRANSPORTATION PROBLEM

THERE IS a type of linear programming problem which may be solved using a simplified version of the simplex technique.[1] Because of its application in solving problems involving several product sources and several destinations of products, this type of problem frequently is called the *transportation* problem. A more general term is *assignment* or *allocation* problem, for the method of solution applies to the assignment of any factors of production to different tasks. A common characteristic of this type of problem is that all the units available must be assigned. For example, if a source supplies 10 units of a product, an assignment of the 10 units must be made to one or another destination; we cannot assign more or less than 10 units.

Example—Basic Method

In this chapter, we shall describe two possible procedures. The first we shall call the "basic" method. Let us assume there are three factories (F_1, F_2, and F_3) supplying three warehouses (W_1, W_2, and W_3). (See Table 19–1.)

TABLE 19–1

Factories	Amount Available	Warehouses	Amount Needed
F_1............	20	W_1............	5
F_2............	15	W_2............	20
F_3............	10	W_3............	20
Total....	45	Total.....	45

[1] The coefficients of all X_{ij}'s in the restraint equations are either zero or one. See the Appendix to this chapter.

The costs of shipping from each factory to each destination are given in the body of Table 19–2. In the margins of the table are the amounts available at the factories and the requirements of the warehouses.

TABLE 19–2
Costs of Shipping and Physical Units

Destination \ Source	F_1	F_2	F_3	Units Demanded
W_1	$0.90	$1.00	$1.00	5
W_2	$1.00	$1.40	$0.80	20
W_3	$1.30	$1.00	$0.80	20
Units available......	20	15	10	45

It is necessary to prepare an initial solution, which may be done in several different ways; the only requirement is that the warehouse needs be met within the constraint of factory production. One popular method is to start in the upper left-hand corner (the northwest corner), first supplying the needs of W_1, then W_2, then W_3. Another procedure (the one we shall employ) is to turn to Table 19–2 and find a box which has the lowest value in both its row and its column; place in that box the lower of the values found in its row or its column margin.

A requirement of the initial solution is that the number of routes used must equal the sum of the number of factories, F, plus the number of warehouses, W, minus one, i.e.:

$$\text{Routes Used} = F + W - 1.$$

If the initial solution uses more routes than $F + W - 1$, then, for one or more zero boxes, there will be more than one possible evaluation. If the initial solution uses less routes than $F + W - 1$, then a problem of degeneracy arises. A method of solving degenerate problems is given later in this chapter.

In establishing early solutions, it is reasonable to aim at using $F + W - 1$ boxes. If more than this number of boxes are used, the solution should be adjusted by making arbitrary changes consistent with the needs of the warehouses and the production capacity of the factories to reduce the number of routes.

The 90 cents in box W_1F_1 of Table 19–2 is the lowest amount in its row and the lowest amount in its column.[2] Since the warehouse only needs five units, even though the factory can supply 20 units, we place a five in the W_1F_1 box of Table 19–3. In Table 19–3 the costs are in the upper left corner of each box, the units shipped in the lower right corner.

The 80 cents of costs in W_2F_3 is equal to the 80 cents of W_3F_3. We could take either value, but we shall arbitrarily choose W_2F_3 and place 10 units in that box (the most that can be supplied by factory 3).

TABLE 19–3
First Solution

Source / Destination	F_1	F_2	F_3	Units Demanded
W_1	$0.90 / 5	$1.00 / 0	$1.00 / 0	5
W_2	$1.00 / 10	$1.40 / 0	$0.80 / 10	20
W_3	$1.30 / 5	$1.00 / 15	$0.80 / 0	20
Units available......	20	15	10	45

To place the remainder of the units, we proceed in a common-sense manner, making certain that no more is taken from a factory than it can produce and no more is sent to a warehouse than it needs. There are 15 units remaining from F_1; we shall assign 10 units to W_2F_1, and five units to W_3F_1. The needs of warehouse 2 are satisfied with this allocation.

The 15 units of F_2 are all assigned to W_3F_2, since warehouse 3 is the only location which has unfilled needs.

Table 19–3 shows the first trial solution. Note that five direct routes are used and $F + W - 1$ equals five (i.e., $3 + 3 - 1 = 5$). If possible, we want a solution which uses $F + W - 1$ boxes, to avoid excess routes or degeneracy. We also require that the solution be

---

[2] W_1F_1 indicates that warehouse 1 is being supplied from factory 1.

consistent with the restraints. It would be a coincidence if the trial solution happened to be the optimum solution; but the closer the first solution is to an optimum solution, the less work is required. In any event, we must test to see if costs may be reduced by some re-arrangement of routes. Total shipment costs for the first solution are:

$$5(0.90) + 10(1.00) + 10(0.80) + 5(1.30) + 15(1.00) = \$44.$$

We shall proceed to test the relative cost advantage of alternative routes. Consider an unused route, such as shipping to warehouse 1 from factory 2 (i.e., box W_1F_2 has a zero entry in its lower right corner). The direct cost of using this route is the amount in the upper left corner of the box, $1.00; this amount is to be contrasted with the current costs of the indirect route from F_2 to W_1. The indirect route is identified as the path a unit would have to follow from a given factory to a given warehouse, using only established channels (i.e., the shipment must avoid zero boxes; otherwise, we are shipping from a box which has no units, or introducing two new boxes into the solution instead of one). In this case the indirect route from F_2 to W_1 for a unit is (the arrows represent cost flows, not the flow of goods):

	F_1	F_2	F_3
W_1...............	5	$\downarrow$	
W_2...............	$\uparrow$	$\downarrow$	
W_3...............	5	15	

The cost of shipping one unit from F_2 to W_1 by this indirect route is:

+$1.00......The charge for shipping from F_2 to W_3
− 1.30......Every unit F_2 sends to W_3 saves the cost
of supplying W_3 from F_1
+ 0.90......The charge for shipping from F_1 to W_1
+$0.60

The cost of presently avoiding box W_1F_2 is 60 cents (the additional outlay of $1.00 for using W_3F_2, the saving of $1.30 resulting from not using W_3F_1 to as large an extent as possible and the 90-cent cost of using box W_1F_1). Compared with this total indirect cost, 60 cents, is a cost of $1.00 which would result from using the direct route W_1F_2; thus the indirect route is to be preferred.

An alternative manner of describing the analysis is to say that the use of W_1F_2 would require the following change in the flow of goods:

	F_1	F_2	F_3
W_1..............	5	↑	
W_2..............		↓	↓
W_3..............	↓	5	

W_1F_1 could supply as many as five units to W_3F_1, and W_3F_2 could supply five units to W_1F_2. The net cost of this indirect route per unit is:

$$
\begin{aligned}
+\$1.00 &\ldots\ldots\ldots \text{Cost of } W_1F_2 \\
-\ 1.00 &\ldots\ldots\ldots \text{Saving of } W_3F_2 \\
+\ 1.30 &\ldots\ldots\ldots \text{Cost of } W_3F_1 \\
-\ 0.90 &\ldots\ldots\ldots \text{Saving of } W_1F_1 \\
\hline
+\$0.40 &\ldots\ldots\ldots \text{Net cost of the change.}
\end{aligned}
$$

The net cost of the change is positive; thus the change is not desirable. If the cost of the direct shipment ($1.00) is greater than the cost of the indirect shipment (60 cents), as in this case, the direct route should not be used (i.e., the zero entry should be retained). There can be only one indirect route for each zero box, unless the previous trial solution contained more than $F + W - 1$ direct routes.

The other zero boxes may be evaluated in a comparable manner. For example, the indirect shipment from F_2 to W_2 is the charge from F_2 to W_3 ($1.00) less the W_3F_1 charge ($1.30) plus the W_2F_1 charge ($1.00) = $0.70. Again, this is less than the cost of direct shipment ($1.40), so the current indirect route should be continued. The W_1F_3 box is also found to have a 70-cent cost for the indirect shipment; and again, this is less than the direct cost ($1.00). However, the evaluation of the last unused route, W_3F_3, yields an indirect cost of $0.80 - $1.00 + $1.30 = $1.10, and this is greater than the direct cost of 80 cents. The direct route W_3F_3 should be used rather than the indirect route of $W_2F_3 - W_2F_1 + W_3F_1$; a saving of

$$\$1.10 - \$0.80 = \$0.30$$

per unit can be made by using the direct route. (See Table 19–4.) How many units can be shifted from the indirect route to the

TABLE 19–4

Unused Route	Direct Cost	Indirect Cost
W_1F_2..........	$1.00	$0.60
W_1F_3..........	1.00	0.70
W_2F_2..........	1.40	0.70
W_3F_3..........	0.80	1.10

direct route? The answer is the minimum number in any of the connections of the indirect route which must supply units for the transfer. This is five units, from box W_3F_1. Thus, we ship five units by the direct route W_3F_3; since F_3 produces only ten units, this imposes a reduction in the W_2F_3 box to five. An additional five units now are required at warehouse 2. This deficiency is met readily by factory 1, which has been forced to reduce its shipment to W_3 by exactly five units as a result of W_3's new source of supply. The new pattern is shown in Table 19–5. Again, all of the unused routes, identified by

TABLE 19–5

Source / Destination	F_1	F_2	F_3	Units Demanded
W_1	$0.90 5	$1.00 0	$1.00 0	5
W_2	$1.00 15	$1.40 0	$0.80 5	20
W_3	$1.30 0	$1.00 15	$0.80 5	20
Units available......	20	15	10	45

the zero entries in Table 19–5, must be evaluated to see if a further reduction in cost is possible. This may be done in the now established manner shown in Table 19–6. In every case the cost of the indirect

TABLE 19–6

Unused Route	Direct Cost	Indirect Cost
W_3F_1..........	$1.30	$1.00
W_1F_2..........	1.00	0.90
W_2F_2..........	1.40	1.00
W_1F_3..........	1.00	0.70

route is less than the cost of the direct route, indicating that we are minimizing the shipment costs. The total cost of shipment from factories to warehouses is:

$$(5)(\$0.90) + (15)(\$1.00) + (15)(\$1.00) + 5(\$0.80) + 5(\$0.80) = \$42.50.$$

Note that the final solution uses five direct routes, where

$$F + W - 1 = 5$$

F plus W may be generalized and called the sum of the number of margin requirements, since we may be dealing with entities other than warehouses and factories.

DEGENERACY—BASIC METHOD

In some programming situations the problem of degeneracy appears. Degeneracy is caused by less than $F + W - 1$ boxes being used, which makes it impossible to evaluate a zero box by the direct methods described above.[3]

To resolve the degeneracy case, record some small amount, say d, in one of the zero boxes. We shall treat d as if it were a standard quantity, and therefore an eligible node for evaluating indirect routes. The box with the d entry may either ship or receive goods, but in the final solution the d is assigned a value of zero if it is still present in the calculations.

Degeneracy Example

Consider the same problem as previously discussed, but let us choose a first trial solution that is degenerate. Say the first solution is that shown in Table 19–7. Only four boxes are being used in this trial solution, but $W + F - 1 = 5$; thus the trial solution is de-

TABLE 19–7

Source \ Destination	F_1	F_2	F_3	Units Demanded
W_1	$0.90 \quad 0	$1.00 \quad 5	$1.00 \quad 0	5
W_2	$1.00 \quad 20	$1.40 \quad 0	$0.80 \quad 0	20
W_3	$1.30 \quad 0	$1.00 \quad 10	$0.80 \quad 10	20
Units available......	20	15	10	45

---

[3] Degeneracy may also occur where a factory ships its entire output to one warehouse and satisfies the total needs of that warehouse.

generate. The zero boxes cannot be evaluated without introducing d. Let us put d units in box W_1F_1, so that the shipping schedule appears as shown in Table 19–8. Total shipping cost for this example is $43.

TABLE 19–8

Source \ Destination	F_1	F_2	F_3	Units Demanded
W_1	d	5	0	$5 + d$
W_2	20	0	0	20
W_3	0	10	10	20
Units available.....	$20 + d$	15	10	$45 + d$

The zero boxes now may be evaluated in the established manner. Consider W_3F_1. The direct cost of shipping to W_3 from F_1 is $1.30. The indirect route is from F_1 to W_1, which may be used by virtue of the d, which permits a reduction of shipment from F_2 to W_1; but this, in turn, requires an increase in the shipment from F_2 to W_3. This completes the indirect shipment from F_1 to W_3, with these costs:

$$
\begin{array}{lr}
W_1F_1. \dots\dots\dots\dots\dots\dots\dots\dots\dots\dots\dots\dots\dots & \$0.90 \\
-W_1F_2. \dots\dots\dots\dots\dots\dots\dots\dots\dots\dots\dots\dots\dots & -1.00 \\
W_3F_2. \dots\dots\dots\dots\dots\dots\dots\dots\dots\dots\dots\dots\dots & 1.00 \\
\hline
\text{Cost of indirect shipment from } F_1 \text{ to } W_3. \dots\dots\dots & \$0.90
\end{array}
$$

This indirect cost is lower than the direct cost ($1.30); therefore the indirect route should continue to be used. The other zero boxes may be evaluated in the same manner, with the result shown in Table 19–9. The direct cost of using the zero box is in the upper left corner

TABLE 19–9

Source \ Destination	F_1	F_2	F_3
W_1			$1.00 \; / \; 0.80$
W_2		$1.40 \; / \; 1.10$	$0.80 \; / \; 0.90$
W_3	$1.30 \; / \; 0.90$		

of the box; the indirect cost of using the zero box is in the lower right of the zero box. The indirect cost exceeds the direct cost in only one instance, shipping from F_3 to W_2 (this indirect route is F_3 to W_3, less W_3F_2, plus W_1F_2, less W_1F_1, plus W_2F_1). This is the only place it pays to shift from the indirect to the direct route. The maximum amount which can be shifted is five units, since this is the minimum amount in a box which must be reduced (box W_1F_2). The new trial solution is shown in Table 19–10. The zero boxes of this trial solution must be

TABLE 19–10

Source / Destination	F_1	F_2	F_3	Units Demanded
W_1	$0.90 — 5	$1.00 — 0	$1.00 — 0	5
W_2	$1.00 — 15	$1.40 — 0	$0.80 — 5	20
W_3	$1.30 — 0	$1.00 — 15	$0.80 — 5	20
Units available......	20	15	10	45

evaluated. This procedure is not subject to degeneracy, for we now have five boxes being used, which meets the standard requirement. As was established before, all these zero boxes have direct costs which exceed their indirect costs, and exactly $F + W - 1$ boxes are being used; thus, this solution is optimal.

Same Example—Henderson-Schlaifer Method

Henderson and Schlaifer (1954) have developed a method for testing alternative routes which is more systematic than the basic method illustrated above. The same problem described in the previous section will be used to illustrate the Henderson-Schlaifer method.

Returning to the example in the beginning of this chapter, we shall prepare an array of costs using the direct costs where the warehouse-factory combination is used in the solution, and the indirect costs where the combination is not used (there is a line under each indirect cost).

Now, for each warehouse, take the difference between the amounts in columns F_1 and F_2, and note that for each line the dif-

	F_1	F_2	F_3
W_1............$0.90	$0.60	$0.70
W_2............ 1.00	0.70	0.80
W_3............ 1.30	1.00	1.10

ference is 30 cents. We can do the same for columns F_2 and F_3; note the difference for each line is 10 cents. The Henderson-Schlaifer method is a means of using these relationships to find the cost array reproduced above.[4]

The first trial solution appearing in Table 19–2 would apply here, just as it did in the basic method. Table 19–3 is now separated into three tables (Tables 19–11, 19–12a, and 19–12b). This is done to make the cost information more accessible for computation.

TABLE 19–11
Units—First Solution

Source / Destination	F_1	F_2	F_3	Units Demanded
W_1	5			5
W_2	10		10	20
W_3	5	15		20
Units available....	20	15	10	45

TABLE 19–12a
Unit Costs—First Solution

Source / Destination	F_1	F_2	F_3	Row Value
W_1	$0.90			$0.00
W_2	$1.00		$0.80	$0.10
W_3	$1.30	$1.00		$0.40
Column value........	$0.90	$0.60	$0.70	

[4] The reader is also referred to G. B. Dantzig's paper, "Applications of the Simplex Method to a Transportation Problem," in T. C. Koopmans (ed.), *Activity Analysis of Production and Allocation* (New York: John Wiley & Sons, Inc., 1951). This paper is the basis of the several procedures presented in this chapter.

TABLE 19–12b

Computation of Unit Costs—First Solution

Destination \ Source	F_1	F_2	F_3	Row Value	
W_1	$0.90			$0.00 ← ①	Arbitrary Choice
W_2	$1.00		$0.80	$0.10 ← ③	($1.00 − $0.90)
W_3	$1.30	$1.00		$0.40 ← ④	($1.30 − $0.90)
Column value.........	$0.90	$0.60	$0.70		

②   ⑤   ⑥
($0.90 − $0.00)   ($1.00 − $0.40)   ($0.80 − $0.10)

In order to start the calculation, the first-row value is arbitrarily chosen to be zero cents. Each cost figure in the body of Table 19–12a is equal to the sum of amounts in the margins of its row and its column. We have presented Table 19–12b to show the computation of the row values and column values. The steps are numbered in sequential order.

Table 19–13 shows the unit costs of all direct routes; the unit cost of indirect routes is calculated by summing the cost entries in the relevant column and row margins; these computations are shown in Table 19–13.

The next step is to compare the unit costs of each route as shown in Table 19–13 with the costs of Table 19–10. Comparison of the ta-

TABLE 19–13

Unit Costs and Cost Savings—First Solution

($0.60 + $0.10)   ($0.60 + $0.00)   ($0.70 + $0.00)

Destination \ Source	F_1	F_2	F_3	Row Value	
W_1	$0.90	$0.60	$0.70	$0.00	
W_2	$1.00	$0.70	$0.80	$0.10	
W_3	$1.30	$1.00	$1.10 ←	$0.40	($0.70 + $0.40)
Column value.....	$0.90	$0.60	$0.70		

bles shows that only one box of Table 19–13, W_3F_3, is larger than the comparable box of Table 19–10. Thus, that direct route is more desirable than the indirect route presently being used. The basic method indicated the same decision by means of the same calculations.

Table 19–14 shows the rearrangement of units shipped (X is the number of units transferred). The maximum size of X is five, if we

TABLE 19–14

Units

Add X units

Destination \ Source	F_1	F_2	F_3	Units Demanded	
W_1	5			5	
W_2	▼ $10 + X$		$10 - X$ ◄	20	
W_3	$5 - X$	15	X	20	Subtract X units
Units available....	20	15	10	45	

Subtract X units   Add X units

obey the requirement that no deliveries may be negative. Box W_3F_1 is the limiting factor, since it can supply only five units of product.

Table 19–15 shows the number of units shipped from each factory to each warehouse after the adjustment. Table 19–16 shows the unit costs of using the routes specified in Table 19–15. Table 19–17 adds the information concerning the cost saving which will result from using routes not presently being used.

TABLE 19–15

Units Shipped—Second Solution

Destination \ Source	F_1	F_2	F_3	Units Demanded
W_1	5			5
W_2	15		5	20
W_3		15	5	20
Units available....	20	15	10	45

TABLE 19–16

Cost per Unit—Second Solution

Destination \ Source	F_1	F_2	F_3	Row Value
W_1	$0.90			$0.00
W_2	$1.00		$0.80	$0.10 ◄─② ($1.00 − $0.90)
W_3		$1.00	$0.80	$0.10 ◄─④ ($0.80 − $0.70)
Column value..........	$0.90	$0.90	$0.70	

$$\underset{(\$0.90 - \$0.00)}{①} \qquad \underset{(\$1.00 - \$0.10)}{⑤} \qquad \underset{(\$0.80 - \$0.10)}{③}$$

TABLE 19–17

Cost per Unit and Cost Savings—Second Solution

($0.90 + $0.00)   ($0.90 + $0.10)

Destination \ Source	F_1	F_2	F_3	Row Value
W_1	$0.90	$0.90	$0.70 ◄	$0.00
W_2	$1.00	$1.00	$0.80	$0.10
W_3	►$1.00	$1.00	$0.80	$0.10
($0.90 + $0.10) Column value....	$0.90	$0.90	$0.70	

($0.70 + $0.00)

Box	From Table 19–17: Cost of Using Indirect Route	From Table 19–2: Cost of Using Direct Route	Net Profit (or Loss) of Using Direct Route
W_1F_2...............	$0.90	$1.00	$(0.10)
W_1F_3...............	0.70	1.00	(0.30)
W_2F_2...............	1.00	1.40	(0.40)
W_3F_1...............	1.00	1.30	(0.30)

None of the presently unused routes will reduce costs if they are substituted for currently employed routes. We have reached an optimum solution, as shown in Table 19–15.

Comparison of the two methods illustrated in this chapter reveals that they differ only in technique. The Henderson-Schlaifer method would seem to be simpler to execute, though the basic method tends more to connect the computations with their meaning. Both methods have the nice feature that an error made in one table may be eliminated in future tables.

In some situations the amount demanded will be less than the amount supplied. The solution is to introduce a destination—say, W_4—which is a fiction, but which receives the slack. A cost of zero may be placed in these slack boxes, since no transportation is involved.

DEGENERACY

In some situations, it is necessary to alter normal procedures because of degeneracy. When the problem is degenerate and the basic method is used, one of the zero boxes cannot be evaluated. That is, one of the boxes being tested for supplying units to the new box does not have any units to supply. In the Henderson-Schlaifer method of solution, degeneracy makes it impossible to complete the row and column values which are necessary to determine the cost savings of the routes which are currently not being used.

Alter the unit cost table so that it appears as shown in Table 19–18.

Let us choose the initial solution as shown in Table 19–19. This is consistent with choosing the best of each row and column (an arbitrary decision was made to supply twenty units of F_3 to W_2).

When the zero boxes are evaluated, difficulty is encountered, since the number of zero boxes is too great. The number of boxes (direct routes) used is less than $F + W - 1$. Now, in Table 19–20, we at-

TABLE 19–18

Unit Costs and Units Supplied and Demanded

Destination \ Source	F_1	F_2	F_3	Units Demanded
W_1	$0.90	$1.00	$1.00	5
W_2	$1.00	$1.40	$0.80	20
W_3	$1.30	$1.00	$0.80	20
Units available......	5	15	25	45

TABLE 19–19

First Solution

Source〰Destination	F_1	F_2	F_3	Units Demanded
W_1	5			5
W_2			20	20
W_3		15	5	20
Units available....	5	15	25	45

TABLE 19–20

Unit Costs

Source〰Destination	F_1	F_2	F_3	Row Value
W_1	$0.90			$0.00
W_2			$0.80	
W_3		$1.00	$0.80	
Column value........	$0.90			

($0.90 − $0.00)

tempt to compute the costs for the row and column margins; at the second computation, we are met with resistance. We must have an entry in either W_2F_1 or W_1F_2 to continue the calculations. Since there is no entry, we must improvise.[5]

TABLE 19–21

Units Shipped

Source〰Destination	F_1	F_2	F_3	Units Demanded
W_1	5			5
W_2	d		20	$20 + d$
W_3		15	5	20
Units available.....	$5 + d$	15	25	$45 + d$

---

[5] The method used here is somewhat different than the method suggested by Henderson and Schlaifer.

TABLE 19–22
Cost per Unit

Source / Destination	F_1	F_2	F_3	Row Value	
W_1	$0.90			$0.00	
W_2	$1.00		$0.80	$0.10	②($1.00 − $0.90)
W_3		$1.00	$0.80	$0.10	④($0.80 − $0.70)
Column value.........	$0.90	$0.90	$0.70		③($0.80 − $0.10)

①($0.90 − $0.00)   ⑤($1.00 − $0.10)

TABLE 19–23
Direct and Indirect Cost per Unit

Source / Destination	F_1	F_2	F_3	Row Value
W_1	$0.90	$0.90	$0.70	$0.00
W_2	$1.00	$1.00	$0.80	$0.10
W_3	$1.00	$1.00	$0.80	$0.10
Column value........	$0.90	$0.90	$0.70	

When the problem is degenerate, the "Units Shipped" table (Table 19–19) must be adjusted. The necessary adjustment is to store d, a very small amount, in the box W_2F_1. This change, as shown in Table 19–21, will allow us to complete the calculations. The cost table can then be completed, as shown in Table 19–22.

The completed direct and indirect cost table will be as shown in Table 19–23.

Comparison of Table 19–23 and Table 19–18 shows that no box in Table 19–23 is greater than the comparable box of Table 19–18, so we have reached an optimum solution (presented in Table 19–21).

Note that we solved the problem of degeneracy and finished the cost table by assuming a small amount of product to be present in box W_2F_1. The amount d is set equal to zero after the solution is obtained.

APPENDIX

THE TRANSPORTATION PROBLEM EXPRESSED IN CONVENTIONAL EQUATION FORM

F_1, F_2, and F_3 are the production capacities of three factories. W_1, W_2, and W_3 are the needs of three warehouses.

C_{11}, C_{12}, . . . , C_{ij}, . . . , C_{33} are the costs associated with factory i, supplying warehouse j.

The total transportation cost is f (we want to minimize f).

X_{ij} the amount transferred from the ith factory to the jth warehouse. This amount may be zero.

$$\text{Minimize:} \quad f = C_{11}X_{11} + C_{12}X_{12} + \ldots + C_{ij}X_{ij} + \ldots + C_{33}X_{33}$$
$$\text{Subject to:} \quad X_{11} + X_{12} + X_{13} \leq F_1$$
$$X_{21} + X_{22} + X_{23} \leq F_2$$
$$X_{31} + X_{32} + X_{33} \leq F_3$$
$$X_{11} + X_{21} + X_{31} = W_1$$
$$X_{12} + X_{22} + X_{32} = W_2$$
$$X_{13} + X_{23} + X_{33} = W_3.$$

All $X_{ij} \geq 0$. Note that the coefficients of all X_{ij} in the restraint equations will be either zero or one. Also, there are six restrictions. With the choice of five appropriate values of X_{ij}, we can effectively limit the choice of the rest of the X_{ij}'s; thus, $W + F - 1$ is the required number of positive values of X_{ij} in order to avoid degeneracy.

BIBLIOGRAPHY

See the Bibliography of Chapter 17.

PROBLEMS

19–1. Using the "basic" method of solving the transportation type of problem, prepare a table of optimum allocation of shipments from the factories to the warehouses:

Factories	Amount Available	Warehouses	Amount Needed
F_1.	10	W_1.	15
F_2.	20	W_2.	28
F_3.	30	W_3.	17
Total. . . .	60	Total. .	60

The costs of shipping are:

	F_1	F_2	F_3
W_1............	$0.90	$1.00	$1.05
W_2............	0.95	1.40	0.85
W_3............	1.30	0.95	1.10

19-2. Solve Problem 19–1 using the Henderson-Schlaifer method. Use the same first trial solution as you used in Problem 19–1.

19-3. Using the basic method of solution, prepare a table of optimum allocation of shipments from the factories to the warehouses:

Factories	Amount Available	Warehouses	Amount Needed
F_1..........	20	W_1........	10
F_2..........	15	W_2........	26
F_3..........	30	W_3........	29
Total....	65	Total..	65

The costs of shipping are:

	F_1	F_2	F_3
W_1............	$1.10	$1.20	$1.10
W_2............	1.12	1.00	0.90
W_3............	1.20	1.05	0.95

19-4. Solve Problem 19–3 using the Henderson-Schlaifer method. Use the same first trial solution as you used in Problem 19–3.

19-5. Using the basic method of solution, attempt to prepare a table of optimum allocation of shipments from the factories to the warehouses. Use the initial solution which is given.

Unit Costs and Units Supplied and Demanded

Source / Destination	F_1	F_2	F_3	Units Demanded
W_1	$0.80	$0.90	$1.00	10
W_2	$0.85	$0.70	$0.60	28
W_3	$1.45	$1.05	$1.15	22
Units available......	10	20	30	60

First Solution

Source \ Destination	F_1	F_2	F_3	Units Demanded
W_1	10			10
W_2		20	8	28
W_3			22	22
Units available....	10	20	30	60

19–6. Instead of using the first solution as given in Problem 19–5, solve Problem 19–5 starting from the solution given below:

First Solution

Source \ Destination	F_1	F_2	F_3	Units Demanded
W_1	5	5		10
W_2	5		23	28
W_3		15	7	22
Units available....	10	20	30	60

19–7. Solve Problem 19–5 using the Henderson-Schlaifer method. Use the same first trial solution as in Problem 19–5.

19–8. Three classifications of workers (P_1, P_2, P_3), may be used on three jobs (J_1, J_2, J_3). Each man has a different cost for each job, as follows:

Direct Costs

Source \ Destination	P_1	P_2	P_3	Workers Needed
J_1	$1.00	$0.90	$0.80	5
J_2	$1.10	$0.80	$0.85	10
J_3	$1.20	$1.10	$1.15	30
Workers available.....	10	15	20	45

The number of workers required on each job and the number of workers available are in the margins of the above table.

Use the basic method to find the optimum allocation.

19–9. Solve Problem 19–8 using the Henderson-Schlaifer method.

19–10. A firm has two factories that ship to three regional warehouses. The costs of transportation are:

Transportation Costs

	Factory	
Warehouse	F_1	F_2
W_1.........$2.00	$4.00
W_2......... 2.00	1.00
W_3......... 5.00	1.00

Factory 2 is old and has a variable manufacturing cost of $2.00 per unit. Factory 1 is modern and produces for $1.00 per unit. Factory 2 has a capacity of 25 units, and factory 1 has a capacity of 40 units. The needs at the warehouses are:

Warehouse	Need
W_1.............	20
W_2.............	10
W_3.............	25

How much should each factory ship to each warehouse? (Hint: Add the manufacturing cost to the transportation cost to obtain a "unit delivered" cost. Minimize this. Also, set up a dummy warehouse to handle the excess capacity.)

Chapter 20

WAITING LINES AND SIMULATION

QUEUES or waiting lines are very common in everyday life. There are few individuals in modern society who have not had to wait in line for a bus, a taxi, a "movie" ticket, a grocery check-out, a haircut, or registration material at the beginning of the school year. Most of us consider lines an unavoidable part of our civilized life, and we put up with them with more or less good humor. Occasionally, the size of a line or the wait we encounter discourages us, and we abandon the project, and a sale is lost by some enterprise. This chapter is concerned with the decision-making process of the business firm (or government agency) which has charge of the queue and makes decisions relative to the number of service facilities which are operating.

Queuing theory or waiting line theory is primarily concerned with processes which have the characteristics of having random arrivals (i.e., arrivals at random time intervals), and the servicing of the customer is also a random process. If we assume there are costs associated with waiting in line, and if there are costs of adding more channels (i.e., adding more service facilities), we want to minimize the sum of the costs of waiting and the costs of providing service facilities. The computations will lead to such measures as the expected number of people in line or the expected waiting time of the arrivals. These measures can then be used in the cost computations to determine the number of service facilities which are desirable.

Queuing theory may be applied to determining the optimum number of:

Toll booths for a bridge or toll road
Doctors available for clinic calls
Repairmen servicing machines
Landing strips for aircraft
Docks for ships
Clerks for a spare-parts counter
Windows for a post office.

The above are a few examples of the many different waiting line situations encountered by business managers.

EXPERIENCE AND QUEUES

Fortunately for the businessman, reasonable queuing decisions can frequently be made based on past experience or on the facts of the current situation. Thus the management of a grocery chain knows approximately how many check-out counters should be installed in a new store by looking at the experience of comparable stores. At any time of the day the store manager can tell how many of the installed counters should be manned by noting the lengths of the queues and adding personnel from other chores, or sending the present check-out personnel to other tasks. Also, historical records (say, of machine down time) can indicate the amount of time that machines had to queue for repairs rather than relying upon the computations resulting from a mathematical model to determine the amount of down time.

While a number of problems encountered by an executive can be reasonably solved by the use of intuition or past experience, there will be many situations which are too complex for our intuition or where we desire a more accurate answer than we can expect to be supplied by intuition. In these situations the problem can be approached by either simulation or a mathematical model procedure. We shall first investigate several mathematical models and then illustrate a simulation procedure.

MATHEMATICAL MODELS OF QUEUING

The presentation of this section has been designed so that no special mathematical knowledge is required. An Appendix to the chapter contains a derivation of a model, but we have not tried to show the origin of the formulas in the body of the chapter. We could consider the following types of situations:

1. Arrivals and services occurring following a given time schedule
2. Arrivals coming randomly from an infinite universe where there are:
   a) One service facility
   b) Multiple service facilities
3. Arrivals coming from a finite population where there are:
   a) One service facility
   b) Multiple service facilities

A solution to the first situation is to have the facilities exactly scheduled to meet the arrivals. A mass production assembly line could be an example of arrivals with a given time schedule.

Both single- and multiple-service facility situations will be illustrated for the situation where arrivals come from an infinite universe, but only the single-service facility situation will be explained if the arrivals come from a finite universe.

A SINGLE-SERVICE FACILITY: ARRIVALS FROM AN INFINITE POPULATION

To simplify the analysis, we shall first assume there is one channel or service facility. Those waiting accept service on a "first come, first served" basis and do not get discouraged by the length of the line (i.e., there is no balking and going elsewhere for service). We shall assume that arrivals and services are coming from an infinite universe and that the process for both arrivals and services is Poisson.[1] The assumptions are:

1. Arrivals are independent of each other. Services are also independent. That is, what happened in previous time periods is not relevant to the future (we can start at time t, or time t plus x, and it does not affect the probability of an arrival or of a service).
2. Both arrivals and services are homogeneous relative to time. That is, the average arrival and service rates do not change over time.

These assumptions may seem somewhat restrictive. Later, we shall relax the assumption of one channel and an infinite universe, but we shall retain the other assumptions in this chapter. The flavor of queuing theory may be gained for the described models, but the expert operations researcher has at his disposal many more models than the ones described in this chapter. However, the business manager should realize that any model will have to make assumptions about the probabilities of arrivals and services. There are three basic elements of uncertainty:

1. We may not know the exact probability distribution which applies.
2. Even if we know which probability distribution applies, we shall probably not know the parameters of the process.
3. If items 1 and 2 were known, we would still not know the actual outcome.

---

[1] See Appendix 1 of this chapter for a description of the Poisson process.

Thus, while the model builder may seem to come up with exact answers as a result of applying his model, there is a great deal of uncertainty associated with solutions. Even if the probability distribution were known (say, we knew the distribution was Poisson), and even if we knew the parameters of the process (say, we knew the mean), the output of the model would still be in the form of an expected value, and the distribution would have a variance. Thus, we are still solving a problem under conditions of uncertainty.

THE MODEL

We shall assume there is one service facility and the arrivals are emanating from an infinite universe. The arrivals and services occur in accordance with a Poisson process. Arrivals are served on a "first come, first served" basis. All the formulas assume the process has been operating long enough to reach an equilibrium. Let:

A = The average number of customers arriving in one unit of time
S = The average number of customers the service facility completes in one unit of time, assuming no shortage of customers
n = The number of units either being serviced or waiting in the system
w = The number in the queue (the number in the queue does not include the unit being serviced)
p_n = The probability of having n units in the system
t = The time an arrival must wait for service.

There are several relationships of interest:[2]

$$(20\text{-}1) \qquad\qquad p_0 = 1 - \frac{A}{S}$$

$$(20\text{-}2) \qquad\qquad p_n = \left(\frac{A}{S}\right)^n p_0$$

$$(20\text{-}3) \qquad\qquad p_n = \left(\frac{A}{S}\right) p_{n-1}.$$

The expected number in the waiting line or being serviced is:

$$(20\text{-}4) \qquad\qquad E(n) = \frac{A}{(S - A)}.$$

The expected number in the queue is:

$$(20\text{-}5) \qquad\qquad E(w) = \frac{A^2}{S(S - A)}.$$

---

[2] See Appendix 2 for the derivation of equation of 20-2.

The average waiting time (in the queue) of an arrival is:

(20–6)
$$E(t) = \frac{E(w)}{A}.$$

The probability that the number in the queue and being serviced is greater than n is:

(20–7)
$$P(N > n) = \left(\frac{A}{S}\right)^{n+1}.$$

Equations 20–1 to 20–7 apply only if $\frac{A}{S} < 1$. If the arrival rate, A, is greater than the service rate, the queue will grow without end.

Example

Assume patients for the medical office of a very large plant arrive randomly following a Poisson process. The office processes an average of five patients an hour. Patients arrive at an average of four per hour (we shall assume the process is Poisson, though this is not exact, since the population is not infinite, although it is very large). The plant operates twenty-four hours a day.

$$A = 4$$
$$S = 5.$$

Since $\frac{A}{S} < 1$, we can use the following relationships:

$$E(n) = \frac{A}{(S - A)} = \frac{4}{(5 - 4)} = 4.$$

There will be an average of four persons in line or being serviced.

$$E(w) = \frac{A^2}{S(S - A)} = \frac{4 \times 4}{5(5 - 4)} = \frac{16}{5} = 3.2.$$

There will be an average of 3.2 persons in line.

$$E(t) = \frac{E(w)}{A} = \frac{16/5}{4} = \frac{4}{5} = 0.8.$$

The average waiting time of a patient is 0.8 of an hour. All of the above measures assume the process has been operating long enough for the probabilities resulting from the physical characteristics of the problem to have made themselves felt; i.e., the system is in equilibrium.

We now know:

1. The average number of patients in the office is four.
2. The average number of patients waiting is 3.2.
3. A patient will wait for four fifths of an hour, on the average.

If we assume a 24-hour workday, there will be an average of 96 patients arriving per day, and the expected total time of patients lost waiting will be:

$$T = A \times 24 \text{ hours} \times E(t)$$
$$T = 4 \times 24 \times \tfrac{4}{5} = 76.8 \text{ hours.}$$

There will be a cost associated with these 76.8 hours. Assume the cost to the corporation is $10 for each hour lost by a worker waiting. The average cost per day from waiting is:

$$76.8 \times \$10 = \$768.$$

We can also compute the probability of different numbers of patients in the office being greater than different amounts. (See Table 20–1.)

TABLE 20–1

Number in Office: n	$P(N > n) = \left(\dfrac{A}{S}\right)^{n+1} = \left(\dfrac{4}{5}\right)^{n+1}$
0	0.8000
1	0.6400
2	0.5120
3	0.4096
4	0.3277
5	0.2621
6	0.2097

It may be that we want to limit the probability of a given occurrence. For example, if we are willing to accept a 0.41 probability that three or more persons will be in line, then one office is acceptable.

Suppose that we could in some fashion increase the service rate to six per hour. What would be the effect of this change?

With $S = 6$, the expected number in the queue, $E(w)$, is 1.3 instead of the 3.2 found above. This can be seen as follows:

$$E(w) = \frac{A^2}{S(S - A)} = \frac{4 \times 4}{6(6 - 4)} = \frac{16}{12} = 1.33.$$

The average wait for a patient is:

$$E(t) = \frac{E(w)}{A} = \frac{1.33}{4} = \tfrac{1}{3}.$$

The total waiting time per day for all patients is:

$$T = 4 \times 24 \times \tfrac{1}{3} = 32 \text{ hours per day.}$$

At the above cost of \$10 per hour, the total cost of waiting is \$320 per day. It would be worth \$448 per day (\$448 = \$768 − \$320) to the company to increase the service rate to six per hour.

Another approach which could be used to reduce the cost of \$768 per day for waiting would be to open another office (that is, another channel). This situation would involve a multiple-service facility.

MULTIPLE-SERVICE FACILITIES

We shall now assume there are C channels and there is one waiting line if all the service facilities are busy. Each channel has the same service rate, S. We shall again use n to represent the sum of the customers being served and in the waiting line.

(20–8)

$$p_0 = \left[\frac{(A/S)^C}{C! \left(1 - \dfrac{A/S}{C}\right)} + 1 + \frac{(A/S)^1}{1!} + \frac{(A/S)^2}{2!} + \cdots + \frac{(A/S)^{C-1}}{(C-1)!} \right]^{-1}$$

(20–9) $$p_n = p_0 \frac{(A/S)^n}{n!} \text{ if } n \le C$$

(20–10) $$p_n = p_0 \frac{(A/S)^n}{C! \, C^{n-C}} \text{ if } n > C.$$

We can use the above equations if $\dfrac{A}{S} < C$. If $\dfrac{A}{S} > C$, then the waiting line grows larger and larger; i.e., n becomes infinite if the process runs long enough.

When $C = 1$ (there is one service facility), equations 20–9 and 20–10 reduce to equation 20–2. From equation 20–9, we have:

$$p_n = p_0 \frac{(A/S)^n}{n!}.$$

But n can only take on values of zero or one if $n \le C = 1$; thus:

(20–2) $$p_n = p_0 \left(\frac{A}{S}\right)^n.$$

If $C = 1$, equation 20–10 also reduces to equation 20–2.

With C service facilities, the average number of customers in the queue is:

$$(20\text{–}11) \qquad E(w) = \frac{(A/S)^{C+1}}{C \cdot C! \left(1 - \frac{A/S}{C}\right)^2} \, p_0$$

and, as before, the expected waiting time for an arrival is:

$$(20\text{–}12) \qquad E(t) = \frac{E(w)}{A}.$$

Example

We shall continue the medical example of the previous section and consider the characteristics of the process if a second office is added.

$$A = 4$$
$$S = 5$$
$$C = 2$$
$$\frac{A}{S} = 0.8$$

$$p_0 = \cfrac{1}{\cfrac{(A/S)^C}{C!\left(1 - \cfrac{A/S}{C}\right)} + 1 + \cfrac{(A/S)^1}{1!} + \cdots + \cfrac{(A/S)^{C-1}}{(C-1)!}}$$

$$p_0 = \cfrac{1}{\cfrac{(0.8)^2}{2\left(1 - \cfrac{0.8}{2}\right)} + 1 + \cfrac{0.8}{1}} = \cfrac{1}{\cfrac{0.64}{1.2} + 1.8}$$

$$= \frac{1}{2.3} = 0.43.$$

For different values of n, we would obtain:

$$n = 1 \quad p_1 = p_0 \frac{(A/S)^n}{n!} = 0.43 \times \frac{0.8}{1} = 0.34 \qquad n \leq C$$

$$n = 2 \quad p_2 = 0.43 \times \frac{(0.8)^2}{2} = 0.13$$

$$n = 3 \quad p_3 = p_0 \frac{(A/S)^n}{C! C^{n-C}} = 0.43 \times \frac{0.8^3}{2 \times 2} = 0.06 \qquad n > C$$

$$n = 4 \quad p_4 = 0.43 \times \frac{0.8^4}{2 \times 2^2} = 0.02$$

$$n = 5 \quad p_5 = 0.43 \times \frac{0.8^5}{2 \times 2^3} = 0.01$$

The average number in the queue is shown in Table 20–2.

TABLE 20–2

n	p_n	np_n
0	0.43	0.00
1	0.34	0.34
2	0.13	0.26
3	0.06	0.18
4	0.02	0.08
5	0.01	0.05

Approximately 0.91
(ignoring the values greater than $n = 5$)

The expected number in the waiting line is:

$$E(w) = \frac{(0.8)^3}{2 \cdot 2\left(1 - \frac{0.8}{2}\right)^2} \times 0.43 = \frac{0.512 \times 0.43}{4 \times 0.36} = 0.15.$$

The expected waiting time is:

$$E(t) = \frac{E(w)}{A} = \frac{0.15}{4} = 0.0375 \text{ hours.}$$

We previously computed the average number of arrivals per day to be 96. The expected total time lost waiting is now:

$$T = A \times 24 \text{ hours} \times E(t)$$
$$= 4 \times 24 \times 0.0375 = 3.60 \text{ hours.}$$

Again assuming a cost of $10 for each hour, the average cost per day of waiting is:

$$3.60 \times \$10 = \$36.$$

There has been a saving in expected cost of $732 (i.e., $768 − $36). If the cost of adding the second office is less than $732 per day, then the decision should be to go from one to two offices. We could also consider adding a third office; but since the expected cost of waiting is now only $36 per day, the adding of a third office is not likely to be worth while from an economic standpoint.

ONE-SERVICE FACILITY: ARRIVALS FROM A FINITE SOURCE

Assume a situation where one repairman is servicing m machines. The Poisson probability law does not apply, since the arrivals are not independent.

A = Average number of machines needing repairs during a unit time period

$S =$ Average number of machines that can be repaired in a unit of time, assuming machines are available for repair

$\dfrac{A}{S} =$ Service factor, and $\dfrac{A}{S} < 1$

$m =$ Total number of machines
$n =$ Number of machines being serviced plus the queue
$k =$ Number of machines operating.

The probability of all m machines waiting or being serviced, assuming the process has been operating long enough to reach a period of equilibrium, is:

$$(20\text{-}13) \qquad p_m = \left\{ 1 + \frac{1}{1!}\left(\frac{S}{A}\right)^1 + \cdots + \frac{1}{m!}\left(\frac{S}{A}\right)^m \right\}^{-1}.$$

The probability of $m - k$ machines waiting or being serviced is:

$$(20\text{-}14) \qquad p_{m-k} = \frac{1}{k!}\left(\frac{S}{A}\right)^k p_m.$$

The expected number of machines in the waiting line is:

$$(20\text{-}15) \qquad E(w) = m - \frac{A + S}{A}(1 - p_0).$$

The average time spent by a machine in the waiting line is:

$$(20\text{-}16) \qquad E(t) = \frac{1}{S}\left(\frac{m}{1 - p_0} - \frac{1 + \dfrac{A}{S}}{\dfrac{A}{S}} \right).$$

Example 1

There is one repairman servicing three machines.

$$A = \text{One machine per day}$$
$$S = \text{Ten machines per day}$$
$$\frac{A}{S} = 0.1$$
$$\frac{S}{A} = 10$$
$$\frac{A}{S} < 1$$
$$m = \text{Three machines}$$

$$(20\text{-}17) \qquad p_m = \left\{ 1 + \frac{1}{1}\left(\frac{S}{A}\right)^1 + \cdots \frac{1}{m!}\left(\frac{S}{A}\right)^m \right\}^{-1}$$

$$p_3 = \left\{1 + (10) + \frac{1}{2}(10)^2 + \frac{1}{3 \cdot 2}(10)^3\right\}^{-1}$$

$$= \{228\}^{-1} = \frac{1}{228}.$$

Table 20–3 shows the computation of p_{m-k}.

TABLE 20–3

k	$\frac{1}{k!}(10)^k\frac{1}{228}$	$= p_{m-k}$	
0...................	$\frac{1}{228}$	$\frac{1}{228}$	p_3
1...................	$10 \times \frac{1}{228}$	$\frac{10}{228}$	p_2
2...................	$\frac{1}{2}(10)^2 \times \frac{1}{228}$	$\frac{50}{228}$	p_1
3...................	$\frac{1}{(3 \cdot 2)}(10)^3 \times \frac{1}{228}$	$\frac{167}{228}$	p_0
Total...........		$\frac{228}{228}$	

The expected number of machines in the waiting line is:

(20–18)

$$E(w) = m - \frac{A + S}{A}(1 - p_0)$$

$$= 3 - \frac{11}{1}\left(1 - \frac{167}{228}\right) = 3 - 11\left(\frac{61}{228}\right) = 3 - 2.94 = 0.06.$$

The average time spent waiting is:

(20–19) $$E(t) = \frac{1}{S}\left(\frac{m}{1 - p_0} - \frac{1 + \frac{A}{S}}{\frac{A}{S}}\right)$$

$$= \frac{1}{10}\left(\frac{3}{\frac{61}{228}} - \frac{1.1}{0.1}\right) = \frac{1}{10}(11.21 - 11) = 0.021 \text{ days.}$$

Example 2

In the second example the likelihood of breakdown will be increased. There is one repairman servicing three machines.

$$A = \text{Two machines per day}$$
$$S = \text{Two and one-half machines per day}$$

$m = $ Three machines

$$\frac{A}{S} = 0.8$$

$$\frac{S}{A} = 1.25$$

$$\frac{A}{S} < 1.$$

$$p_m = \left\{1 + (1.25)^1 + \frac{1}{2}(1.25)^2 + \frac{1}{6}(1.25)^3\right\}^{-1}$$
$$= \{1 + 1.25 + 0.7812 + 0.3255\}^{-1}$$
$$= (3.36)^{-1} = \frac{1}{3.36} = 0.298.$$

TABLE 20–4

k	$\frac{1}{k!}(1.25)^k 0.298$	$= p_{m-k}$	
0....................	0.298	0.298	p_3
1....................	1.25×0.298	0.372	p_2
2....................	$\frac{1}{2} \times 1.25^2 \times 0.298$	0.233	p_1
3....................	$\frac{1}{6} \times 1.25^3 \times 0.298$	0.097	p_0
		1.000	

$$E(w) = m - \frac{A+S}{A}(1 - p_o) = 3 - \frac{4.5}{2}(0.903) = 3 - 2.03 = 0.97.$$

$$E(t) = \frac{1}{S}\left(\frac{m}{1 - p_o} - \frac{1 + \frac{A}{S}}{\frac{A}{S}}\right) = \frac{1}{2.5}\left(\frac{3}{0.903} - \frac{1.8}{0.8}\right)$$

$$= \frac{1}{2.5}(3.32 - 2.25) = \frac{1}{2.5}(1.07) = 0.44.$$

The average waiting time is 0.44 days. Machines are breaking down at the rate of two per day, so the average time lost per day is 2×0.44, or 0.88 equipment-days. Assuming a value per equipment-day of $100 per machine, this would be a waiting cost of $88 (i.e., $0.88 \times \$100$).

If we discard the assumption that the process is Poisson and constant parameters, or increase the number of service facilities and the number of units being serviced, we may find it easier to use the simulation technique rather than a mathematical solution.

SIMULATION

It is generally accepted practice that an airplane manufacturer will test a scale model of a new type of aircraft in an air tunnel before building a full-sized plane. Flood control measures are frequently tested on scale models before the actual projects are carried out. In recent years, techniques for testing the results of some business decisions before they are actually executed have been developed. The anticipated actual business processes are simulated using either manual labor (pencil, paper, and desk calculator) or large electronic computers. The electronic computers have the advantage of being able to handle large amounts of data rapidly. However, the basic procedure is independent of how the computations are made.

Waiting line problems of the type discussed previously in this chapter could be analyzed by building such an artificial or simulation model. Where we can adequately solve the problem by mathematical methods, it is generally preferable to do so. There are many queuing situations which cannot be solved easily by mathematics, and hence we must resort to simulation.

Consider, as an example, a warehouse that has one dock which is used to unload railroad freight cars. Incoming freight cars are delivered to the warehouse during the night. It takes exactly half a day to unload a car. If more than two cars are waiting to be unloaded on a given day, some are postponed until the following day.

Past experience has indicated that the number of cars arriving during the night have the frequencies shown in Table 20–5.

TABLE 20–5

x Number of Cars Arriving	$f(x)$ Relative Frequency
0	0.23
1	0.30
2	0.30
3	0.10
4	0.05
5	0.02
6 or more	0.00
	1.00

Average $= E(x) = 1.5$ cars per night

Furthermore, there is no apparent pattern, so that the number arriving on any night is independent of the number arriving on any other night.

This is a one-channel queuing problem with a service rate of two per day and an arrival rate of 1.5 per day. However, it can be shown that the arrivals are not Poisson; and the services clearly are not, since the service time is fixed at exactly half a day. Hence the queuing model presented before does not apply.

The first step in simulating this queuing process is to generate a history or time series of arrivals for a number of nights. One way to do this would be to take 100 chips and write the number "0" on 23 of them; the number "1" on 30 of them; the number "2" on 30 of them; and so on, corresponding to the frequences in Table 20–5. We could then draw a chip from the hat, and the number on the chip would indicate the number of freight cars arriving in a given simulated period.

A simpler procedure is to use a table of random numbers such as Table 20–6. Each entry in Table 20–6 was drawn in such a way that each digit (zero through nine) had an equal chance of being drawn.

We could then assign two-digit random numbers to each of the possible outcomes (i.e., to the number of arrivals) as shown in Table 20–7.

There are 100 two-digit pairs of numbers. Note that 23 are assigned to the event "zero cars arrive"; 30 to the event "one car arrives"; 30 to the event "two cars arrive"; etc. Since each two-digit number has a 1/100 chance of coming up, the probability that the event "zero cars arrive" will occur is 23/100, or 0.23.

We are now prepared to simulate the queuing process. This is done in Table 20–8.

Three days are used to start the process (marked "x"). For the first day, the random number (taken from Table 20–6) is 97 (assume the table is entered randomly). Since 97 corresponds to the event "four cars arrive" in Table 20–7, we list four in the third column. Of these four cars, two are unloaded, and two are postponed until the following day. The random number for the second day is 02 (again from Table 20–6). This means zero cars arriving, and the two cars from the previous day are unloaded. We continue in the same fashion.

Table 20–8 simulates 50 days' operations (in addition to the three days to get started). During most of the period, there is little delay. Note that there is, however, considerable delay starting around period 36. The average number of arrivals per day (1.58) over the 50 days is slightly larger than the expected average (1.50). On the average, 0.90 cars are delayed per day. For more accurate results, the simulation could be carried on for more days.

We could use the simulation model in much the same way that we

TABLE 20–6
Table of Random Digits

97	95	12	11	90	49	57	13	86	81
02	92	75	91	24	58	39	22	13	02
80	67	14	99	16	89	96	63	67	60
66	24	72	57	32	15	49	63	00	04
96	76	20	28	72	12	77	23	79	46
55	64	82	61	73	94	26	18	37	31
50	02	74	70	16	85	95	32	85	67
29	53	08	33	81	34	30	21	24	25
58	16	01	91	70	07	50	13	18	24
51	16	69	67	16	53	11	06	36	10
04	55	36	97	30	99	80	10	52	40
86	54	35	61	59	89	64	97	16	02
24	23	52	11	59	10	88	68	17	39
39	36	99	50	74	27	69	48	32	68
47	44	41	86	83	50	24	51	02	08
60	71	41	25	90	93	07	24	29	59
65	88	48	06	68	92	70	97	02	66
44	74	11	60	14	57	08	54	12	90
93	10	95	80	32	50	40	44	08	12
20	46	36	19	47	78	16	90	59	64
86	54	24	88	94	14	58	49	80	79
12	88	12	25	19	70	40	06	40	31
42	00	50	24	60	90	69	60	07	86
29	98	81	68	61	24	90	92	32	68
36	63	02	37	89	40	81	77	74	82
01	77	82	78	20	72	35	38	56	89
41	69	43	37	41	21	36	39	57	80
54	40	76	04	05	01	45	84	55	11
68	03	82	32	22	80	92	47	77	62
21	31	77	75	43	13	83	43	70	16
53	64	54	21	04	23	85	44	81	36
91	66	21	47	95	69	58	91	47	59
48	72	74	40	97	92	05	01	61	18
36	21	47	71	84	46	09	85	32	82
55	95	24	85	84	51	61	60	62	13
70	27	01	88	84	85	77	94	67	35
38	13	66	15	38	54	43	64	25	43
36	80	25	24	92	98	35	12	17	62
98	10	91	61	04	90	05	22	75	20
50	54	29	19	26	26	87	94	27	73

TABLE 20–7

Number of Cars Arriving	Random Digits	Relative Frequency
0..............	00 to 22	0.23
1..............	23 to 52	0.30
2..............	53 to 82	0.30
3..............	83 to 92	0.10
4..............	93 to 97	0.05
5..............	98 and 99	0.02
		1.00

TABLE 20–8

Day Number	Random Number	Number of Arrivals	Total Number to Be Unloaded	Number Unloaded	Number Delayed to Following Day
x..........	97	4	4	2	2
x..........	02	0	2	2	0
x..........	80	2	2	2	0
1..........	66	2	2	2	0
2..........	96	4	4	2	2
3..........	55	2	4	2	2
4..........	50	1	3	2	1
5..........	29	1	2	2	0
6..........	58	2	2	2	0
7..........	51	1	1	1	0
8..........	04	0	0	0	0
9..........	86	3	3	2	1
10..........	24	1	2	2	0
11..........	39	1	1	1	0
12..........	47	1	1	1	0
13..........	60	2	2	2	0
14..........	65	2	2	2	0
15..........	44	1	1	1	0
16..........	93	4	4	2	2
17..........	20	0	2	2	0
18..........	86	3	3	2	1
19..........	12	0	1	1	0
20..........	42	1	1	1	0
21..........	29	1	1	1	0
22..........	36	1	1	1	0
23..........	01	0	0	0	0
24..........	41	1	1	1	0
25..........	54	2	2	2	0
26..........	68	2	2	2	0
27..........	21	0	0	0	0
28..........	53	2	2	2	0
29..........	91	3	3	2	1
30..........	48	1	2	2	0
31..........	36	1	1	1	0
32..........	55	2	2	2	0
33..........	70	2	2	2	0
34..........	38	1	1	1	0
35..........	36	1	1	1	0
36..........	98	5	5	2	3
37..........	50	1	4	2	2
38..........	95	4	6	2	4
39..........	92	3	7	2	5
40..........	67	2	7	2	5
41..........	24	1	6	2	4
42..........	76	2	6	2	4
43..........	64	2	6	2	4
44..........	02	0	4	2	2
45..........	53	2	4	2	2
46..........	16	0	2	2	0
47..........	16	0	0	0	0
48..........	55	2	2	2	0
49..........	54	2	2	2	0
50..........	23	1	1	1	0
Totals..		79			45
Average		1.58			0.90

used mathematical waiting line models. That is, we can compare the effects of feasible alternatives upon waiting time and cost. For example, in this case we could compare delays under the current service rate of two per day with a service rate of three per day. Or we could introduce one or more additional channels.

SIMULATION AND INVENTORY CONTROL

The use of simulation is not restricted to the use of queuing processes. Many phases of business operations have been simulated with successful results. We shall illustrate by a brief example how simulation could be applied to the solution of an inventory problem.

Suppose that the weekly demand of a certain product has the distribution shown in Table 20–9.

TABLE 20–9

Number Demanded	Probability	Random Numbers Assigned
0.	0.10	00 to 09
1.	0.40	10 to 49
2.	0.30	50 to 79
3.	0.20	80 to 99
	1.00	

When an order is placed to replenish inventory, there is a delivery lag which is a random variable, as shown in Table 20–10.

TABLE 20–10

Number of Weeks from Order to Delivery	Probability	Random Numbers Assigned
2.	0.20	00 to 19
3.	0.60	20 to 79
4.	0.20	80 to 99
	1.00	

We would like to determine an order quantity, Q, and an order point, R. We can do this by trying several values of Q and R, and simulating to determine the best.

An illustration with $Q = 15$ and $R = 5$ is shown in Table 20–11.

TABLE 20–11

Inventory Simulation Illustration

Week Number	Re-ceipts	Begin-ning Inven-tory	Ran-dom Num-ber	Sales (Units)	Ending Inven-tory	Lost Sales (Out-ages)	Orders	Random Number for Orders	Number of Weeks Hence When Order Will Arrive
0..........	15	15	11	1	14				
1..........		14	91	3	11				
2..........		11	99	3	8				
3..........		8	57	2	6				
4..........		6	28	1	5		15	61	3
5..........		5	70	2	3				
6..........		3	33	1	2				
7..........	15	17	91	3	14				
8..........		14	67	2	12				
9..........		12	97	3	9				
10..........		9	61	2	7				
11..........		7	11	1	6				
12..........		6	50	2	4		15	86	4
13..........		4	25	1	3				
14..........		3	06	0	3				
15..........		3	60	2	1				
16..........	15	16	80	3	13				
17..........		13	19	1	12				
18..........		12	88	3	9				
19..........		9	25	1	8				
20..........		8	24	1	7				
21..........		7	68	2	5		15	37	3
22..........		5	78	2	3				
23..........		3	37	1	2				
24..........	15	17	04	0	17				
25..........		17	32	1	16				
26..........		16	75	2	14				
27..........		14	21	1	13				
28..........		13	47	1	12				
29..........		12	40	1	11				
30..........		11	71	2	9				
31..........		9	85	3	6				
32..........		6	88	3	3		15	15	2
33..........		3	24	1	2				
34..........	15	17	61	2	15				
35..........		15	19	1	14				
36..........		14	90	3	11				
37..........		11	24	1	10				
38..........		10	16	1	9				
39..........		9	32	1	8				
40..........		8	72	2	6				
Totals....		412				0			
Average		10.3							

We assume that no back orders are allowed. If we established the cost of ordering, the cost of holding inventory, and the cost of being out of stock, we could estimate the cost of the inventory system under the rule $Q = 15$, $R = 5$. Alternative rules could be compared to this.

Simulation is a powerful tool of analysis and business decision making. By constructing a model of a business process, we can analyze different courses of action. We should do this when the causal relationships are too complex to yield simple analytical solutions. Even where a mathematical solution is possible, simulation may be a cheaper and quicker method than analysis by pure mathematical means.

APPENDIX 1

THE POISSON PROCESS AND DISTRIBUTION

In a Poisson process the probability of occurrence of a success or failure is constant, and the occurrence of a success or failure is independent of what has happened immediately preceding the present observation. We may be interested in what happens over a continuous interval. This interval might be a measure of distance—for example, a yard or a unit of time such as a day. Printing errors per page of a book is an example of a process which may be Poisson; other examples are the manufacturing of textiles, rolled steel, pipe, wire, etc., where there are X defects per unit measure of product.

The sales for a product may behave like a Poisson process. Suppose we have had 1,500 individual sales of one unit of product per person during the last fifty weeks, or an average sale of 30 per week. We may wish to know the probability of different weekly sales in the next five weeks.

The Poisson probability distribution applied to a Poisson process gives the probability of a number of successes in a measure of distance or time, given that we know (1) the probability of a success *per unit* of distance or time and (2) the length of distance or time. Suppose we use the symbol L to be the expected number of successes per unit measure, i.e., the intensity of the process.[3] Examples of L are 60 units of sales per month, two units of sales per day, 25 telephone calls per hour, three defects per 100 feet of pipe, etc. We shall

---

[3] Frequently in literature in this area the Greek letter λ (lambda) is used to represent the process intensity.

let t be the unit of time or space during which successes are to be counted. For example:

$$P_{po}(R = r|L, t) = \frac{e^{-Lt}(Lt)^r}{r!}$$

is the Poisson probability of r defects during time t when the average number of defects per unit of time is L.

In using the Poisson probability distribution, we may combine L and t by multiplication to obtain m; i.e., $m = Lt$, where m is the expected number of successes in the specified time period. We *expect* m successes in a specified time, t. For example, if $L = 2$ (the average number of successes per week) and $t = 5$ (the time period is five weeks), the average number of successes per five-week period is $2 \cdot 5 = 10$. The variance of a Poisson distribution is also m, so the standard deviation is $\sqrt{m}$.

If the number of Bernoulli trials, n, is large, and if p, the probability of success, is small, the Poisson probability distribution may be used as an approximation to the binomial probability distribution in obtaining solutions to problems involving Bernoulli trials. This approximation is especially useful when n is large, since the computations involved in solving the binomial problem become tedious (even with a computer).

THE EXPONENTIAL DISTRIBUTION

In connection with the Poisson process, we have discussed the Poisson probability distribution, which gives the probability of the number of occurrences (successes or defectives), given an intensity

FIGURE 20–1

Exponential Probability Density Function

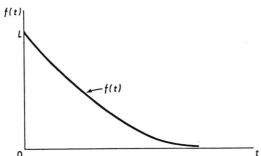

L and a certain time period t.[4] For the same process, we could ask about the waiting time until the first success. In other words, what is the time, t, to the first occurrence? This probability distribution is called the exponential distribution (see Figure 20–1).[5] The right-hand tail of the exponential distribution is:[6]

$$P(T > t) = e^{-m}$$

That is, the probability that the first occurrence will take place after a time lapse of t is e^{-m}. Note that this is also the value of a Poisson mass function for zero occurrences.

APPENDIX 2

DERIVATION OF BASIC QUEUING FORMULA

We want to derive the relationship:

$$p_n = \left(\frac{A}{S}\right)^n p_0.$$

Assume arrivals and services occur in accordance with a Poisson process. There is one service facility with a single "first come, first served" queue. Let:

A = Average number arriving in one unit of time.
S = Average number the station can service in one unit of time.
n = Number of units in the system either being serviced or waiting.
Sh = Probability of a service in time period h.
$P_n(t)$ = Probability of having n units in the system at time t.

---

[4] The Poisson mass function is:
$$P_{po}(R = r \,|\, L, t) = e^{-m} \frac{m^r}{r!}$$

If $r = 0$, then:

$$P_{po}(R = 0 | L, t) = e^{-m}$$

i.e., the probability of no successes in time t is e^{-m}.
   If $r = 1$, then:
$$P_{po}(R = 1 | L, t) = me^{-m}$$

i.e., the probability of one success in time t is me^{-m}.

[5] The exponential probability density function is:
$$f(t) = Le^{-m}.$$

$$[6] \int_t^\infty Le^{-Lx}dx = -e^{-Lx}\Big|_t^\infty = 0 + e^{-Lt} = e^{-Lt} = e^{-m}.$$

p_n = Probability of having n units in the system, assuming equilibrium.

Ah = Probability of an arrival during time period h, when h is very small.

Computation of $P_1(h)$:

$$P_n(h) = \frac{(Ah)^n e^{-Ah}}{n!}$$

$$P_1(h) = Ah\, e^{-Ah}.$$

If h is very small, e^{-Ah} goes to one, and

$$P_1(h) = Ah.$$

We can reasonably assume that the probability of more than one change during time period h is very close to zero; to simplify the development, we shall assume it actually to be zero (i.e., the probability of two or more services or arrivals or a service and arrival is zero). Thus:

$$1 - Ah - Sh = \text{Probability of No Changes.}$$

We can reach state n (i.e., n units in the system) by one of four events occurring as follows:

Event (a)—Be at n, and no change occurs.
Event (b)—Be at $n - 1$, and have an arrival take place.
Event (c)—Be at $n + 1$, and have a service.
Event (d)—Be at $n - y$ or $n + y$, and have y changes take place when $y > 1$ (we have assumed the probability of this event to be zero).

Since the events a, b, and c are mutually exclusive events, we may add their probabilities:

$$P_n(t + h) = P(a) + P(b) + P(c).$$

(20-20)
$$P_n(t + h) = P_n(t)(1 - Ah - Sh) + P_{n-1}(t)(Ah) + P_{n+1}(t)(Sh)$$
(20-21)
$$\frac{P_n(t + h) - P_n(t)}{h} = -(A + S)P_n(t) + AP_{n-1}(t) + SP_{n+1}(t).$$

Rearranging terms and letting h approach zero:

(20-22) $$\frac{dP_n(t)}{dt} = AP_{n-1}(t) - (A + S)P_n(t) + SP_{n+1}(t)$$

In equilibrium, $\dfrac{dP_n(t)}{dt} = 0$, and we obtain:

$$(20\text{--}23) \qquad p_{n+1} = -\frac{A}{S} p_{n-1} + \frac{A+S}{S} p_n.$$

Returning to equation 20–20:

$$(20\text{--}24) \quad P_n(t+h) = P_n(t)(1 - Ah - Sh) + P_{n-1}(t)(Ah) + P_{n+1}(t)(Sh).$$

If we solve for $P_0(t+h)$, then $n = 0$, and $P_{n-1}(t) = 0$, and we obtain:

$$(20\text{--}25) \qquad P_0(t+h) = P_0(t)(1 - Ah - Sh) + P_1(t)(Sh)$$

Subtract $P_0(t)$ from both sides and divide by h:

$$(20\text{--}26) \qquad \frac{P_0(t+h) - P_0(t)}{h} = -(A+S)P_0(t) + SP_1(t)$$

With zero customers a service is impossible, and $SP_0(t) = 0$; thus:

$$(20\text{--}27) \qquad \frac{P_0(t+h) - P_0(t)}{h} = -AP_0(t) + SP_1(t) .$$

In equilibrium, this last equation is equal to zero as h goes to zero:

$$-Ap_0 + Sp_1 = 0$$
$$(20\text{--}28) \qquad p_1 = \frac{A}{S} p_0 .$$

Using equation 20–23, we obtain:

$$(20\text{--}29) \qquad p_2 = -\frac{A}{S} p_0 + \frac{A+S}{S} p_1 .$$

Substituting $\dfrac{A}{S} p_0$ for p_1:

$$-\frac{A}{S} p_0 + \frac{A+S}{S} \left(\frac{A}{S} p_0\right) = \left(-\frac{AS}{S^2} + \frac{A^2 + AS}{S^2}\right) p_0 = \frac{A^2}{S^2} p_0 = \left(\frac{A}{S}\right)^2 p_0.$$

Continuing this procedure, we find:

$$(20\text{--}30) \qquad p_n = \left(\frac{A}{S}\right)^n p_0 .$$

The reader interested in further derivations is referred to W. Feller, *An Introduction to Probability Theory and Its Applications;* and

A. Kaufman, *Methods and Models of Operations Research* (see the Bibliography that follows for these references and others).

BIBLIOGRAPHY

BELLMAN, R. "Top Management Decision and Simulation Processes," *Journal of Industrial Engineering*, September-October, 1958.

FELLER, W. *An Introduction to Probability Theory and Its Applications.* 2d ed. New York: John Wiley & Sons, Inc., 1957.

FISHER, R. A., and YATES, F. *Statistical Tables for Biological, Agricultural and Medical Research.* London: Oliver & Boyd, Ltd., 1943.

GALLIHER, H. P. "Simulation of Random Processes," in *Notes on Operations Research, 1959.* Cambridge: Technology Press, 1959.

HARLING, J. "Simulation Techniques in Operations Research—A Review," *Operations Research*, May-June, 1958.

KAUFMAN, A. *Methods and Models of Operations Research.* Englewood Cliffs, N.J.: Prentice-Hall, Inc., 1963.

MEYER, H. A. (ed.). *Symposium on Monte Carlo Methods.* London: Chapman & Hall, Ltd., 1956. New York: John Wiley & Sons, Inc., 1956.

RAND CORPORATION. *A Million Random Digits.* Glencoe, Ill.: Free Press, Inc., 1955.

SAATY, T. L. *Elements of Queueing Theory.* New York: McGraw-Hill Book Co., Inc., 1961.

SIMON, H. A., and NEWELL, A. "Heuristic Problem Solving: The Next Advance in OR," *Operations Research*, January-February, 1958.

PROBLEMS

20–1. Ace Airline has one reservations clerk on duty at a time. He handles information about flight schedules and makes reservations. All calls to Ace Airline are answered by an operator. If a caller requests information or reservations, the operator transfers the call to the reservations clerk. If the clerk is busy, the operator asks the caller to wait. When the clerk becomes free, the operator transfers to him the call of the person who has been waiting the longest.

Assume that arrivals and services follow a Poisson process. Calls arrive at a rate of ten per hour, and the reservations clerk can service a call in four minutes, on the average (that is, $S = 15$ per hour).

a) What is the average number of calls waiting to be connected to the reservations clerk?

b) What is the average time a caller must wait before reaching the reservations clerk?

c) What is the average time for a caller to complete a call (i.e., waiting time plus service time)?

20–2. Refer to Problem 20–1 above. Suppose that the management of Ace Airline is considering installing some visual display equipment and a new reservations system. One of the benefits of this system is that it will reduce the average time required to service a call from four to three minutes.

a) What would be the average number of calls waiting to be connected to the reservations clerk if this new system were installed?

b) What would be the expected waiting time before a caller was connected to the reservations clerk with the new system?

20–3. Refer to Problems 20–1 and 20–2. Suppose that instead of installing a new reservations system, Ace Airline was considering adding a second reservations clerk. The telephone operator could then refer calls to whichever clerk was free.

a) What would then be the average number of calls waiting to be connected to a reservations clerk?

b) What would then be the expected waiting time before a caller was connected to a reservations clerk?

20–4. Refer to Problem 20–3 above. Suppose that the cost of manning an additional station would be $50 per day. Ace Airline is undecided about incurring this additional cost.

a) If the good will cost of having a customer wait is 10 cents per minute spent waiting (before being connected to a clerk), should Ace Airline add the second clerk?

b) At what good will cost would Ace Airline be indifferent as to whether or not to add the second clerk?

c) What assumption is made about the expected number of calls for each hour of the day?

20–5. Two typists have identical jobs. Each types letters dictated by a manager. Suppose that letters to be typed arrive at random (following a Poisson process) at a rate of three per hour for each typist. Suppose that each typist can type four letters per hour, on the average (also a Poisson process).

a) Assuming that each typist does her own work, what is the expected waiting time for a letter (time before work is started on a letter)?

b) Suppose that the two typists are "pooled." That is, letters are sent to the two together and are done by whoever is free, in the order of arrival. What is the expected waiting time for a letter under this arrangement?

c) Comment on this example.

20–6. The Speedo Computer Company maintains a technical repair man to service the five Speedo electronic computers that are located in Bay City. Speedo receives a rental of $100 per hour on each of these computers. This fee is paid only for the number of hours that the computers are operative and excludes down time (time spent awaiting repair).

Past experience shows that a Speedo computer develops trouble and needs repair about once in five days. Hence, with the five computers in Bay City, requests for repair are made on an average of one per day ($A = 1$). The time required to repair a computer, on the average, takes about one third of a day (i.e., $S = 3$).

a) What is the expected total amount of machine down time per week? Include repair time as well as waiting time. Also, assume an eight-hour day, five-day week for both the computers and the service man.

b) Suppose that some new diagnostic equipment could be developed that would enable the service man to repair four computers per day (instead of the three above). How much would this equipment be worth per week to Speedo?

20–7. a) Using the same history of arrivals shown in Table 20–8, simulate the waiting line process of the warehouse-railroad car example on pages 340–43 with a known service rate of three per day.

b) Assuming that the warehouse company pays $20 per day for freight cars kept over one day, estimate the annual savings (250 days = one year) from a service rate of three per day (instead of two per day).

20–8. Continue Table 20–11 to one hundred periods, using the random numbers from Table 20–6. Estimate the total annual cost (one year = 50 weeks) if the cost of placing an order is $10; the cost of holding one unit of inventory is 50 cents per year; and the cost of outage is $3.00 per unit of lost sales. (Use average beginning inventory in determining cost of holding inventory.)

20–9. Pick an inventory rule that you consider good for the situation described in Problem 20–8. (That is, pick a number Q and a number R.) Compare the cost of your rule with the cost in Problem 20–8.

Chapter 21

THE INVESTMENT DECISION AND UNCERTAINTY

GENERALLY, the capital-budgeting analysis presented in business literature implicitly makes either of two assumptions: (1) The cash flows are known with certainty (as they would be if an individual purchased series H or E United States Savings Bonds), or (2) it is appropriate to use the mean value of cash flows. These assumptions may or may not be reasonable.

Capital budgeting is a broad subject, and we cannot attempt more than a sketch of some of its special aspects in this book.[1] It is assumed that business firms can determine an appropriate rate of interest to be used as the cutoff rate in making investment decisions. Secondly, it is assumed that business firms should use the present value method of judging the acceptance or rejection of investments. The fact that surveys of corporations show that neither assumption is perfectly descriptive of general business practice does not alter the usefulness of a model based on these assumptions. Business investment decisions should be made using the present value method if the interests of the stockholders are to be best served. While the use of the present value method is a necessary part of the decision process, there still remains the problem of risk.

CAPITAL BUDGETING UNDER CERTAINTY

We shall briefly review capital budgeting under certainty. Let us assume an interest rate of 10 per cent and an investment with the following projected cash flows:

---

[1] For a more complete introduction, see Bierman and Smidt (1960).

354

Period	Cash Flows
0	$ (800)
1	1,000

There is a cash outlay at the end of period 0 of $800, followed by a cash inflow of $1,000 at the end of period 1. The present value analysis is as shown in Table 21–1.

TABLE 21–1

Period	Cash Flows	Present Value Factor	Present Value of Cash Flows
0	$(800)	$\frac{100}{100} = 1.000$	$(800)
1	1,000	$\frac{100}{110} = 0.909$	$\frac{909}{\$\ 109}$

The net present value of cash flows is positive; following the present value method, the investment should be undertaken (the present value of the positive cash flows is $109 greater than the present value of the outlays, $800). If the net present value is negative, the investment is considered to be undesirable.

INTRODUCING UNCERTAINTY

An important cause of uncertainty is that the cash flows of future periods are generally estimates; thus, we do not know which of many outcomes will be the actual outcome. In this chapter, we shall ignore the fact that the timing of the disclosure of the true outcome also affects the value of the investment.

Assuming the corporation has a utility function that is linear in money, i.e., it values an extra dollar of profit or loss the same, regardless of the profit level, then, despite the uncertainty, it is appropriate to use the mean values of the distribution of cash flows of each period. We find it convenient to assume that the distributions are normal.[2] See Figure 21–1.

Let us analyze the significance of the fact that the cash flows are not known with certainty. If the cash outlays for the investment have a standard deviation of $200 ($\sigma = 200$), then there is a 50–50

---

[2] The normal distribution is not strictly appropriate, for it assigns some probability to negative values, which are excluded by definition in the case of cash outlays. However, the error introduced by such an assumption is small relative to the computational advantages of using the normal density function.

FIGURE 21–1

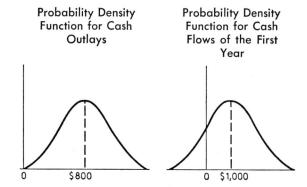

Probability Density
Function for Cash
Outlays

Probability Density
Function for Cash
Flows of the First
Year

chance that the investment will vary $134 or more (⅔ of σ, or ⅔ of $200) from the mean of $800. See Figure 21–2.

There is a 0.25 probability that the investment will cost $934 or more, and a 0.25 probability that the investment will cost $666 or less. Thus, even *if* the remainder of the facts were *known with cer-*

FIGURE 21–2

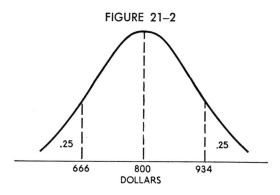

tainty, there would be a 0.25 probability that the investment will have a negative present value of at least $25.

$$\text{Present value of investment outlays:} \quad 934 \cdot \frac{100}{100} = \$(934)$$

$$\text{Present value of cash flows:} \quad 1{,}000 \cdot \frac{100}{110} = \underline{909}$$

$$\text{Negative net present value:} \qquad \$\ (25)$$

The analysis is further complicated by the fact that the cash flows of period 1 may also have a probability distribution. Let us assume that the cash flows of period 1 have a probability distribution which has a standard deviation of $450. We make the very important assumption that the cash flows of successive periods are independent.

We shall assume the interest rate is known to be 10 per cent. The discount rate could be considered a random variable, but it would make the analysis much more complex.

In summary, there are two probability distributions, as shown in Table 21–2. We must determine the mean and the standard devia-

TABLE 21–2
Cash Flows

	Mean	σ—Standard Deviation
Period 0—cash flows......$ (800)		$200
Period 1—cash flows...... 1,000		450

tion of the probability distribution of the net present value distribution.

The mean of the present value distribution is computed summing the means of the other distributions. We shall use as the present value factor $(1 + r)^{-i}$, where r is the interest rate and i is the number of periods. These values may be obtained from present value tables. The basic formula we use is:

$$(21\text{--}1) \qquad \text{Mean} = \sum_{i=0}^{n}(1 + r)^{-i}\bar{Y}_i$$

where $\bar{Y}_i$ is the mean cash flows of period i. Computation of the mean of the present value distribution, using a 10 per cent interest rate, is as follows:

$$\begin{aligned} \text{Period 0—cash flows: } &-800(1 + 0.10)^{-0} = (800) \\ \text{Period 1—cash flows: } &1{,}000(1 + 0.10)^{-1} = \underline{909} \\ \text{Mean—net present value distribution: } &\overline{109.} \end{aligned}$$

The computation of the standard deviation is slightly more complex:

$$(21\text{--}2) \qquad \sigma_Y{}^2 = \sum_{i=0}^{n}(1 + r)^{-2i}\sigma_i{}^2$$

where σ_i is the standard deviation of the cash flows of the ith year, and σ_Y is the standard deviation of the net present value distribution.[3] (See Table 21–3.)

---

[3] If c is a constant, it can be shown that $\text{Var}(cX) = c^2\,\text{Var}(X)$. It can also be shown that with the X's independent, the variance of a sum of random variables is equal to the sum of their variances, i.e., $\text{Var}(X_1 + X_2) = \text{Var}(X_1) + \text{Var}(X_2)$. See Chapter 2. If we let c equal the discount factor for time value, we can derive equation 21–2 from the above relationships. We want the variance of the present value (the present value has a probability distribution).

TABLE 21–3

Period	$(1.10)^{-2i}$	$\sigma_i{}^2$	$(1.10)^{-2i}\sigma_i{}^2$
0....................	$(1.10)^{-2\times0}$	$200^2 = 40,000$	40,000
1....................	$(1.10)^{-2\times1}$	$450^2 = 202,500$	167,000
		$\sigma_Y{}^2 \quad =$	207,000

$$\sigma_Y = \sqrt{207,000} = 455$$

We have now determined the mean ($109) and the standard deviation ($455) of the net present value distribution.

This distribution contains a great deal of information. For example, we can determine the probability of the net present value being zero or less, as follows:

$$D = \frac{109}{455} = 0.24.$$

The probability of zero net present value or less is 0.41 (0.24 standard deviations from the mean). See Figure 21–3.

FIGURE 21–3

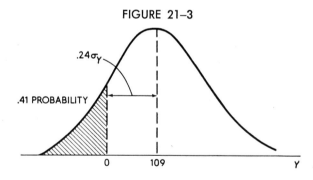

The expected opportunity loss (or the expected value of perfect information) is determined as follows:

$$EOL = \sigma_Y N(D) = 455 \cdot N(0.24)$$
$$= 455 \cdot 0.29 = 132.$$

Should the investment be undertaken? That depends on the preferences of the management of the corporation. Later in this chapter, we shall see how to compute the utility of this investment and incorporate these preferences directly into the computations. It should be remembered that as long as the firm is considered to have a utility function that is linear in money (the firm would be indifferent between an alternative of zero dollars and a lottery with a 0.50 probability of winning x dollars and a 0.50 probability of losing x dollars), use of the mean values is appropriate. The conventional method of solving capital-budgeting decisions using the present value method may be reasonable if the imputed linear utility function is appropriate.

EXPECTED LOSS—DISCRETE EVENTS

There are several methods of presenting information for decision making to management when a nonlinear utility function is used. The method presented in this section is relatively simple in execution. Let us assume there is an investment possibility which has a 0.60 probability of having a positive net present value of $1,000, and a 0.40 probability of having a *negative* present value of $1,200. The expected monetary value of the investment may be computed as follows:

$$\$1,000 \cdot 0.60 = \$\ 600$$
$$(\$1,200) \cdot 0.40 = \underline{(480)}$$
$$\text{Expected Value of Investment} = \$\ 120$$

These numbers may be identified as:

Expected value of the positive present values (profitable operations are
    assumed)..$ 600
Expected value of the loss (EOL).................................. (480)
    Expected Value of the Investment............................$ 120

There is a 0.40 probability that the investment will have a negative present value of $1,200; the $1,200 must be weighted by the probability of the event, 0.40, to obtain the expected value of the loss, $480. The $1,200 is a "conditional" cash flow.

Consider a second investment. The expected monetary value of the investment is also $120, but assume the expected loss is twice the $480 of the first investment, or $960. Is the second investment equally desirable, less desirable, or more desirable than the first? It has the same expected monetary value but twice the expected loss. Before drawing a conclusion, we should look at the array of present values for the second investment:

Expected value of the positive present values[4].....................$1,080
Expected value of the negative present values[4]..................... (960)
    Expected Value of the Investment............................$ 120

_____

[4] These should be interpreted as two possible events: one leading to an expected positive present value of $1,080, and the other leading to an expected negative present value of $960. Since these expected values are obtained by multiplying the conditional present values by the probability of the event, the conditional positive present value or conditional negative present value actually realized will be different from the expected $1,080, or ($960):

A firm with a utility function that is linear in money would be indifferent between the two investments, since they both have the same expected monetary value. A firm with a strong aversion to losses would favor the first investment; a firm with strong preferences for large gains might favor the second investment.

EXPECTED LOSS—CONTINUOUS EVENTS

In the above example, two investments had negative expected values of $960 and $480 if an event with a 0.40 probability occurred. These two numbers give some indication of the risk of loss associated with the two investments. We can compute comparable measures of loss when there are many possible events by making use of calculus (see Figure 21–4).

FIGURE 21–4
Present Value

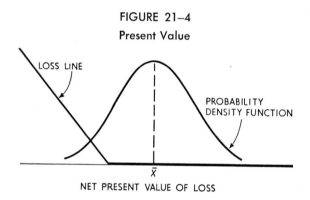

NET PRESENT VALUE OF LOSS

We want to take the expectation of the product of the loss line and the probability density function of the loss. Fortunately, this process can be accomplished making use of the relatively simple formula:

(21–3)   Expected Opportunity Loss $= \sigma_Y N(D)$

where σ_Y is the standard deviation of the cash flows. Let:

C_b = Cash flows equal to cash outlay, i.e., amount of cash required to break even.

Conditional Present Values	Probability of Event		Expected Present Values
$1,800	· 0.60	=	$1,080
($2,400)	· 0.40	=	(960)
			$ 120

C_E = Mean value of positive cash flows

$N(D)$ = The value of N with a given D (see Table D in Appendix at the end of the text).

D is measured in standard deviations and is equal to *the absolute value* of the difference between C_b and C_E divided by σ_Y.

Example

Assume an investment has a certain cost of \$3,000. The *mean* present value of cash inflows is \$4,000, and the mean net present value is \$1,000. Management says that the present value of the cash inflow has a standard deviation equal to \$1,800.

$$\sigma_Y = \$1,800$$

$$D = \frac{\left| C_b - C_E \right|}{\sigma_Y} = \frac{\left| \$3,000 - \$4,000 \right|}{\$1,800} = \frac{\$1,000}{\$1,800} = 0.555$$

$$N(D) = N(0.555) = 0.1818.$$

Expected Opportunity Loss $= \sigma_Y N(D) = \$1,800 \cdot 0.1818 = \$327$.

We shall assume a second investment with the same cost of \$3,000 and the same mean value of cash inflows of \$4,000. However, the cash inflow has a standard deviation of \$900.

$$\sigma_Y = \$900$$

$$D = \frac{\left| C_b - C_E \right|}{\sigma_Y} = \frac{\left| \$3,000 - \$4,000 \right|}{\$900} = \frac{\$1,000}{\$900} = 1.11$$

$$N(D) = N(1.11) = 0.06727$$

Expected Opportunity Loss $= \sigma_Y N(D) = \$900 \cdot 0.067 = \$60$.

A comparison of the two investments shows there is higher risk of loss with the first investment than the second: an expected loss of \$327 versus \$60. The expected values of both investments, using the mean value of the cash flows, is \$1,000.

NONLINEAR UTILITY FUNCTIONS

Instead of computing the expected opportunity loss giving each dollar equal weight, it is possible to weight the losses, i.e., introduce a nonlinear utility function.

Assume management is asked a series of questions similar to the following: "If you were to be indifferent between not investing, and an investment which has a 0.50 probability of \$100,000 of positive present values and a 0.50 probability of X dollars of negative values, what is your value of X?" If management's utility is linear in money, the answer will be $100,000. Let us assume the answer given is $40,000.

The expected monetary value of the investment is

$$0.50(\$100,000) - 0.50(\$40,000) = \$30,000.$$

However, the expected utility of the investment is equivalent to zero dollars, since management would be indifferent between the investment and an act that yields zero dollars. This discrepancy between expected utility and expected monetary value indicates that management has a nonlinear utility function.

Example

Corporation ABC is considering an investment which would utilize all its funds available for investment. The researchers expect either of two instantaneous events to occur, with the results shown in Table 21–4.

TABLE 21–4

Event	Conditional Net Monetary Value: Y	Probability of Event	Expected Monetary Value
A........................	$1,000,000	0.90	$900,000
B........................	(50,000)	0.10	(5,000)
Expected Monetary Value.			$895,000

Assume the firm has a utility function which may be approximated as follows:

$$U = -0.001Y^2 \text{ if } Y < -1,000$$
$$U = Y \qquad \text{if } Y \geq -1,000.$$

The analysis will be as shown in Table 21–5.

The investment is desirable, assuming we have chosen the correct utility function.

Let us illustrate a second possible utility function (see Table 21–6):

$$U = -0.01Y^2 \text{ if } Y < -100$$
$$U = Y \qquad \text{if } Y \geq -100$$

With this utility function, the investment is undesirable. Obviously, the type of utility function used by management can alter

TABLE 21–5

Event	Conditional Net Monetary Value: Y	Conditional Utility U	Probability of Event	Expected Utility
A..............	$1,000,000	1,000,000	0.90	900,000
B..............	(50,000)	(2,500,000)	0.10	(250,000)
Expected Utility......				650,000

TABLE 21–6

Event	Conditional Net Monetary Value: Y	Conditional Utility U	Probability of Event	Expected Utility
A..............	$1,000,000	1,000,000	0.90	900,000
B..............	(50,000)	(25,000,000)	0.10	(2,500,000)
Expected Utility......				(1,600,000)

the investment decision. It is difficult to derive an appropriate function to represent a decision maker's utility; however, unless he is willing to make decisions on the basis of expected monetary value, it is necessary to search for some nonlinear representation of the decision maker's utility. A convenient form for mathematical analysis is the equation described in Appendix 1 and below.[5]

CONTINUOUS PROBABILITY FUNCTIONS

If, instead of discrete events, we are dealing with a continuous range of possibilities, it is helpful to look at the expectation of the utility function. Assume the utility function is:

$$U = Z - bZ^2$$
$$Z \leq \frac{1}{2b}$$

where U is a measure of utility and Z is dollars.

The expected value of utility is:

$$E(U) = E(Z) - E(bZ^2).$$

$E(Z)$ is the mean, $\bar{Z}$, i.e., the mean of the net present value probability distribution. $E(bZ^2)$ is equal to $bV(Z)$ plus $b\bar{Z}^2$, i.e., b times

---

[5] A simulation procedure is presented in Appendix 2. Also see Chapter 20.

the sum of the variance and the square of the mean of the net present value probability distribution. Thus:

$$E(U) = \bar{Z} - b[V(Z) + \bar{Z}^2].$$

Example

A firm has \$1,500 available for investment. Evaluate an investment with the characteristics shown in Table 21–7.

TABLE 21–7

Period	Means of Cash Flows	Variance of Cash Flows
0.	\$(1,500)*	40,000
1.	1,000	90,000
2.	1,000	160,000

*Cash outlay.

The cash flows of each period are independent.

Assume the appropriate discount rate is 0.10. The utility function, assumed not to change with time and different past income histories, is:

$$U = Z - bZ^2 = Z - 0.0001Z^2.$$

$$Z \le \frac{1}{0.0002}.$$

The expected utility is:

$$E(U) = \bar{Z} - 0.0001[V(Z) + \bar{Z}^2].$$
$$E(U) = \bar{Z} - 0.0001\,[V(Z) + \bar{Z}^2]$$
$$= 235 - 0.0001\,[223,656 + 55,225]$$
$$= 235 - 28 = 207.$$

Computations are as shown in Tables 21–8 and 21–9.

The mean utility is positive, indicating that the investment is

TABLE 21–8

1	2	3	4
Period i	Var(Z) Variance of Cash Flows	c^2 Discount Factor $(1 + r)^{-2i}$	$c^2\,\mathrm{Var}(Z) = \mathrm{Var}(cZ)$ (2×3)
0.	40,000	1.0000	40,000
1.	90,000	0.8264	74,376
2.	160,000	0.6830	109,280
			223,656

TABLE 21–9

Period	Cash Flows	Discount Factor	Present Value of Cash Flows
0..............	$(1,500)	$(1.10)^0$	$(1,500)
1..............	1,000	$(1.10)^{-1}$	909
2..............	1,000	$(1.10)^{-2}$	826
			$ 235

acceptable, since the $U(\$0) = 0$, and the utility of the investment is larger than zero.

The conventional present value computation also indicates the investment is desirable (a positive present value of $235). See Table 21–9.

A COMMON STOCK INVESTMENT MODEL

A type of investment decision is one where an individual must choose the amount to invest. This decision is closely associated with the purchase of securities.

SUMMARY OF THE MODEL

The purchase of securities for investment purposes falls under the heading of decision making under uncertainty. Characteristically, this involves a subjective probability distribution over some future set of events—in this case the possible values of the securities. The individual's reaction to these possible events is reflected in his utility function, which provides a personalistic evaluation of the risk inherent in such decisions. A complicating factor in the investment decision is the time element: Uncertain future flows must be treated in some manner so that they may be compared with flows of the present time period. There is no simple and precise means for handling this problem of prospective uncertain returns over time; certainly, there are weaknesses in the procedure we suggest. Our purpose is to provide an example of the orderly treatment of risk stemming from variance of money flows.[6]

ASSUMPTIONS

In developing this model, we make the following assumptions:

---

[6] We are not considering the companion problem of portfolio selection, i.e., finding the optimum mix of investments. The importance of considering the interrelationships of investments should be stressed.

1. The individual has a fixed stock, F, of monetary assets (cash and readily marketable securities) which he considers eligible for investment.
2. The investment decision is made relevant to a short period of time—say, six months or one year.
3. The relatively brief planning period provides some justification for assuming that the individual's utility function for money is the same at the beginning and at the end of the time period. If his utility for $1.00 is U at time t_0, then at time t_1 his utility for $1.00 is also U.
4. There are no broker's fees.
5. The individual has a nonlinear utility function that in general is subject to diminishing marginal utility. We will define $U(\$0) = 0$.
6. The individual desires to select that act which yields the greatest present utility.
7. The individual is willing to estimate:
   a) The expected monetary value of the security at the end of the time period. The monetary value of the security is its market price at the end of the period plus cash dividends for that period; the dividends are treated as if they were paid at the end of the period.
   b) The reliability of this expected value—that is, the investor estimates the variance of the distribution of possible values.

EXPECTED VALUE OF COMMON STOCK

The distribution of the expected value might be obtained by estimating the distributions for expected dividends and for expected market price. The expected present value then would be the present value of the sum of the expected dividends and the expected price. The variance of the expected present value would be the variance of the sum of the dividends and the price, times the square of the discount factor.

For our purposes in this chapter, there is no need to distinguish between bonds and common stock. If we regard interest as a dividend to the bondholder, then the technique described above is applicable to bonds as well as common stock. The major difference would be the greater reliability in estimating the value of most bonds at the end of the planning period; the variance of such estimates normally is smaller than for common stock.

NET EXPECTED UTILITY

Say an individual has F dollars and is considering an investment, I, in a specific stock, X. He assigns a subjective probability weight to a possible future value (market price plus dividends) of the investment in X. The present value less the cost may be given a utility representation; then, if each of these utility measures is weighted by the relevant probability of that future value, the expected utility of the investment is obtained by aggregating these weighted utilities. The graphic representation of this situation is shown in Figure 21–5.

The expected utility of the investment will vary with I, the size of the investment. For example, assume that an investor believes stock X will have a substantial rise over the planning period (contrary to

FIGURE 21–5

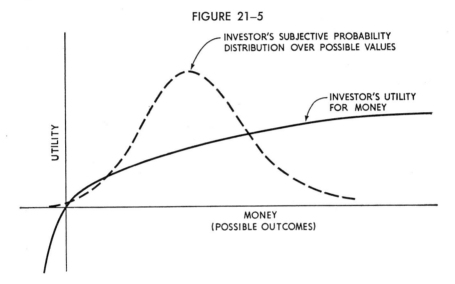

market expectations), but he attaches a moderate amount of variance to this estimate. The expected utility of the present value of one share of the stock might be larger than the current utility representation of the stock's price. However, as larger and larger blocks of stock X are considered for investment purposes, forces act to check the rise of expected utility: The variance of the expected value of the investment increases with the size of the investment; and since most utility functions reflect an aversion to variance, the total expected utility increases at a decreasing rate. The expected utility may increase for a range, but will probably reach a maximum and then fall as I increases and the possibility of large losses is introduced.

MARGINAL UTILITY

If $\overline{U}$, the expected utility, is negative for all levels of investment in a security, that security will be dropped from consideration. We are concerned now with the remaining candidates: those securities with $\overline{U} > 0$ for some values of I, the size of investment. Our objective is to provide a simple rule for selecting the amount of investment in the eligible security. To do this, we define the net marginal utility as

$$m = \frac{\Delta \overline{U}}{\Delta I}$$

where I represents the monetary investment in the security under consideration. We assume a utility function that reflects aversion to risk (the second derivative of the function is negative).

The investor first calculates the expected marginal utility of an eligible security for some initial small investment. The process then is repeated for another small increment of investment. These assignments are continued until either:

1. The marginal utility for the eligible security is zero. If the investor's fund has not been exhausted, he should hold the excess as cash, or seek another investment.
2. The investor's fund is exhausted. In this case the marginal utility of the investment will be greater than zero.

If there are few eligible securities (as would be the case when the investor expects a market decline and has a personal discount rate that is higher than the market rate), the investor will hold most of his fund as cash; if there are many securities with positive net expected utilities, the investor may commit his entire fund to some combination of common stocks and bonds.[7]

Example

We shall illustrate the above discussion with an example. The assumptions used in this example are artificially simple; nevertheless, it has elements of analysis which would be present in a real-world situation. However, the number of alternatives available to the investor and interaction of one investment decision on decisions to invest in other stocks are not considered.

Assume an individual buys stock in 100-share blocks and is considering purchasing 100 shares of a common stock currently selling

---

[7] For the multiple-security case, this method is excessively simplified. We should consider not only the variance of each stock, but also the covariances between stocks. If the prices (and dividends) of stocks are independent, then we may be able to reduce our risk by diversifying our portfolio. See Markowitz (1959).

for $60 per share; he has $6,000 available for investment. His estimate of the next year's performance of the stock is as follows:

Expected dividend for the coming year—$3.00 per share, with a variance of $1.00.

Expected price at the end of the year—$77 per share, with a variance of $400.

A 0.05 rate of discount is appropriate.

The expected dividends plus the expected price, each times the number of shares to be purchased, gives the expected monetary value of the stock at the end of the year:

$$EMV = 100 \cdot \$3.00 + 100 \cdot \$77 = \$300 + \$7,700 = \$8,000.$$

The present value of $8,000 is $7,619. The mean net present value is $1,619 (i.e., $7,619 − $6,000).

If X is a random variable and c a constant, then Var (cX) is equal to $c^2 \text{Var}(X)$. Also, the variance of the sum of two independent random variables is equal to the sum of the variances (we assume price and dividends to be independent).[8] We can now compute the variance of the monetary value of the stock.

Let D be the dividend and P the price per share. The variance of M, the monetary value of the investment in 100 shares, is:

$$\text{Var}(M) = \text{Var}\ \frac{100}{1.05} D + \text{Var}\ \frac{100}{1.05} P$$
$$= \frac{100^2}{(1.05)^2}\text{Var}(D) + \frac{100^2}{(1.05)^2}\text{Var}(P)$$

where $\text{Var}(D)$ is the variance of the dividend and $\text{Var}(P)$ is the variance of the price of the stock.

$$\text{Var}(M) = \frac{100^2}{1.1025}\ (1) + \frac{100^2}{1.1025}\ (400) = \frac{10,000 + 4,000,000}{1.1025} = \$3,600,000.$$

We can find the expected utility of a distribution with a mean of $1,619 and a variance of $3.6 million by simulation (see Appendix 2 at the end of this chapter) or by using a quadratic utility function. We shall use the quadratic utility function, since it is easier to show the computations, though as a general method the simulation pro-

---

[8] This assumption is not required and may be dropped; however, the computations would become somewhat more involved.

cedure is to be preferred. Assume the following quadratic formula applies:

$$U = Y - bY^2.$$

Take the expectation of both sides; then:

$$E(U) = \bar{Y} - b[V(Y) + \bar{Y}^2]$$

where b is assumed to be equal to $\dfrac{1}{20,000}$.

Substituting the mean of $1,619 and the variance of $3.6 million, we obtain an expected utility of 1,309:

$$E(U) = 1,619 - \frac{1}{20,000}(3,600,000 + 1,619^2)$$

$$= 1,619 - \frac{1}{20,000}(3,600,000 + 2,600,000)$$

$$= 1,619 - \frac{1}{20,000}(6,200,000)$$

$$= 1,619 - 310 = 1,309.$$

The net marginal utility, m, is obtained by dividing the change in utility—in this example the expected utility—by the dollar cost of the investment:

$$m = \frac{\Delta \bar{U}}{\Delta I} = \frac{1,309}{6,000} = 0.22.$$

Since m is positive, the investment is worthy of consideration. The net marginal utility is a measure of the desirability of this investment compared to other investments. Actually, the $6,000 investment is too large an increment, and smaller investment increments than 100 shares might also be considered.

In the next section, we shall consider the desirability of investing in 200 shares instead of 100 shares.

Example—Marginal Investment Analysis

If 100 shares are desirable as an investment, as indicated above, would a larger quantity be more desirable? Consider the purchase of 200 shares of the same stock. Let the price remain at $60 per share, and let the investor's stock of money now be $12,000.

The decision maker expects the same market price and dividend at the end of the year, with the same variance characteristics.

$$EMV = 2(\$1,619) = \$3,238$$

$$\text{Var } (M) = \frac{(200^2)}{1.05^2}(1) + \frac{(200^2)}{1.05^2}(400) = \frac{40,000 + 16,000,000}{1.1205} = 14,300,000.$$

The expected utility is:

$$E(U) = 3{,}238 - \frac{1}{20{,}000}\,(14{,}300{,}000 + 10{,}500{,}000)$$
$$= 3{,}238 - 1{,}240 = 1{,}998.$$

Since we are interested in making a marginal decision about this particular security, we should deduct the utility of the first $6,000 invested, which is 1,309. The expected utility associated with the incremental investment is 689 (that is, $1{,}998 - 1{,}309 = 689$).[9]

The investment is worthy of consideration, since the marginal utility for the investment in the second 100 shares is:

$$m = \frac{689}{6{,}000} = 0.11.$$

Note that the net marginal utility (m) has declined for the second 100 block of shares purchased. It would continue to decline for each additional block.

CONCLUSIONS AND LIMITATIONS OF THE ANALYSIS

We have attempted to provide a procedure for determining the amount of a security which should be purchased and helping the investor to act consistently with (1) his judgment of the market and (2) his personal evaluation of risk and time preference.

The application of the rule does not imply that the investment would be liquidated at the end of the planning period. Rather, the investment should be reviewed at that time (and possibly at several intervening times as well), and the process repeated. This would result in the addition of some new holdings, or increases in old investments, as well as some selling, provided the investor had changed his evaluation of the market.

This type of analysis is worthy of study and development. Intuitively, we know that variance in earnings will have different effects on the desirability of investments to different individuals. A reasonable measure of stock value should take this factor into consideration. The conventional present value method of evaluating invest-

---

[9] The $U(A + B)$ is not equal to $U(A)$ plus the $U(B)$; for example, the utility of $800 is not equal to twice the utility of $400. However, $U(\Delta_A) \equiv U(A + \Delta_A) - U(A)$, where $U(\Delta_A)$ is defined as the utility of moving a distance Δ from A. We can compute the utility of moving from $1,000 by an amount of $100 by taking the utility of $1,100 and subtracting the utility of $1,000. The symbol $\equiv$ means the relationship is an identity; that is, it holds true for all values of A and Δ_A.

ments makes use of the mean values of the cash flows, and the dispersions of the flows are not generally incorporated into the analysis. This chapter suggests methods of including the probability of realizing different amounts of net present value. Secondly, we computed the expected loss. The third computation involved the inclusion of a utility function in the computations. The utility function brings investors' attitudes towards the dispersion of the cash flows directly into the present value analysis.

For corporations, there is the added complication that they are more complex than individuals (since the well-being of many individuals is affected). The determination of a market utility function or the utility function of a complex corporation and its behavior over time is a problem to which there is not currently a completely satisfactory solution. On the other hand, an alternative to employing some approximate nonlinear utility function is to use the mean cash flows in analyzing the desirability of an investment. This choice implies the assumption that the firm has a linear utility function for money. So, whether we want to or not, we shall be assuming one or another utility function.

APPENDIX 1

AN ALGEBRAIC MODEL OF UTILITY

In analysis involving a utility function, it is sometimes assumed that the individual's utility function is of the quadratic form:

$$U = Y - bY^2$$

where Y is money and b is some constant. The behavior of this function is consistent with the assumption of diminishing marginal utility and the approximate characteristics of many individuals' utility functions, at least over some range of money values. One limitation of the function is that U reaches a maximum at $Y = \dfrac{1}{2b}$, and declines for values of Y greater than this amount. If this behavior is inappropriate, a restraint must be placed on the magnitude of Y, generally that $Y < \dfrac{1}{2b}$.

The great advantage of the quadratic utility function is the convenient form it assumes when uncertainties are involved. If we take the expectation of both sides of the utility function, we obtain:

$$E(U) = E(Y - bY^2) = E(Y) - E(bY^2).$$

Since the expectation of Y is the mean of Y, we write:

$$E(U) = \bar{Y} - bE(Y^2).$$

But we know that $V(Y) = E(Y^2) - E(Y)^2$, or $E(Y^2) = V(Y) + \bar{Y}^2$. Substituting this value of $E(Y^2)$, we obtain:

$$E(U) = \bar{Y} - b[V(Y) + \bar{Y}^2]$$

where $E(U)$ may be interpreted as the expected utility of the investment at the end of the planning period, $\bar{Y}$ is the expected monetary value of the investment, and $V(Y)$ is the variance of the expected monetary values.

APPENDIX 2

SIMULATION OF THE UTILITY FOR AN EARNING DISTRIBUTION

Not all utility functions should be described by a simple quadratic function.

One possibility is to become expert curve fitters (fitting mathematical equations to curves), but this is a complex operation. An easier procedure, and one which can be quickly mastered, is to determine the mean utility of a distribution of earnings (earnings is a random variable) by simulation. All we require is that we specify the mean and the variance of the earning distribution (assuming the distribution is normal), and that we know the utility function of the individual. Figure 21–6 shows the earning distribution and the utility function.

FIGURE 21–6

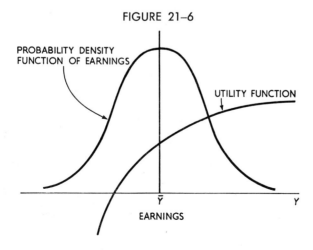

PROBABILITY DENSITY
FUNCTION OF EARNINGS

UTILITY FUNCTION

$\bar{Y}$

EARNINGS

Y

FIGURE 21–7
A Standard Normal Curve (Mean $= 0$, $\sigma_u = 1$)

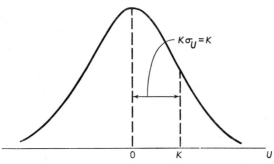

We want to determine the utility of earnings with mean $\overline{Y}$ and standard deviation σ_Y.

The procedure we shall follow is to go to a table of random normal deviates (which may also be generated on a computer) and enter the table randomly. By taking a series of observations (i.e., numbers from the table), we can determine the average utility of the earnings distribution.

Procedure:

1. Take a number, say k, from a table of standard normal deviates. See, for example, W. J. Dixon and F. J. Massey (1957), Table A–z, pages 371–80. Figure 21–7 illustrates the meaning of k.
2. Convert k to earnings (see Figure 21–8):

$$Y = \overline{Y} + k\sigma_Y.$$

3. Go to Figure 21–8 and read the utility for Y earnings. This is one observation of utility.

FIGURE 21–8

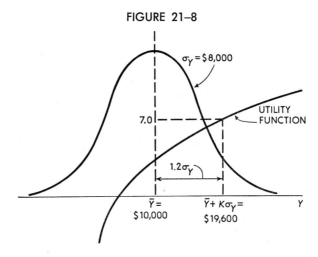

4. Take 100 observations; obtain 100 utilities; divide the total of the 100 observations by 100 to obtain the mean utility of the earning distribution.

Example

Assume the mean earnings, $\overline{Y}$, equal \$10,000 and the standard deviation of earnings, σ_Y, is \$8,000.

We take a random normal deviate and find it to be $+1.2$. The earnings observation is:

$$Y = \overline{Y} + k\sigma_Y$$
$$Y = \$10,000 + 1.2(\$8,000) = \$19,600 = \text{First Observation of Earnings.}$$

The next step is to measure the utility of \$19,600 earnings. We see the utility measure is 7.0. This is our first observation of utility. We would repeat this process 100 times (or more) to obtain a series of observations which would be summed and divided by the number of observations to obtain the expected utility of the earnings distribution. Thus, we have simulated the utility value of the expected earnings distribution.

BIBLIOGRAPHY

BIERMAN, H., JR., and SMIDT, S. *The Capital Budgeting Decision*. New York: Macmillan Co., 1960.

DEAN, J. *Capital Budgeting*. New York: Columbia University Press, 1951.

DIXON, W. J., and MASSEY, F. J. *Introduction to Statistical Analysis*. 2d ed. New York: McGraw-Hill Book Co., Inc., 1957.

DURAND, D. "Growth Stocks and the St. Petersburg Paradox," *Journal of Finance*, September, 1957.

FISHER, I. *The Theory of Interest*. New York: Macmillan Co., 1930.

HIRSHLEIFER, J. "On the Theory of Optimal Investment Decision," *Journal of Political Economy*, August, 1958.

LUTZ, F., AND LUTZ, V. *The Theory of Investment of the Firm*. Princeton: Princeton University Press, 1951.

MARKOWITZ, H. M. *Portfolio Selection*. Cowles Foundation Monograph 16. New York: John Wiley & Sons, Inc., 1959.

SCHLAIFER, R. *Probability and Statistics for Business Decisions*. New York: McGraw-Hill Book Co., Inc., 1959.

SOLOMON, E. *The Management of Corporate Capital*. Glencoe, Ill.: Free Press, Inc., 1959.

PROBLEMS

21-1. Assume a discount rate of 0.10 and an investment with the following projected cash flows:

Year	Cash Flows
0	$(1,600)
1	1,500
2	1,000

Assuming the firm has a linear utility function for money, should the investment be accepted?

21–2. Assume the cash flows of Problem 21–1 have the following probability distributions:

Period	Mean	σ
0	$(1,600)	$400
1	1,500	500
2	1,000	600

The distributions are assumed to be normal and independent of each other.

a) Compute the mean of the present value distribution.

b) Compute the standard deviation of the present value distribution.

c) Compute the probability of the investment having a net present value of zero or less.

d) Compute the expected value of the loss (or the expected value of perfect information).

21–3. Assume a discount rate of 0.10 and an investment with the following projected cash flows:

Year	Mean Cash Flow	σ of Cash Flow Distributions
0	$(1,600)	$ 700
1	2,000	1,000
2	1,000	1,500

The distributions are assumed to be normal and independent of each other.

a) Compute the mean of the present value distribution. Using just the mean value, would the investment be accepted?

b) Compute the standard deviation of the present value distribution.

c) Compute the probability of the investment having a net present value of zero or less.

d) Compute the expected value of the loss (or the expected value of perfect information).

e) Compare the desirability of investments of Problems 21–2 and 21–3.

21–4. A firm is considering an investment which has the following characteristics:

Period	Mean Cash Flow	Variance
* 0.............	$(1,000)	10,000
1.............	2,100	1,102,500

The appropriate discount rate to apply to future cash flows is 0.05. The firm has only $1,000 to invest.

The firm has the following utility function:

$$U = Y \text{ if } Y \geq 0$$
$$U = Y - 0.0001 Y^2 \text{ if } Y < 0.$$

Using a simulation technique, compute the mean present utility of the investment using the standard normal deviates below for the net present value of the cash flows:

Trial	Normal Deviates for Cash Flows
1......................	−2.015
2......................	−0.623
3......................	0.699
4......................	0.481
5......................	−0.586

21-5. Using the utility function below and the ten normal deviates, simulate the mean utility of the earnings. The mean earnings are $15,000; and the standard deviation, σ, is $10,000.

Ten Normal Deviates

−0.38	−0.56
+0.49	+0.33
+0.03	−0.98
−0.77	+1.47
−0.06	−2.32

Utility Function
$$U = Y \text{ if } Y \geq 0$$
$$U = Y - 0.001 Y^2 \text{ if } Y < 0.$$

Chapter 22

THE PRICING DECISION

OUR PURPOSE in Chapters 22 to 24 is to suggest an analytical framework within which business decisions affecting sales may be made. The initial task is to identify those factors or forces which influence the firm's sales. A further division may be made in terms of those factors over which the firm has some control and those factors which are beyond the discretion of management. Finally, for those factors within the jurisdiction of the firm's management, alternative decision strategies will be analyzed.

THE FACTORS AFFECTING SALES

We define sales as the quantity (units) of a given product the firm sells over a specific period of time, and designate this variable by Q_i, where i identifies the product. This is a critical variable for the firm, and considerable attention has been devoted to the factors that determine its magnitude. The following variables have been considered significant in influencing the firm's sales:

1. The price the firm charges for the product, which we shall designate by P_i.
2. The prices charged by other firms for closely related products, which we shall identify by a composite variable P_j.
3. The purchasing power, or disposable income (designated by Y), of consumers in the markets which the firm services.
4. The magnitude and quality of the firm's merchandising (sales promotion) effort, relative to the industry, which we shall represent by M.

There are many other variables which have a direct and powerful effect on sales, such as natural disasters or momentary quirks in the public taste. However, these forces are not only outside management's realm of influence, but they are so random and irregular in

378

their appearance and effects that it is impossible to derive orderly patterns of relationship between the causes and the result, or make any reliable prediction about the time and place of the next appearance of the causative force. We include them only indirectly in our analysis.

We may express the relationships under consideration as an equation:

$$(22\text{--}1) \qquad Q_i = A + bP_i + c_jP_j + dY + eM.$$

The dependent variable is Q_i, the quantity of product sold for a given period. The magnitude A is a catchall, which incorporates, on the average, the type of windfalls and catastrophes discussed above. The independent variables which affect sales are P_i, P_j, Y, and M; their respective coefficients represent the amount of change in Q_i per unit change in the associated independent variable.

THE EFFECT OF A CHANGE IN PRICE

The coefficient b is the change in Q_i caused by a unit change in P_i (the price of product i). More generally, b is the ratio of the change in Q_i induced by a change in P_i. If we represent a small change in a variable by the symbol Δ, we may define b as $\dfrac{\Delta Q_i}{\Delta P_i}$. If the price of an article falls, the sales of the article almost always will increase, and vice versa (assuming the other independent variables remain unchanged). Therefore, ΔQ_i and ΔP_i almost always will have opposite signs, so the ratio of the changes is usually negative. Thus, $b < 0$ for most commodities.

PRICES OF OTHER PRODUCTS

There may be several prices in the P_j category (prices charged by other firms), and the sign of

$$\frac{\Delta Q_i}{\Delta P_j} = c_j$$

their respective coefficients, will depend upon the nature of the relationship between the products sold by the other firms and product i. If the other product (or products) is designed to meet the same consumer needs as product i, then the two products are substitutes, and c_j will be positive. This follows from the observation that if a firm marketing a competing product raises the price of that product, your sales will tend to increase, for some of its customers will be tempted to switch to your product.

The coefficient c_j will be negative if the product produced by the other firm is complementary to the product you produce. For example, if the price of automobiles fell, the manufacturers of gasoline would expect to increase their sales.

DISPOSABLE INCOME

The income coefficient

$$\frac{\Delta Q_i}{\Delta Y} = d$$

may be positive or negative. If d is positive, it follows that the sales of the product will increase with the rising real income of the consumers. Such a product is classified as a superior good. If d is negative, sales and income are inversely related, and the product is technically defined as inferior. Some products will experience sales booms while incomes are falling (usually inexpensive goods which are substituted for relatively more costly products), but most products are superior in the above sense.

MERCHANDISING EXPENDITURES

Merchandising expenditures consist of advertising, sales and promotion efforts, and the general effort of the firm to create a favorable image of its product in the consumer's mind.[1] The coefficient of merchandising expenditures,

$$\frac{\Delta Q_i}{\Delta M} = e$$

is positive in all but the most ill-conceived campaigns.

In summary, the forces which affect sales in a consistent and orderly fashion may be classified under four headings:

1. Price of the product under consideration.
2. Other products' prices.
3. Consumer real disposable income.
4. Merchandising.

---

[1] Usually, merchandising is defined broadly so as to cover all selling effort, including the pricing decision. In our treatment, however, we have abstracted the pricing decision from its usual merchandising setting for special consideration; thus, when we use the term "merchandising," we refer to all selling effort except pricing.

The first and fourth of these factors are subject to some degree of control by company management; the other two factors are beyond the usual impact of a specific firm's decisions. We shall consider the price of the firm's product in this chapter and the next, and merchandising decisions are considered in Chapter 24.

CONSUMER DEMAND

We are concerned with the relationship between the price of an article and its unit sales. The traditional tool for summarizing this relationship is the concept of consumer demand. The demand relationship may be approximated from equation 22–1 by letting the independent variables, P_j, Y, and M, remain constant, while P_i is allowed to change and thus be the sole source of changes in Q_i. Since only P_i is allowed to vary, the expression $(A + c_jP_j + dY + eM)$ is a constant—say, K. We may rewrite equation 22–1 as:

$$(22\text{--}2) \qquad\qquad Q_i = K + bP_i.$$

Equation 22–2 is the general form of a linear demand equation. Among economists, it is conventional to graph such an equation with the independent variable, P_i, on the vertical axis and the dependent variable, Q_i, on the horizontal axis, as in Figure 22–1 (this is the reverse of the convention followed by mathematicians). In effect, this is the graphic representation of equation 22–3), which is derived from equation 22–2 by solving for P_i.

$$(22\text{--}3) \qquad\qquad P_i = \frac{1}{b}Q_i - \frac{K}{b}.$$

The price axis intercept of the curve is $-\dfrac{K}{b}$, and the slope is $\dfrac{1}{b}$, as shown in Figure 22–1, where $\dfrac{1}{b}$ is equal to the value of ΔP_i divided by ΔQ_i and is less than zero. If $K = 100$ and $b = -2$, then the demand equation would be $P_i = \dfrac{100}{2} - \frac{1}{2}Q_i$, or $P_i = \$50 - 0.5Q_i$, indicating that if, say, 60 units were sold, they would bring a price of $P_i = \$50 - 0.5(60) = \$20$. The price would have to be reduced $1.00 for every two-unit increase in sales.

It should be noted that movements along the demand curve are not shifts in demand, since the demand function relates price and quantity. In the previous example, if the price was reduced to $15, the demand equation indicates that 70 units could be sold. This increase in sales from 60 to 70 is not an increase in the demand function, since it was induced by an appropriate reduction in price. A shift in the demand function is induced by a chance in one of the independent variables, P_j, Y, or M, which we have considered to be constant. Demand will shift in the same direction as changes in these variables for products that are classified as substitutes and superior products. Conversely, if the price of a related product rises and the demand curve falls (shifts down and to the left), then the two prod-

FIGURE 22–1

Consumer Demand

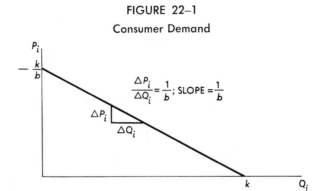

ucts are complements; or if demand falls in response to an increase in consumer disposable income, the product is identified as an inferior one. Shifts in demand then are induced through changes in K where K is defined as $(A + c_j P_j + dY + eM)$.

SLOPE AND ELASTICITY OF DEMAND

The two basic measures of a demand curve are slope and elasticity. Slope is defined as the ratio $\dfrac{\Delta P_i}{\Delta Q_i}$, or the reciprocal of b. The slope is almost always negative, indicating that an increase in price (a positive ΔP_i) will cause sales to fall (a negative ΔQ_i), and vice versa. For a linear demand curve the slope is constant, regardless of price (it would be -0.5 in our example).

Elasticity (E) is defined as the ratio of the relative change in quantity divided by the relative change in price,

$$E = \frac{\dfrac{\Delta Q_i}{Q_i}}{\dfrac{\Delta P_i}{P_i}} = \left(\frac{\Delta Q_i}{Q_i}\right)\left(\frac{P_i}{\Delta P_i}\right)$$

which is readily changed to the algebraic expression in equation 22–4:

$$(22\text{–}4) \qquad E = \frac{\Delta Q_i}{\Delta P_i}\frac{P_i}{Q_i} = b\frac{P_i}{Q_i}.$$

A *linear* demand curve will have a different elasticity at each price or quantity. In the example we considered above, when $b = -2$, $P_i = \$20$, and $Q_i = 60$, the elasticity would be:

$$E = b\frac{P_i}{Q_i}$$

$$E = -2\frac{\$20}{60} = -\frac{2}{3}.$$

If the price is $15 and sales are 70 units, the elasticity would be:

$$E = -2\frac{\$15}{70} = -\frac{3}{7}.$$

For a general elasticity formula for a linear demand curve, we could substitute the value of P_i from equation 22–3 in equation 22–4 and obtain:[2]

$$E = b\frac{P_i}{Q_i} = \frac{b}{Q_i}\left(\frac{1}{b}Q_i - \frac{K}{b}\right)$$

or

$$(22\text{–}5) \qquad E = 1 - \frac{K}{Q_i}$$

$$K \geq Q_i.$$

This indicates that demand elasticity will be zero or negative ($K \geq Q_i$; thus, $K/Q_i \geq 1$) and will vary between zero and $-\infty$. The customary classification is as follows:

Elastic.................	$-1 > E \geq -\infty$
Unit elasticity.........	$E = -1$
Inelastic...............	$0 \geq E > -1.$

In our example of $P_i = \$50 - 0.5Q_i$, the curve would have unit elasticity at $P_i = \$25$, be elastic at higher prices, and inelastic at lower prices.[3]

TOTAL REVENUE

Demand is an important conceptual linkage between the consumer and the producer of a product. If we multiply expected sales,

---

[2] Since $P_i \geq 0$, $b < 0$, then, from the demand equation $Q_i = K + bP_i$, it may be seen that $K \geq Q_i$.

[3] If $P_i = \$25$ and $b = -2$, Q_i will equal 50; $E = b\frac{P_i}{Q_i} = -2\frac{25}{50} = -1.$

Q_i, by the expected price, P_i, we obtain the expected consumption expenditures of consumers, which, from the business viewpoint, will become total revenue. This important variable may be derived from demand by multiplying both sides of equation 22–2 by P_i, or both sides of equation 22–3 by Q_i.

(22–3)
$$P_i = \frac{1}{b}Q_i - \frac{K}{b}$$

(22–6)
$$R = P_iQ_i = \frac{1}{b}Q_i^2 - \frac{K}{b}Q_i$$

The total revenue curve and the related linear demand curve are plotted in Figure 22–2. The total revenue curve has a positive slope

FIGURE 22–2

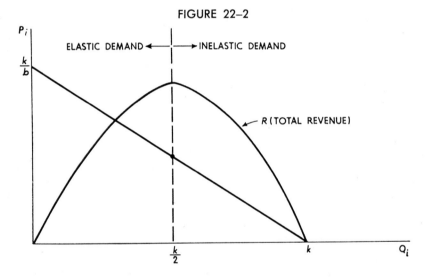

(the total revenue is increasing) over the range of sales where demand is elastic; total revenue is at a maximum when the demand curve has unit elasticity; total revenue declines in the range where demand is inelastic.

SIGNIFICANCE OF PRICE TO THE FIRM

The selection of a pricing strategy is of great importance in the operation of a business firm. Poor decisions in this area are met with immediate and severe retribution, more so perhaps than in any other area of business decision making. Price is a potent variable for two reasons:

1. In conjunction with expenses of making the sales, it is a prime determinant of the company's profits.
2. Purchasers are quite sensitive to this variable, which results in competitors also being sensitive to your pricing strategy.

Consider the first of these characteristics. An impression of the significance of P_i may be obtained from the algebraic definition of profits. The firm's total profits, π, are defined as the difference between total revenues (R) and total expenses (C):

$$(22\text{--}7) \qquad \pi = R - C \text{ or } \pi = P_iQ_i - C.$$

It can be seen that changes in P_i have a direct effect on the firm's profits (remember that Q_i is also a function of P_i).

With regard to the price sensitivity of consumers, they are usually concerned with the prices of the products they buy. Such prices determine the consumer's standard of living, given his income. If a consumer's income remained constant while the prices of the things he bought doubled, his real income would be cut in half, since

$$(22\text{--}8) \qquad \frac{\text{Money Income}}{\text{Price Level}} = \text{Real Income Index}.$$

THE USE OF MARGINS AS A PRICING DEVICE[4]

A popular means of pricing in retail or wholesale business firms is the use of margins or markups. The price of an article is determined by adding a margin to the article's wholesale cost. Thus:

$$(22\text{--}9) \qquad \text{Price } (P_i) = \text{Wholesale Cost } (w) + \text{Margin } (m)$$
$$P_i = w + m.$$

The purpose of this section is to derive some general guides for management's decisions regarding margin policy. Specifically, we are concerned with the proper behavior of the relative margin, $\dfrac{m}{P_i}$, as the wholesale price varies. By proper behavior, we mean a margin practice that will be consistent with maximum profits.

For purposes of exposition, we shall make the following simplifying assumptions:

1. At any given time the firm can buy any amount of the article at the same wholesale price. Therefore, w is both the average and the marginal cost to the firm; w is the entire marginal (variable) cost of buying and selling the article; all other costs are fixed.

---

[4] See L. Tarshis (1947) for a similar approach.

2. The firm prefers more total profits (π) to less; i.e., maximum profits are the most satisfactory profit level.

Total profits will be maximized when the firm extends sales to include all units which might contribute a positive increment to π, but stops short of that range of sales which contribute negative increments to π. Let us give the previous sentence a quantitative representation: $\pi = R - C$ and $\Delta\pi = \Delta R - \Delta C$. Dividing by ΔQ_i:

$$(22\text{--}10) \qquad \frac{\Delta\pi}{\Delta Q_i} = \frac{\Delta R}{\Delta Q_i} - \frac{\Delta C}{\Delta Q_i} = 0$$

i.e., marginal revenues minus marginal costs equal zero. Therefore:

$$(22\text{--}11) \qquad \frac{\Delta R}{\Delta Q_i} = \frac{\Delta C}{\Delta Q_i}.$$

Equation 22–11 states that marginal revenues $\left(\dfrac{\Delta R}{\Delta Q_i}\right)$ equal marginal costs $\left(\dfrac{\Delta C}{\Delta Q_i}\right)$ when total profits are at a maximum. By assumption, the marginal costs are the same as the wholesale costs (w), so we may write:

$$w = \frac{\Delta C}{\Delta Q_i} = \frac{\Delta R}{\Delta Q_i}$$

$$(22\text{--}12) \qquad w = P_i - m = \frac{\Delta R}{\Delta Q_i}.$$

The ratio $\dfrac{\Delta R}{\Delta Q_i}$ therefore bears the key to the relationship among the variables which interest us—w, P_i, and m. Let us break down this ratio by an analogue to a simple operation in differential calculus. Recall that total revenue is the product of price and quantity.[5]

$$(22\text{--}13) \qquad \frac{\Delta R}{\Delta Q_i} = \frac{\Delta(P_i Q_i)}{\Delta Q_i} = P_i \frac{\Delta Q_i}{\Delta Q_i} + Q_i \frac{\Delta P_i}{\Delta Q_i} = P_i + Q_i \frac{\Delta P_i}{\Delta Q_i}.$$

If we substitute this solution in equation 22–12, we may write:

$$(22\text{--}14) \qquad P_i - m = \frac{\Delta R}{\Delta Q_i} = P_i + Q_i \frac{\Delta P_i}{\Delta Q_i}$$

or

$$(22\text{--}15) \qquad m = -Q_i \frac{\Delta P_i}{\Delta Q_i}.$$

---

[5] See Appendix 1 at the end of this chapter for derivation of equation 22–13.

If we divide each side by price, we obtain:

(22-16)
$$\frac{m}{P_i} = -\frac{Q_i \Delta P_i}{P_i \Delta Q_i} = -\frac{1}{E}.$$

The profit-maximizing relative margin $\left(\dfrac{m}{P_i}\right)$ is the negative recipro-cal of the price elasticity of demand. Equation 22–16 may be written:

$$\frac{\text{Margin}}{\text{Price}} = -\frac{1}{E}.$$

Several important guides may be developed from this relation-ship. If we rewrite equation 22–16 as:

(22-17)
$$-E = \frac{P_i}{m} \text{ or } -E = \frac{\text{Price}}{\text{Margin}}$$

we see that since $P_i > m$ (i.e., the price of product i is greater than the margin of product i), $\dfrac{P_i}{m} > 1$, and $-E > 1$, or $E < -1$. When $E < -1$, this is designated as the elastic range of the demand curve. *A profitable margin practice therefore results in a price in the elastic range of the firm's demand curve.*

The firm should charge a price equal to

$$\frac{w}{1 + \dfrac{1}{E}}.$$

We derive the optimum price making use of equation 22–17:

(22-17)
$$-E = \frac{\text{Price}}{\text{Margin}} = \frac{P_i}{m}.$$

But m is equal to $(P_i - w)$; thus:

$$-E = \frac{P_i}{P_i - w}.$$

Solving for P_i:

(22-18)
$$P_i = \frac{Ew}{1 + E} = \frac{w}{1 + \dfrac{1}{E}}.$$

To set a profit-maximizing price, we need to know the marginal cost, w, and the elasticity of demand, E. We do not need to know the conventional markups or the "desired" profit.

USING DEMAND ELASTICITY

The directions for a profitable margin policy may be expressed in the context of elasticity considerations. This relationship may be helpful in deciding upon a margin practice, for the management may have definite opinions regarding the approximate elasticity of demand at various prices. For example, if management feels the demand curve of the product has the same price elasticity at all feasible prices, then the relative margin $\frac{m}{P_i}$ should be maintained at a constant level of $\frac{-1}{E}$. If the demand curve has a constant elasticity of -2, the firm will maximize profits by maintaining a relative margin of $0.5 \left(\frac{-1}{-2} = 0.5 \right)$; i.e., the margin m will equal the wholesale cost w, and $P_i = 2w$. The equation for a demand curve with constant elasticity is $Q_i = aP_i^E$, where E is the elasticity.

If a firm follows a policy of maintaining a constant relative margin, no matter what the wholesale cost, that policy implies a demand curve with a constant elasticity (subject to the assumptions specified above). This implied characteristic may or may not be consistent with the management's feelings about the probable elasticity of demand. Thus the appropriateness of such a margin practice is not obvious.

If management feels that price elasticity increases with price for a given demand curve confronting the firm, then management should let the relative margin vary inversely with the level of the wholesale cost. If wholesale costs rise, the relative margin should be reduced, and vice versa.

For example, a linear demand curve may be characterized as being more elastic at high prices than at lower prices.[6] Say the firm is confronted by a demand curve of the form $P = 12 - Q$, and wholesale costs are equal to two. Our rule is that the decision maker should choose a price so that $\frac{m}{P} = -\frac{1}{E}$. This occurs when $P = 7$,

---

[6] Remember, $E = \frac{\Delta Q_i}{\Delta P_i} \frac{P_i}{Q_i}$. In a linear demand curve, $\frac{\Delta Q_i}{\Delta P_i}$ is a constant. Hence, when P_i is large, then $\frac{P_i}{Q_i}$ is large, and E is large. Conversely, if Q_i is large and P_i is small, then $\frac{P_i}{Q_i}$ is small, and E is small.

FIGURE 22–3

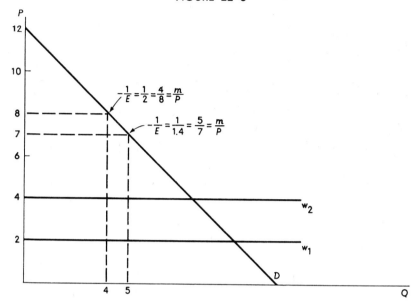

$m = 5$, and $E = -1.4$, as shown in Figure 22–3.[7] This is the same price indicated by the equality of marginal revenue and marginal cost, for it is the maximum profit position; the means of arriving at that position do not alter its basic characteristic. Now, let the whole-sale cost rise from two to four; the equality $-\dfrac{1}{E} = \dfrac{m}{P}$ is re-estab-

---

[7] We are given $w = 2$ and $P = 12 - Q$. By (22 – 3), $P = \dfrac{1}{b}Q - \dfrac{K}{b}$, thus, in this ex-

ample, $b = -1$. Using equation 22–4, $E = b\dfrac{P}{Q}$, and the fact that $P = 12 - Q$, we solve

for E in terms of P:

$$E = b\frac{P}{Q} = -\frac{P}{Q} = -\frac{P}{12 - P} = \frac{P}{P - 12}$$

Equation 22–18:

$$P = \frac{w}{1 + \dfrac{1}{E}}$$

allows us to solve for the profit-maximizing price, P:

$$P = \frac{w}{1 + \dfrac{1}{E}} = \frac{2}{1 + \dfrac{P - 12}{P}}$$

Solving for P, we find the optimum price to be seven; and using the relationship

$$P = 12 - Q$$

the quantity to be sold is five.

By equation 22–4, $E = b\dfrac{P}{Q} = -\dfrac{7}{5} = -1.4$.

lished by changing price from seven to eight, so that the new elasticity is -2, the new margin is four, and the new relative margin is one half, which is lower than the five-sevenths relative margin which was optimal before the increase in wholesale cost.

If management feels that price elasticity decreases for some range of higher prices for a given demand curve, then the relative margin should be varied directly with the wholesale cost for that relevant range.

It is difficult to construct a simple example of a demand curve which will have the desired characteristics. However, let the demand curve be of the form $P = 20 - 2Q$ for $0 \leq Q \leq 5\frac{5}{7}$, and of the form $P = 10 - \frac{1}{4}Q$ for $Q \geq 5\frac{5}{7}$. Assume the wholesale price is four. Total profits will be at a maximum in two neighborhoods, corresponding to the two segments of the demand curve. For the first segment, a price of 12 will yield sales of four units and profits of $(8 \cdot 4 = 32)$. The elasticity at this point of the demand curve is $-1\frac{2}{8}$, which satisfies our rule. However, the rule also is satisfied at another price: seven, with sales of 12 units and profits of 36 (the elasticity is $-\frac{7}{3}$). Since 36 exceeds 32, we assume the decision maker will choose a margin of three and a price of seven. However, this demand curve is less elastic over some range of higher prices, as just demonstrated; so if wholesale prices rise, the decision maker may increase the relative margin. For example, if the wholesale cost increases to six, the total profits again will have two neighborhood maxima: one at a price of 13, sales of 3.5, and profits of 24.5; the second at a price of eight, sales of eight, and profits of 16. The price adjustment at 13 is to be preferred; it should be noted that the relative margin increases from $\frac{3}{7}$ to $\frac{7}{13}$ in response to an increase in wholesale cost.

If the altered circumstances come about through a change in consumer demand rather than through a change in wholesale costs, then the elasticity at the new prices must be considered. Usually, an increase in demand will reduce the elasticity of the new relevant prices, so that the relative margin should be increased. However, this is not an analytically necessary relationship, and it is possible for an increase in demand to be accompanied by an increase in elasticity and a fall in the relative margin (the price of the product also must fall).

We have seen that it is quite possible for a firm to achieve a satisfactory adjustment to changes in demand and supply by means of a margin or markup means of pricing. While it is always true that marginal costs and marginal revenues are equal when profits are at a maximum, it is not true that the only way to approach maximum profits is by these marginal calculations. If the alternate means are constructed with care, there is no reason for them not to be consistent with profit maximization and marginal calculations, if such calculations are possible.

COMPETITION

So far in this chapter, we have discussed management's approach to the pricing decision as if it were a straightforward maximization problem against nature. This, of course, is generally not characteristic of the pricing problem. The pricing decision of one firm will affect the sales and profits of competing firms. The competing firms are very likely to choose a pricing strategy that takes account of this relationship. The pricing problem takes on the features of a conflict situation involving thoughtful opponents—the situation analyzed in the game framework in Chapter 16.

Let us start with a simple situation:

1. There are only two competitors, who produce a standardized product.
2. Competition is restricted to price. The competitor who offers the lowest price in a given period will get all the business. The high-price firm will get none. If the offered price is the same, the competitors will share the market equally for that period.
3. The demand is represented by the equation $Q = 12 - 2P$ for each period, where Q is the amount sold and P is the low price offered for that period.
4. Each firm has a fixed cost of six for each period and no variable costs.
5. The firms are managed by profit maximizers.
6. Price offers must be in integer form.

If the firms could co-operate, they would maximize their joint profits by each choosing a price of three. Each would then sell three units, have revenues of nine, and make a profit of:

$$\pi = 9 - 6 = 3$$

The independent, competitive entrepreneur faces a strong temptation, however. If he cuts his price to two, while his opponent holds his at three, the innovator will earn a profit of ten, and incidentally impose a loss of six on his opponent. The opponent may retaliate by matching the price cut, so that each charges a price of two and earns a profit of two. But once again, temptation faces the price cutter: By offering a price of one, he can earn twice as much as he can at a price of two. If the opponent follows this price cut, so that each offers the product for one, each will incur losses of -1. This is an equilibrium adjustment in game theoretic terms—an unhappy situation that has the same properties as the "prisoner's dilemma" we discussed in an earlier chapter. This can be seen by constructing a game matrix for the competitors (assuming they have utilities that are linear in the profit units). Entries in the body of Table 22–1 are profits resulting from an intersection of price strategies. Firm 1's profits are in the upper right-hand corner; firm 2's profits are in the lower left.

TABLE 22–1

Firm 2's Prices \ Firm 1's Prices	3	2	1	0
3	3 / 3 (π_1, π_2)	10 / −6	4 / −6	−6 / −6
2	−6 / 10	2 / 2	4 / −6	−6 / −6
1	−6 / 4	−6 / 4	−1 / −1	−6 / −6
0	−6 / −6	−6 / −6	−6 / −6	−6 / −6

It is apparent that the strategy of bidding price 2 dominates the strategy of bidding price 3. That is, if a firm bids two, all of the profits are as good as or better than if it bids three, regardless of the opponent's price choice. If strategy 3 is eliminated for each firm, then it follows that a price bid of one dominates the other alternatives, and the firms will tend toward the pay-off of -1 for each.

Of course, these results may be modified by a number of factors. If this situation is repeated over and over, the parties may learn to communicate and eventually co-operate in some tacit manner. This is especially true if they begin in a situation where they have relatively little information about the pay-off matrix, and gradually acquire more information through time.

The relative magnitude of the pay-offs will also affect the strategy choices. If a price cutter gains very little, but knows that he imposes a large loss on his competitor, most firms will respond in a co-operative manner. Conversely, if the rewards for price cutting are great and the penalty for having a high price is small, firms are likely to respond in a more competitive manner.

In any event, the pressures generated by such a situation are likely to force the firms toward some sort of co-operative behavior. In some instances, this takes the form of overt collusion, or even merger. The legal restraints on this form of response are severe and exacting. As a result, many firms seek some approved mechanism for achieving tacit co-operation. Quite often, this takes the form of developing a set of rules of thumb for decision making which are widely recognized and accepted throughout the industry. Generally, these rules of thumb seem crude and far from efficient means of adjustment, but they may be the instruments of survival in a "prisoner's dilemma" situation.

Let us study one means by which the competitors described above might mitigate their situation short of collusion. Remember that this market is characterized by the demand curve $Q = 12 - 2P$. Let us assume:

1. Each competitor imagines a demand curve for his individual product, of the form $q_1 = a_1 - b_1 P_1$ for the first firm, and $q_2 = a_2 - b_2 P_2$ for the second. In this form of a demand equation $b_i \geq 0$.
2. Each competitor is fairly confident that he can predict the reaction of his customers to a given price change. That is, firm 1 thinks it knows the value $-b_1$, the slope of its demand curve; and firm 2 thinks it knows the value $-b_2$. However, each is uncertain about the parameter a, which indicates the general level of demand.
3. The entrepreneurs' psychology is consistent with the level of aspiration model: If a firm makes an estimate of a and therefore establishes a profit goal, and the actual profits fall short of this goal, the firm will tend to reduce its estimate of a. Conversely, if the realized profits are greater than the profit goal, the firm will tend to raise its estimate of a.
4. Each firm will try to maximize its profits consistent with the individual demand for its product.
5. Only one price can rule in the market at one time.

Consider firm 1. It desires to maximize its profits subject to the demand $q_1 = a_1 - b_1 P_1$ and the fixed charges of six. Profits are defined for firm 1 as $\pi_1 = a_1 P_1 - b_1 P_1^2 - 6$. They will be maximized with respect to a price choice when:[8]

$$\frac{d\pi_1}{dP_1} = a_1 - 2b_1 P_1 = 0$$

or

$$a_1 = 2b_1 P_1$$

---

[8] The second-order condition holds.

If we substitute this value for a_1 in the individual demand for firm 1, we get $q_1 = b_1 P_1$. Similar calculation for firm 2 yields $q_2 = b_2 P_2$.

The sum of the outputs of the two firms must equal the market production, Q. Substituting $q_1 + q_2$ for Q in the equation

$$Q = 12 - 2P$$

the market demand may be written:

$$q_1 + q_2 = 12 - 2P$$

or

$$q_1 + q_2 + 2P = 12.$$

We now have three independent equations. Since only one price may rule in the market, $P_1 = P_2 = P$, and we have only three unknowns:

$$\begin{aligned} q_1 + q_2 + 2P &= 12 \\ q_1 - b_1 P &= 0 \\ q_2 - b_2 P &= 0 \end{aligned}$$

The equilibrium price is defined (after substitution) as:

$$P = \frac{12}{2 + b_1 + b_2}.$$

Will the parties actually converge on this price? They might if they make reasonably conservative adjustments in the direction suggested by the level-of-aspiration model.

What does the model mean? For an example, assume each firm estimates that the slope of its individual demand curve is the same as the slope of the market demand curve. Thus, $b_1 = b_2 = 2$, and $P = \dfrac{12}{2 + 2 + 2} = 2$. Each firm will produce four units and make a profit of two units. These profits are at a maximum with respect to the individual demand curve assumed to face the firms.

It might be charged that it is naïve for the entrepreneurs to ignore their mutual dependence and assume that their individual demand curves have the same slope as the market demand curve.[9] But if they are prohibited by law from open collusion or merger, and if there is no such prohibition against naïveté, this approach may be the most direct means for avoiding the losses associated with the "rational" prisoner's dilemma solution.

If each entrepreneur estimated his customers' response to be of

---

[9] This is, in effect, what Cournot does in the development of his model. The result described above coincides with the Cournot result. See Chamberlin (1956).

the sort such that $b_1 = b_2 = 1$, then the monopoly solution would obtain. Thus:

$$P = \frac{12}{2 + 1 + 1} = 3$$
$$q_1 = 3$$
$$q_2 = 3$$
$$\pi_1 = 3$$
$$\pi_2 = 3$$

This might very well happen for only two firms competing over a period of time (with a stable demand and good market information). However, it would seem unlikely that several firms would be capable of making and maintaining estimates of the sort that would produce a monopoly adjustment. For example, if there were four firms in this industry, the monopoly adjustment would obtain if each estimated b equal to $\frac{1}{2}$; twenty firms would achieve the maximum joint profits with b values of $\frac{1}{10}$, and so forth. Firms with many competitors would have to imagine that their customers were less responsive to price changes than firms with few competitors. Therefore, it seems reasonable to suppose that such industries might find an adjustment somewhere between the monopoly solution and the "prisoner's dilemma."

APPENDIX

DERIVATION OF MARGINAL REVENUE RELATIONSHIP

To see why

$$\frac{\Delta(P_i Q_i)}{\Delta Q_i} = P_i + Q_i \frac{\Delta P_i}{\Delta Q_i}$$

interpret $P_i Q_i$ as an area obtained by multiplying Q_i width by P_i height (see Figure 22–4).

A small change in the area is approximated by $P_i \Delta Q_i + \Delta P_i Q_i$. The area $\Delta P_i \Delta Q_i$ (a very small quantity times a very small quantity) is assumed to approach zero if Δ is very small. Thus:

$$\Delta(P_i Q_i) = P_i \Delta Q_i + Q_i \Delta P_i$$

or, dividing both sides by ΔQ_i:

$$\frac{\Delta(P_i Q_i)}{\Delta Q_i} = P_i \frac{\Delta Q_i}{\Delta Q_i} + Q_i \frac{\Delta P_i}{\Delta Q_i}$$

FIGURE 22–4

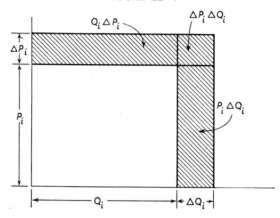

and since

$$\frac{\Delta Q_i}{\Delta Q_i} = 1$$

$$\frac{\Delta(P_iQ_i)}{\Delta Q_i} = P_i + Q_i\frac{\Delta P_i}{\Delta Q_i}.$$

BIBLIOGRAPHY

CHAMBERLIN, E. H.   *The Theory of Monopolistic Competition.* Cambridge: Harvard University Press, 1956.

FOURAKER, L. E.   "Product Differentiation and Straight Line Indifference Curves," *American Economic Review*, May, 1958.

NUTTER, H. M.   "The Plateau Demand Curve and Utility Theory," *Journal of Political Economy*, December, 1955.

SAMUELSON, P. A.   *Economics: An Introductory Analysis.* New York: McGraw-Hill Book Co., Inc., 1961.

SCITOVSKY, T.   *Welfare and Competition.* Homewood, Ill.: Richard D. Irwin, Inc., 1951.

SHUBIK, M.   *Strategy and Market Structure.* New York: John Wiley & Sons, Inc., 1959.

TARSHIS, L.   *The Elements of Economics.* Boston: Houghton Mifflin Co., 1947.

PROBLEMS

22–1. You are trying to estimate the parameters of a linear demand curve of the form $Q = A + bP$. You estimate that the market would absorb 500 units of the product if it were free. Further, if you charged a price of eight, you estimate that you could sell 100 units.

Determine the values for A and b, and plot the curve on graph paper.

22–2. You are given this sales equation:

$$Q_i = 100 - 10P_i - 5P_j - 0.001Y + 4M$$

a) What will the sales be if $P_i = P_j = Y = M = 0$?
b) If P_i alone is increased by two units, what will happen to sales?
c) Is product j a complement or a substitute for product i?
d) If income increases by 5,000 units, what will happen to sales?
e) Is product i an inferior or a superior good?

22–3. For the demand curve $Q = 500 - 50P$:
a) What is the elasticity of demand when $P = 1$ and when $P = 8$?
b) At what price does the demand curve have unit elasticity?
c) What is total revenue when $E = -1$?

22–4. The consumer price index is 100, and your income is $400 per month. Next year, you get a raise to $500 per month, but the price index goes up to 200. Has your real income increased?

22–5. Say that you are given a demand curve of the form $P = \dfrac{A}{b} + \dfrac{1}{b}Q$, specifically $P = 10 - 0.1Q$. Wholesale costs are constant and equal to two.
a) What is the equation for total revenue?
b) What is the total revenue when $Q = 39$ and when $Q = 41$? What is marginal revenue over this interval? What is your estimate of marginal revenue at $Q = 40$?
c) What is the equation for total wholesale costs?
d) What is the total wholesale cost when $Q = 39$ and when $Q = 41$? What is marginal cost over this interval? What is your estimate of marginal cost at $Q = 40$?
e) What output and price maximize profits in this example? What are those profits?
f) What is the relative margin at this price?
g) What is the negative reciprocal of elasticity $\left(-\dfrac{1}{E} \right)$ at this price?
h) Plot the demand curve and the constant wholesale cost on graph paper. Plot the value of $-\dfrac{1}{E}$ for several different quantity values. If you connected these points with a line, what sign would its slope have? Plot the value of $\dfrac{m}{P}$ for several different quantity values. If you connected them with a line, what sign would its slope have? Where would the lines intersect?

22–6. In the course of an interview, a businessman discloses that his firm follows a practice of maintaining a constant 0.25 relative margin for a certain product, even though its wholesale price varies substantially. In another part of the interview the businessman indicates that for this product, he thinks sales will increase from their current level of 100,000 units to 120,000 units in response to a reduction in price from $3.00 to $2.70. Is the management's margin practice consistent with its judgment regarding demand elasticity and profit maximization?

22-7. Plot the demand curve $P = \dfrac{100}{Q_i}$ What is the elasticity between any two prices?

22-8. If wholesale costs are constant and there is an increase in a linear demand curve, how should the absolute and relative margins behave if profits are maximized?

22-9. Given the following relationship between sales and other factors:

$$Q_i = 10 - 0.04P_i + 0.02P_j + 0.01Y + 0.1M.$$

a) What are sales when $P_i = 100$, $P_j = 50$, $Y = 1,000$, and $M = 20$?

b) Assuming P_j, Y, and M are fixed, what is the demand curve of this firm?

c) What is the relationship between product i and product j?

d) Is product i inferior or superior?

e) Graph the effect on demand of an increase in M of 30 units to a level of 50.

22-10. It has been observed that absolute margins rise with the wholesale price of fresh produce, but the relative margin falls. What type of demand curve does this imply for this product, assuming the firms are maximizing profits?

22-11. a) Derive the game matrix for two price competitors faced with the market demand $Q = 100 - P$ and individual fixed costs of $500 each. Assume the only available prices are in multiples of $10.

b) What is the equilibrium price, quantity, and profit in game theory terms?

c) What is the monopoly solution?

d) What would be the solution if each firm acted as if it were confronted with a demand curve of the form $q = a - P$? What would be the effect of a third firm entering this market, with the same assumptions regarding consumer behavior?

Chapter 23

PRICES AND CONSUMER PREFERENCES

CONSUMERS have preferences, or brand loyalties, among the various products designed to meet identical consumer needs. It is possible, in most markets, for rival products to be priced differently without causing all of the customers to shift to the lowest priced product. Many buyers will pay a premium for some preferred product, indicating that their preference is, in some sense, stronger than the price differential. Clearly, the preference position of a product should be considered when determining a price policy.

The measure we shall employ in the analysis of consumer preferences is the marginal rate of substitution of competing products for your product. This ratio, S_{ri}, reflects the rate at which a specific consumer is willing to exchange a rival product, r, for your product, i. Since the products are designed to meet the same consumer needs, we assume S_{ri} to be a constant for any given consumer at a given time. For empirical support of this assumption and a more extensive theoretical treatment, see Fouraker (1958) and Nutter (1955). For example, say a customer has a marginal rate of substitution of two units of r for one unit of i. This degree of preference could be represented by linear indifference curves, as in Figure 23–1. The first indifference curve, I_1, indicates that the consumer derives a certain amount of satisfaction, measured by the index I_1, from two units of product r, and the same amount of satisfaction from one unit of product i. Further, any linear combination of r and i such as $Q_r + 2Q_i = 2$, where $Q_r \geq 0$ and $Q_i \geq 0$, will yield the same satisfaction associated with I_1.

The second indifference curve indicates that satisfaction measured by I_2 is derived from the various combinations $Q_r + 2Q_i = 4$, $Q_r \geq 0$, $Q_i \geq 0$, and $I_2 > I_1$.

Now, say the price of r and the price of i are the same, and the individual has enough income to buy two units of one or the other.

FIGURE 23–1

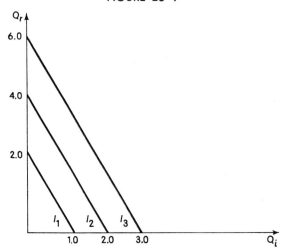

FIGURE 23–1

Would he buy r exclusively, i exclusively, or some combination of the two products? The solution may be seen in Figure 23–2, where the dotted line represents the budget line of the consumer (i.e., he can afford any combination of Q_r and Q_i on the dotted line). If the consumer bought r exclusively, he would derive satisfaction associated with I_1; if he bought some combination of Q_r and Q_i (represented by a point on the budget line), he would receive satisfaction I_j where $I_1 < I_j < I_2$. If he bought product i exclusively, he would achieve the highest level of satisfaction consistent with his budget constraint, I_2. Since we assume consumers prefer more satisfaction to less, we

FIGURE 23–2

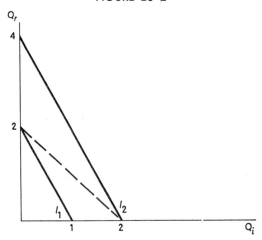

would predict that this consumer would buy product i exclusively. Indeed, as long as product i costs less than twice as much as product r, this consumer would continue to buy product i exclusively (he could be said to prefer product i in this price range). If product i costs exactly twice as much as product r, the consumer would be indifferent between buying r exclusively, i exclusively, or some combination of the products. If the price of i was more than twice the price of r, this consumer would switch to the exclusive purchase of r.

Other consumers will not have the same degree of preference between products r and i (if they did, the two products would be parts of a homogeneous commodity, a rare phenomenon outside of agriculture). Say another consumer will want one unit of i for 0.8 units of r, i.e., he has a marginal rate of substitution between r and i of 0.8 ($S_{ri} = 0.8$).[1] If $P_r = P_i$, this consumer will buy product r. In general, if $S_{ri} < \dfrac{P_i}{P_r}$, the consumer will buy product r; if $S_{ri} = \dfrac{P_i}{P_r}$, the consumer is indifferent between the products; if $S_{ri} > \dfrac{P_i}{P_r}$, the consumer will buy product i.

FREQUENCY DISTRIBUTION OF PREFERENCES

Consider the set of all customers in the market for which products r and i are competing. It is conceivable that the S_{ri} for each of these consumers can be estimated and placed in an array, from the lowest value to the highest. If we associated the number of units of the commodity (either product r or product i) purchased by the consumer with his S_{ri}, and plotted the result, we might get a distribution such as that shown in Figure 23–3. Such a distribution might be considered the parent population of preferences between products r and i. Such a distribution would have a central tendency which might be measured by one of the averages, say the arithmetic mean. We define the mean preference $\overline{S}_{ri}$ as the sum of individual consumers' marginal rates of substitutions weighted by the quantity of purchases of either product r or product i ($Q_{r,i}$), divided by total sales (Q) in the market. Thus, for n consumers:

---

[1] Think of S_{ri} as being $S_{r \to i}$, where the arrow indicates we are moving from product r to i and the S_{ri} of 0.8 measures the amount of r we shall give up for each unit of i. Technically, as we use it in this book, S_{ri} is the absolute value of the marginal rate of substitution.

FIGURE 23–3

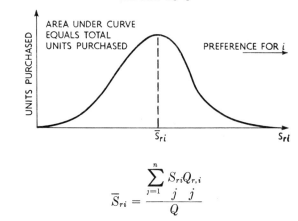

$$(23-1) \qquad \overline{S}_{ri} = \frac{\sum_{j=1}^{n} S_{r i} Q_{r,i}}{Q}$$

where the j marks the preferences and purchases of the jth person.

The preferences among the consumers are dispersed around this mean, reflecting differences in tastes. A measure of the dispersion is the standard deviation, which is defined as follows:

$$(23-2) \qquad \sigma_{S_{ri}} = \sqrt{\frac{\sum_{j=1}^{n} (S_{ri} - \overline{S}_{ri})^2 \, Q_{r,i}}{Q}}.$$

If consumers do not distinguish between products r and i (i.e., if they are parts of a homogeneous commodity), the σ_{Sri} will be zero. The more consumers differentiate between the products and disagree on their relative merits, the larger σ_{Sri} will become. Therefore, it is an index of the degree of differentiation or brand loyalty between the products.

For any price ratio P_i/P_r, it will be possible to determine how the market will be divided between the two products. For all $S_{ri} > P_i/P_r$ the consumers will buy product i; for $S_{ri} < P_i/P_r$ the consumers will buy product r; for $S_{ri} = P_i/P_r$, they are indifferent. In terms of the graphic analysis, let Figure 23–4 represent a preference distribution with a specific price ratio, P_i/P_r. The area under the curve represents the entire market for both products; the shaded area to the right of P_i/P_r represents product i's share of the market; the unshaded area to the left of P_i/P_r represents product r's share of the market. The producer of product i can increase his share of the market by reducing the ratio P_i/P_r. This might be accomplished by (1) reducing P_i faster than the rival reduces P_r and (2) increasing P_i slower than the rival increases P_r. Thus the ratio P_i/P_r is not under the exclusive control of either producer, and plans or programs must be contingent upon the anticipated behavior of the rival. For example, if the producer of i knew that the producer of r would match by a proportionate reduction any price cuts he instituted, it would be impossible for producer i to reduce the ratio P_i/P_r, and he would probably be reluctant to start a price war. While proportionate price reductions

FIGURE 23-4

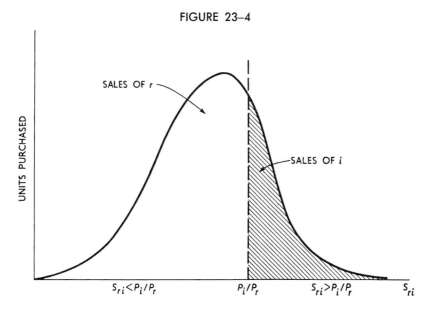

by both parties would increase the size of the market, they would leave the shares unchanged.

ESTIMATING THE DISTRIBUTION OF PREFERENCES

The producer generally does not know the dimensions of the preference distribution between his product and those of competitors. This is especially true when a new product is being considered, or when a competitor brings out a new product. A survey of the entire population of potential customers usually is too expensive to be considered, and the manager must rely on partial information derived from samples. We shall outline sampling procedures in the context of a pricing decision where share of the market is the major criterion.

Assume you devise an experimental means of approximating a consumer's marginal rate of substitution between r and i. A random sample of seventeen potential buyers of the product is selected (a sample is random if each element in the population has an equal chance of being chosen for the sample), and the marginal rate of substitution of r for i for each of the subjects is estimated. The resulting data are presented in Table 23–1, where $X = S_{ri}$. It is our purpose to use this sample in creating a satistical description of consumer preferences in the entire market for products r and i. This must be done if we are to judge what effect our pricing decision will have on share of market.

TABLE 23–1

Subject's Marginal Rate of Substitution between r and i $X = S_{ri}$	Deviation $X - \overline{X}$	Squared Deviations $(X - \overline{X})^2$
0.9	−0.4	0.16
0.8	−0.5	0.25
1.0	−0.3	0.09
1.6	0.3	0.09
1.3	0.0	0.00
1.0	−0.3	0.09
1.4	0.1	0.01
1.3	0.0	0.00
1.5	0.2	0.04
1.1	−0.2	0.04
1.8	0.5	0.25
1.3	0.0	0.00
1.7	0.4	0.16
1.4	0.1	0.01
1.7	0.4	0.16
1.0	−0.3	0.09
1.3	0.0	0.00
22.1	0.0	1.44
$\overline{X} = 1.3$		

$$\sigma_P = \sqrt{\frac{\Sigma(X - \overline{X})^2}{N - 1}} = \sqrt{\frac{1.44}{16}} = 0.3$$

$$\sigma_{\overline{x}} = \frac{0.3}{\sqrt{17}} = 0.073.$$

A statistical description consists of statements regarding the central tendency and dispersion of a distribution; in this case the distribution is that of measures of consumer preferences.

If we were limited to one estimate of the true arithmetic mean of marginal rates of substitution between r and i, we would guess 1.3, the arithmetic mean of the sample. However, it would be a coincidence if the sample mean and the true mean were identical. It is known, from the central limit theorem, that sample means will in general form a normal distribution around the true mean of the population. The dispersion of this distribution of sample means is measured by the standard deviation of sample means, $\sigma_{\bar{x}}$. This statistic is calculated from the following formula:

$$(23\text{-}3) \qquad \sigma_{\bar{x}} = \frac{\sqrt{\dfrac{(X - \bar{X})^2}{N - 1}}}{\sqrt{N}} = \frac{\sigma_P}{\sqrt{N}}$$

where

    X = Observed value
    $\bar{X}$ = Sample mean
    N = Number of observations in sample
    σ_P = Estimated standard deviation of the population.

The relationships are sketched in Figure 23–5. In our example, from Table 23–1, we see that $\sigma_P = 0.3$ and $\sigma_{\bar{x}} = 0.073$. If the sample means are distributed normally, we can make probability statements about intervals around the sample mean including the true

FIGURE 23–5

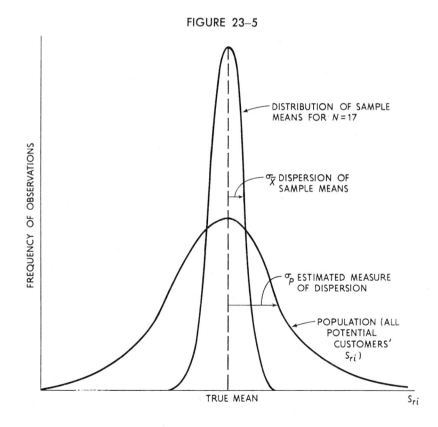

mean. From the normal table, we know that 0.95 of the sample means will fall within ±1.96 standard deviations of sample means of the true mean. An equivalent statement would be: "If you take a sample mean and add and subtract 1.96 standard deviations of sample means, the resulting range will include the true mean in approximately 95 out of 100 such experiments." Thus, in our problem the *0.95 confidence interval* may be calculated as follows:

$$\overline{X} \pm 1.96 \, \sigma_{\bar{x}} = 1.30 \pm 0.14, \text{ or } 1.16 \text{ to } 1.44.$$

Other intervals pertaining to the true mean might be desired for decision purposes. They can be calculated readily when given the sample mean, the standard deviation of sample means, and Table B (in the Appendix at the end of the text). For example, the 0.5 confidence interval would be:

$$\overline{X} \pm 0.67 \, \sigma_{\bar{x}} = 1.30 \pm 0.05, \text{ or } 1.25 \text{ to } 1.35.$$

The proper interpretation of such a statement is: "For a large number of sample means, it is expected that the construction of this interval $(\overline{X} \pm 0.67 \, \sigma_{\bar{x}})$ will include the true mean in half the cases."

We have seen that the standard deviation of the population may be estimated from the sample. If the population has a distribution that is approximately normal, this parameter may be used in making statements about the distribution of the population. In our example the estimated standard deviation of the population σ_P was 0.3. From Table B (in the Appendix at the end of the text), we can see that, for example, the probability of an item deviating by +2.33 standard deviations from the mean is roughly 0.01. If the true mean of consumers' preferences were 1.44, we could conclude that if we set a price of 2.14 times the price of product r, only 0.01 of the customers would continue to buy our product, for only 0.01 of the customers would have a marginal rate of substitution of 2.14 or greater.[2] Similarly, if the true mean marginal rate of substitution is 1.16, we could acquire half of the market by setting our price at 1.16 times the price of r (since 0.50 of the customers will have preference ratios greater than this number). If the true mean was 1.25 and we wanted approximately 0.80 of the market, we would set our price at one $[1.25 - 0.84(0.3) = 1.00]$ times r, i.e., we would set the same price as the competing price. Since we do not know the true mean for certain but can make confidence interval statements about it, it would seem appropriate to develop a table such as Table 23–2. The specific

---

[2] $1.44 + 2.33 \, (\sigma_P) = 1.44 + 0.7 = 2.14.$

TABLE 23–2

Price Ratio $\dfrac{P_i}{P_r}$	Your Share of the Market if the True Mean, $\bar{S}_{ri}$, Is—				
	1.44	1.35	1.30	1.25	1.16
0.70............0.99		0.98	0.98	0.96	0.93
0.85............0.97		0.95	0.93	0.91	0.85
1.00............0.93		0.88	0.84	0.80	0.70
1.15............0.83		0.75	0.69	0.63	0.51
1.30............0.69		0.57	0.50	0.43	0.31
1.45............0.49		0.37	0.31	0.25	0.17
1.60............0.30		0.20	0.16	0.12	0.07
1.75............0.15		0.09	0.07	0.05	0.03
1.90............0.07		0.04	0.02	0.02	0.01

confidence interval or intervals that are used are a matter of discretion of the decision maker; there is nothing intrinsically superior about the levels we have selected. Ideally they should be derived from cost considerations.

Figure 23–6 may be viewed from different perspectives, each having some merit for the decision-making process confronting the management. One approach is implicit in the construction of Table 23–2. For any price ratio selected by the management of the firm producing product i, the probable share of the market going to the firm may be read from Figure 23–6. The best single estimate of the share of market is read from the central solid line, which is associ-

FIGURE 23–6

Relative Demand for Product i with 0.95 Probability

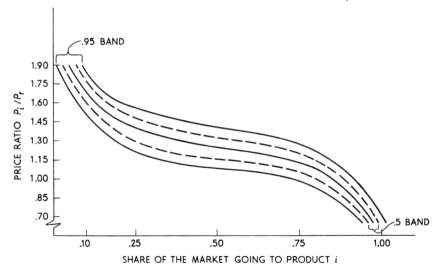

ated with the proposition that the true mean marginal rate of substitution and the sample mean marginal rate of substitution are
the same. If the selected price ratio is 1.15, the best single estimate
of share of market is 0.69, since the sample mean was 1.3. However,
the probability that the share of market will be exactly 0.69 is quite
small, even allowing for rounding. A more informative statement is
that if the price ratio is 1.15, the chances are 50–50 that the share of
market will fall in the range 0.63 to 0.75. This range is symmetric—
we would assign a probability of 0.25 that the share of market for
product i would be below 0.63 and a probability of 0.25 that the
share of market would be greater than 0.75 (see Table 23–2).

If a wider confidence interval was required, we could assert that a
price ratio of 1.15 would lead to a share of market between 0.51 and
0.83, with a probability of 0.95. Since this interval also is symmetric,
you could make the alternative statement to management that a
price ratio of 1.15 would assure it of over half the market, with a
probability of 0.975.

An alternative approach to the interpretation of Figure 23–6 is to:

1. Select the desired share of market.
2. Move vertically until the desired band is reached.
3. Read the associated price ratio from the vertical axis.

The selection of the band depends upon management's willingness not to achieve the desired share of market. If the price ratio
is read from the reference point of the lowest solid line, the probability is 0.975 that the product will acquire at least the share of market which served as a point of departure. If the price ratio is taken
from the lowest broken line, the probability of achieving at least the
desired share of market is reduced to 0.75. The central solid line
yields a probability of 0.50, and so forth.

CONCLUSION

We have seen how share of the market is determined by the price
ratio P_i/P_r. However, this price ratio is not subject to the exclusive control of either producer. You may try to increase your share
of the market by reducing P_i and therefore reducing the ratio
P_i/P_r. Such a strategy will work only against weak, sluggish, or
timorous opposition. Many active competitors would meet your price
reduction (thus keping P_i/P_r a constant), or join battle by reducing
P_r by more than your cut in P_i (thereby giving you a smaller share of
market).

The trend of pricing patterns in American industry is to establish a price ratio by institutional means such as customary prices, rules of thumb, price leadership, and traditional ratios. Rivalry among producers then is directed to the area of merchandising.

BIBLIOGRAPHY

See the Bibliography of Chapter 22.

PROBLEMS

23–1. A certain customer has a marginal rate of substitution between your product (i) and your rival's product (r) of $S_{ri} = 1.2$. Explain what this means in your own words.

    a) If you and your rival charge the same price, which product will this customer buy?

    b) If your price is 0.50 higher than your rival's price, which product will this customer buy?

    c) If your price is 0.20 higher than your rival's, which product will this customer buy?

23–2. The marginal rate of substitution between products x and y is $S_{xy} = 2$ for a certain customer. Plot a typical indifference curve for this customer, with product x on the vertical axis and product y on the horizontal axis. What is the absolute value of the slope of this indifference curve?

23–3. If $S_{xy} = 2$ and $P_y/P_x = 1.5$, which product will the consumer buy, and why?

23–4. The dispersion of preferences between products z and m is $\sigma_{Szm} = 0$. What does this mean?

23–5. If a consumer's marginal rate of substitution of a for b is 1.5, what is his marginal rate of substitution of b for a?

23–6. You are given this information: $P_i/P_r = 0.9$. There are three customers: a, with $S_{ri} = 1.3$, who will buy six units of the product; b, with $S_{ri} = 0.8$, who will buy nine units of the product; and c, with $S_{ri} = 1.4$, who will buy five units of the product. Calculate the mean preference and the standard deviation of the preferences.

23–7. For product a and its rival the dispersion of preferences is $\sigma_{Sri} = 1.6$; for product b and its rival the dispersion of preferences is $\sigma_{Sri} = 6.3$. Which product is more susceptible to encroachment by the rival product via the means of price reduction?

23–8. You are given the following information: A sample of preferences of twenty-five customers is taken (they buy only one unit of the product per period, so weights are identical). The sample mean preference is $\bar{S}_{ri} = 1.2$. The estimate of the standard deviation of population preferences (σ) is 1.0. What price should you charge if you want at least half of the market, with probability 0.95?

Chapter 24

MERCHANDISING DECISIONS

UNDER CERTAINTY

By MERCHANDISING, we mean efforts to change the consumer's preferences in favor of the product being offered for sale. Merchandising activity would include all selling effort: advertising, sales promotion, salaries of salesmen, etc.

Merchandising may affect consumer preferences in two fundamentally different ways:

1. It may induce customers to buy the commodity produced by the industry of which your firm is a part, rather than either buying commodities produced by other industries or saving such funds. This type of merchandising effect increases the size of the market, which we shall identify by the symbol Q.
2. It may induce established consumers of rival products to switch to the purchase of your product. This type of merchandising effect increases your share of the market, designated by the fraction a (that is, $0 \leq a \leq 1$). We shall separate these two types of merchandising effects for analytical purposes.

Another basis of classification is in terms of the assumed relationship between the merchandising expenditures of other firms and the merchandising outlay of the decision maker. In this chapter, we shall assume that the merchandising efforts of other firms can be estimated independently, and are not directly altered by the decision of the firm under consideration.

SIZE-OF-MARKET DECISION

The sales of the commodity, Q, will be related in some manner to the aggregate of the merchandising efforts of the firms in the industry. Let A_i represent the merchandising expenditures of the ith firm, and assume that these expenditures are designed solely to increase the size of the market, it being assumed that the firm's share of the market will remain constant. If there are n firms in the industry, the sum of all such expenditures will be designated by

$$\sum_{i=1}^{n} A_i = A_1 + A_2 + , \ldots , + A_n.$$

We assume that the normal relationship between Q and $\sum_{1=i}^{n} A_i$ will be as shown in Figure 24–1; that is, we assume that merchandising efforts are subject to diminishing returns, so that continued applica-

FIGURE 24–1

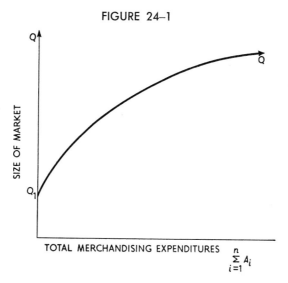

tion of uniform increments of merchandising effort will eventually lead to smaller and smaller positive increments to total sales. The sales of the industry represented in Figure 24–1 would be Q_1 if there was no merchandising effort to increase the size of market. Sales increase at a decreasing rate as merchandising expenditures rise. A large number of algebraic functions would have this desired property; a specific algebraic example of this type of function would be

$$Q = Q_1 + \left(\sum_{i=1}^{n} b_i A_i \right)^{\frac{1}{K}}, \quad (K > 1)$$

where b_i is some index of the effectiveness of the ith firm's merchandising effort and K is some index of consumer resistance to sales effort for this commodity. For example, let $Q_1 = 800$ units, $n = 2$, $b_1 = 1.0$, $b_2 = 1.2$ (indicating that the second firm was more effective in its merchandising effort than the first), and $K = 2$. Then the equation would read:

$$Q = 800 + (A_1 + 1.2A_2)^{1/2}.$$

If the first firm spent 13 units on merchandising and the second firm spent 10 units, the sales would be:

$$Q = 800 + (13 + 12)^{1/2}$$
$$Q = 800 + (25)^{1/2} = 805.$$

If these expenditures were approximately doubled to $A_1 = 25$ and $A_2 = 24$, sales would increase only to 807. Larger selling expenditures would exert even less proportional leverage on the amount of sales.

The optimum merchandising strategy for firm y may be approximated as follows: The operating profit, exclusive of selling costs and fixed overhead, which we shall call gross profit (G), will be the amount of the product sold multiplied by the margin per unit, m. The amount sold is determined by multiplying the size of the market, Q, by a, y's share of the market. Profit, π_y, will be this amount of gross profit (G) less the costs of merchandising, A_y. Thus:

$$\pi_y = G - A_y = aQm - A_y.$$

We want to choose that level of merchandising expenditures, A_y, which results in profit being as large as possible. The objective is to increase expenditures as long as increments to merchandising expense (ΔA_y) induce even larger positive increments to gross profit (ΔG), i.e., positive increments to profit $(\Delta \pi_y)$. We would not spend that increment on merchandising when $\Delta G < \Delta A_y$, for this would reduce profit. Therefore, profit will be at a maximum when $\Delta G = \Delta A_y$ (incremental profit equals incremental costs) and marginal profit is negative for larger merchandising expenditures.[1] For example, if we define $G = aQm$ and let

$$Q = Q_1 + \left(\sum_{i=1}^{n} b_i A_i \right)^{\frac{1}{K}}$$

---

[1] In terms of calculus, the conditions for π_y to be a maximum are as follows:

$$\frac{d\pi_y}{dA_y} = \frac{dG}{dA_y} - \frac{dA_y}{dA_y} = 0$$

$$\frac{d^2\pi_y}{dA_y^2} = \frac{d^2G}{dA_y^2} < 0.$$

The first-order condition is the equivalent of requiring that incremental gross profit from merchandising $\left(\frac{dG}{dA_y} \right)$ equal the marginal cost of merchandising $\left(\frac{dA_y}{dA_y} = 1 \text{ in this case} \right)$. The second-order condition is satisfied by our assumption that merchandising activity is subject to diminishing returns.

as we did earlier, then multiplying both sides by am gives:

$$amQ = am\left[Q_1 + \left(\sum_{i=1}^{n} b_i A_i\right)^{\frac{1}{K}}\right].$$

Since

$$\pi_y = G - A_y = aQm - A_y$$

we may substitute the value for amQ:

$$\pi_y = aQ_1 m + am\left(\sum_{i=1}^{n} b_i A_i\right)^{\frac{1}{K}} - A_y, \qquad (K > 1).$$

The optimum merchandising expenditure for the y firm would be:[2]

$$A_y = b_y^{\frac{1}{K-1}}\left(\frac{am}{K}\right)^{\frac{K}{K-1}} - \frac{1}{b_y}\sum_{\substack{i=1 \\ i \neq y}}^{n} b_i A_i.$$

This indicates that in this model the amount the firm will increase its merchandising outlay is directly proportional to:

1. The effectiveness of its selling efforts in increasing the size of market (b_y)
2. Its share of market (a)
3. Its margin (m)

The firm will decrease its merchandising expenditures of this type if there are increases in:

1. Consumer resistance to merchandising efforts (K)
2. The size and effectiveness of the expenditures of other firms on this type of merchandising

---

[2] From the calculus:

$$\frac{d\pi_y}{dA_y} = \frac{1}{K}am\left(\sum_{i=1}^{n} b_i A_i\right)^{\frac{1-K}{K}} b_y - 1 = 0$$

$$\frac{d^2\pi_y}{dA_y^2} = \frac{1-K}{K^2}am\left(\sum_{i=1}^{n} b_i A_i\right)^{\frac{1-2K}{K}} b_y^2 < 0$$

$$\left(\sum_{i=1}^{n} b_i A_i\right)^{\frac{1-K}{K}} = \frac{K}{amb_y}$$

$$\sum_{i=1}^{n} b_i A_i = \left(\frac{K}{amb_y}\right)^{\frac{K}{1-K}} = \left(\frac{amb_y}{K}\right)^{\frac{K}{K-1}}$$

$$A_y = b_y^{\frac{1}{K-1}}\left(\frac{am}{K}\right)^{\frac{K}{K-1}} - \frac{1}{b_y}\sum_{\substack{i=1 \\ i \neq y}}^{n} b_i A_i.$$

MERCHANDISING TO INCREASE THE SHARE OF MARKET

In the previous section, we assumed that the share of market, a, was a constant and Q, the size of market, was a variable. In this section, we shall reverse these assumptions and let Q be fixed while the competing firms try to alter their respective shares of Q by merchandising efforts.

SHARE-OF-MARKET DECISIONS

The objective of this type of merchandising is to change consumer preferences in favor of your product rather than your rival's. For

FIGURE 24–2

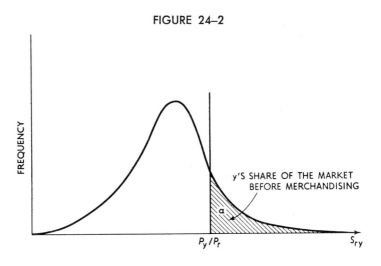

purposes of exposition, let us again assume that we are concerned with a market in which there are two competing products, yours (y) and your rival's (r). Each individual in the market will have a marginal rate of substitution between these products, S_{ry}. The distribution of customer preferences is as shown in Figure 24–2. Assume the rivals have an aversion to price competition so that the price ratio P_y/P_r is a constant. Those customers whose $S_{ry} > P_y/P_r$ will buy y's product; if $S_{ry} < P_y/P_r$, they will buy r's product. The shaded area to the right of the point P_y/P_r represents y's share of the market, a, where $0 \leq a \leq 1$. It is in your interest to shift the *distribution of preferences* to the right, increasing your share of the market, provided this can be done without incurring too much ex-

pense (see Figure 24–3). Such attempts to alter consumer preferences constitute our second class of merchandising efforts.

The merchandising expenditures of this type belonging to y,
represented by A_y, will have some effect on the preferences of the
consumers of the commodity. It is assumed y's expenditures will
have a desirable influence on consumer preferences from y's viewpoint—that they will tend to increase the weighted average marginal
rate of substitution $\bar{S}_{ry}$ (or decrease $\bar{S}_{yr}$). Similarly, the merchandis-

FIGURE 24–3

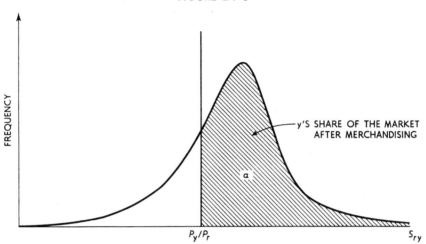

ing efforts of r will tend to have an adverse effect on consumer preferences from y's standpoint. These relationships might be expressed by
some functional arrangement between the marginal rates of substitution and the merchandising activity, such as:

$$\underset{j(t+1)}{S_{ry}} = f(\underset{j(t)}{S_{ry}}, \underset{t}{A_y}, \underset{t}{A_r})$$

where the marginal rate of substitution of the jth individual in time
period $t + 1$ is expressed as a function of his marginal rate of substitution in time period t and the expenditures on merchandising
by y and r in time period t. Further, since

$$\underset{j(t+1)}{S_{ry}} = \left|\frac{\Delta r}{\Delta y}\right|$$

and

$$\underset{j(t+1)}{S_{yr}} = \left|\frac{\Delta y}{\Delta r}\right|$$

we may write

$$\underset{j(t+1)}{S_{ry}} = \underset{j(t+1)}{1/S_{yr}}.$$

It follows that the functional relationship must be one that will satisfy the following requirement:[3]

$$\underset{j(t+1)}{S_{ry}} = \underset{j(t+1)}{1/S_{yr}} = \underset{j(t)\ \ t\ \ t}{f(S_{ry}, A_y, A_r)}.$$

EFFECT OF RIVAL'S EXPENDITURES

Since the effectiveness of y's merchandising expenditures will depend upon r's merchandising expenditures (among other things), an appropriate initial task for y would be to estimate the level of r's outlay for the next period, $\underset{t+1}{A_r}$. Now, on the assumption that r will spend $\underset{t+1}{A_r}$ on merchandising in the $t+1$ period, y may evaluate the profitability of various levels of $\underset{t+1}{A_y}$, y's own merchandising expenditures for the period $t+1$. Specifically, y will be able to assign a certain share of market to each potential level of merchandising expenditure, as shown in Figure 24–4, conditional upon the actual expenditure of r in period $t+1$ being $\underset{t+1}{A_r}$.

This expected share of the market function may be converted into an expected total gross profit function by multiplying it by the factor

---

[3] An example of a function that is satisfactory in this respect is

$$\underset{j(t+1)}{S_{ry}} = \left(\frac{A_y}{A_r}\right)^{\frac{1}{K}} \underset{j(t)}{S_{ry}}$$

$$\underset{j(t+1)}{S_{yr}} = \left(\frac{A_r}{A_y}\right)^{\frac{1}{K}} \underset{j(t)}{S_{yr}} \qquad (K, A_r, A_y \geq 1)$$

where K again is the index of susceptibility of the jth customer to merchandising activity. In this model, if $A_y = A_r$ for period t, the distribution of preferences and the market shares will remain the same. If $A_y > A_r$, for some

$$\underset{g(t)}{S_{ry}} < \frac{P_y}{P_r}$$

$$\underset{g(t+1)}{S_{ry}} > \frac{P_y}{P_r} \qquad (g = 0, \ldots, h)$$

indicating that h customers who had purchased product r in time period t have switched to the purchase of product y in time period $t+1$ as a result of the extra merchandising expenditures on the part of the producer of y. Further increases in the ratio A_y/A_r would induce additional shifts to y's product until, conceivably, y could gain the whole market.

FIGURE 24–4

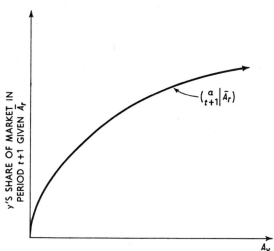

mQ, or margin times the size of the market. This total gross profit function of y is conditional upon manager r doing what is expected of him, since it incorporates such a condition. It may be compared with a total merchandising cost function (which will be a 45-degree line through the origin, since A_y is the variable on the horizontal axis), such as shown in Figure 24–5. The greatest expected profit occurs where $G > A_y$ and the vertical distance between the two functions is at a maximum. This point may be identified in Figure 24–5 as the one where the slope of the total gross profit curve equals the

FIGURE 24–5

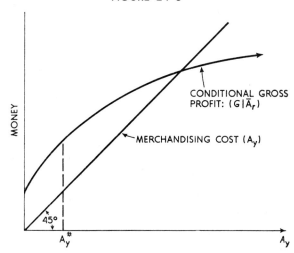

slope of the merchandising cost curve, which in this case is equal to one. The merchandising outlay which provides this adjustment is marked $A_y{}^*$.

Manager r will be faced with a similar decision. Assume he estimates the merchandising expenditures that y might make in time period $t + 1$, and derives an estimate of this parameter. He then may be assumed to calculate his expected gross profit function, conditional upon $_{t+1}A_y$. This function, in conjunction with r's merchandising costs, determines some $_{t+1}A_r{}^*$ which maximizes his expected profits for period $t + 1$. Now, if (1) r's estimate of y's expenditures A_y is correct and (2) y's estimate of r's expenditures A_r is correct, the two firms may be said to be in equilibrium.

Example

A numerical example may be of some use in understanding the model. Let the size of the market be $Q = 80,000$, y's margin be \$3.00 per unit, r's margin be \$4.00 per unit, and the price ratio be

TABLE 24–1

$S_{ry}(t)$	Proportion of Customers	
0.4	0.02 ⎫	
0.6	0.03 ⎪	
0.8	0.06 ⎬ $P_y/P_r = 1.5$	
1.0	0.12 ⎪ $a_r = 0.58$ (r's share of market)	
1.2	0.15 ⎪	
1.4	0.20 ⎭	
1.6	0.18 ⎫	
1.8	0.14 ⎬ Customers with $S_{ry} > P_y/P_r = 1.5$	
2.0	0.06 ⎪ $a_y = (0.18 + 0.14 + 0.06 + 0.04) = 0.42$	
2.2	0.04 ⎭	
	1.00	

$P_y/P_r = 1.5$. The most recent market survey at y's disposal indicates that an approximate discrete distribution of consumer preferences for the current period is as shown in Table 24–1. All customers with an $S_{ry} > P_y/P_r$ will buy product y (0.42 of the market), and all customers with $S_{ry} < P_y/P_r$ will buy product r (0.58 of the market). The problem is to determine the optimum merchandising strategy for the next period, $t + 1$.

The manager of y must:

1. Estimate the merchandising expenditures of the producer of r for the period $t + 1$.
2. Estimate the effectiveness of y's own merchandising efforts in this context.

Say that on the basis of past experience, y feels the expected relationship between consumer preferences in one period and in the ensuing period is given by the equation:

$$S_{ry} \atop t+1 = (A_y/A_r)^{1/2} S_{ry} \atop t .$$

Assume y estimates that his rival will spend \$100,000 on merchandising in period $t + 1$. If y spends \$115,000 on merchandising in period $t + 1$, the expected marginal rate of substitution for the jth individual would be:

$$S_{ry} \atop j(t+1) = (1.15)^{1/2} S_{ry} \atop j(t) = 1.07 S_{ry} \atop j(t) .$$

and the array in Table 24–1 would be transformed to that of Table 24–2.

TABLE 24–2

S_{ry} (t)	$S_{ry} = 1.07 \cdot S_{ry}$ (t + 1) $\qquad$ (t)	Proportion of Customers	
0.4	0.43	0.02	
0.6	0.64	0.03	$P_y/P_r = 1.5$
0.8	0.86	0.06	$a_r = 0.38$
1.0	1.07	0.12	
1.2	1.28	0.15	
1.4	1.50+	0.20	
1.6	1.71	0.18	Customers with $S_{ry} > P_y/P_r = 1.5$
1.8	1.93	0.14	$a_y = 0.62$
2.0	2.14	0.06	
2.2	2.35	0.04	

Thus, y would expect to get 0.62 of the market of 80,000 units, or sales of 49,600 units. Since the margin of y's product is \$3.00 per unit, y would expect gross profit (net of manufacturing costs) of \$3.00 · \$49,600, or \$148,800. The resulting profit would be \$148,800 less \$115,000 (the merchandising costs), or \$33,800. Since this is the greatest profit among the available alternatives, this is the strategy y would select (see Table 24–3).

Now, assume that the producer of r receives estimates from his research staff and feels he must restrict his action to one of these al-

TABLE 24–3

Computation of Profit for Different Merchandising
Expenditures

1 Merchandising Expenditures A_y $t + 1$	2 Gross Profit $(G\|A_r{}^* = 100,000)$ $t + 1$	3 Profit (Col. 2 − Col. 1)
$ 10,000	$ 0	−$ 10,000
50,000	9,600	− 40,400
57,000	24,000	− 33,000
70,000	57,600	− 12,400
88,000	100,800	12,800
115,000	148,800	33,800
158,000	184,800	26,800
225,500	213,600	− 11,900
354,000	228,000	− 126,000
1,407,000	240,000	− 1,167,000

TABLE 24–4

Expenditures by r A_r	Conditional Gross Profit $(G\|A^*_y = 115,000)$	Profit $G − A_r$
$ 60,000	$ 73,600	$13,600
100,000	121,600	21,600
300,000	320,000	20,000

ternatives (see Table 24–4). The estimated expenditure by y is
$115,000, and the resulting profit associated with the expenditure
levels on A_r under consideration is as shown in Table 24–4. The
greatest profit results from an expenditure of $100,000; and if he
follows this course, an equilibrium will obtain. However, it is a very
unstable equilibrium, resulting largely from the narrow range of r's
alternatives.

SHARE-OF-MARKET AND SIZE-OF-MARKET DECISIONS

In many cases the management may hope that a given merchandising campaign will increase both the size and the share of the
market (in comparison with the results in the absence of merchandising outlays). If we can assume the rival's merchandising expenditures are fixed, the task of selecting the optimum outlay is only
slightly more complicated than the partial cases discussed above.
We have defined the firm's profit as $\pi_y = a_y Qm − A_y$, where a_y is

y's share of market, Q is the size of market, m is the margin, and A_y is the level of merchandising expenditures. Now, if we consider *both* a_y and Q to be functions of A_y and A_r (the rival's merchandising expenditures), then it can be shown by means of the calculus [4] that for a given level of A_r, y's profit is maximized when A_y is chosen so that $E_a + E_Q = D_A$, where E_a is defined as the *share* elasticity of merchandising (the ratio of the relative change in share of market divided by the relative change in y's merchandising expenditures); E_Q is the *size* elasticity of merchandising (the ratio of the relative change in size of market divided by the relative change in your merchandising expenditures); D_A is $\left(\dfrac{1}{1 + \dfrac{\pi}{A}}\right)$. For profit to be maximized, it is necessary for the present value of G minus the present value of A to be positive, using the cost of capital as the discount rate. If these conditions are not met, it is in the interest of the firm not to operate for the next period.[5]

[4] Let $\pi = aQm - A$, where a is some function of A, $a = f(A)$, and Q is some function of A, $Q = g(A)$. Further, say

$$\frac{d^2\pi}{dA^2} < 0$$

Then the first-order condition is:

$$\frac{d\pi}{dA} = \frac{da}{dA}Qm + \frac{dQ}{dA}am - 1 = 0$$

or

$$\frac{da}{dA}Qm + \frac{dQ}{dA}am = 1$$

Divide each side of the equation by Qam:

$$\frac{da}{dA}\cdot\frac{1}{a} + \frac{dQ}{dA}\cdot\frac{1}{Q} = \frac{1}{Qam}$$

Multiply each side of the equation by A:

$$\frac{da}{dA}\cdot\frac{A}{a} + \frac{dQ}{dA}\cdot\frac{A}{Q} = \frac{A}{Qam} = \frac{A}{A + \pi} = \frac{1}{1 + \pi/A}$$

But the first term is E_a, the share elasticity of merchandising; the second term is E_Q, the size elasticity of merchandising; the term $\dfrac{1}{1 + \pi/A}$ is defined as D_A. Therefore:

$$E_a + E_Q = D_A$$

It follows that in the special case, when the size of market is fixed, then $E_a = D_A$; when the share of market is fixed, then $E_Q = D_A$.

[5] It is necessary to remember that π is a profit figure on variable costs and does not reflect fixed costs; i.e., we are not considering the possibility of liquidation. Also, this is a one-period analysis where one outlay is followed by positive proceeds; thus, D_A is unique.

BIBLIOGRAPHY

DORFMAN, R., and STEINER, P. "Optimal Quality and Optimal Advertising," *American Economic Review*, May, 1954.

EVANS, F. B. "Discussion of the Strategy of Market Segmentation," in STOCKMAN, L. H. (ed.). *Advancing Marketing Efficiency*. Chicago: American Marketing Association, 1959.

FRIEDMAN, L. "Game Theory Models in the Allocation of Advertising Expenditures," *Operations Research*, September-October, 1958.

GILLMAN, L. "Operations Analysis and the Theory of Games: An Advertising Example," *Journal of the American Statistical Association*, December, 1950.

MAGEE, J. F. "The Effect of Promotional Effort on Sales," *Journal of the Operations Research Society of America*, February, 1953.

VIDALE, M. L., and WOLFE, H. B. "An Operations Research Study of Sales Response to Advertising," *Operations Research*, June, 1957.

PROBLEMS

24-1. If the size of the market increased from 100,000 units to 108,000 units in response to an increase in total merchandising expenditures from \$600,000 to \$630,000, and then, under comparable conditions, from 140,000 to 154,000 units in response to an increase in expenditures from \$720,000 to \$756,000, are these reactions consistent with our assumptions about diminishing returns?

24-2. If the standard deviation of preferences, $\sigma_{S_{ri}}$, is very large, does this contribute to the attractiveness of an aggressive merchandising campaign or detract from it, other things being equal?

24-3. Let the preference relationship for some customer be given by

$$S_{ry} \atop t+1 = \left(\frac{A_y}{A_r}\right)^{1/3} S_{ry} \atop t.$$

If $S_{ry} \atop (t) = \frac{1}{2}$, how much larger would A_y have to be than A_r to raise $S_{ry} \atop (t+1)$ to 1?

24-4. A customer's preferences may be represented as follows:

$$S_{ry} \atop t+1 = \left(\frac{A_y}{A_r}\right)^{1/2} S_{ry} \atop t.$$

If $S_{ry} \atop t = 2$, $A_r = A_y$, and $P_r = P_y$, which product will the customer buy in time period t? How large would A_r have to grow relative to A_y before the customer would shift in period $t + 1$?

24–5. Say that manager y underestimates r's merchandising expenditures that affect the size of the market in making his decision on how much y should spend on size-of-market merchandising. Will y's profits for the next period be more or less than anticipated?

24–6. Say that manager y underestimates r's share-of-market merchandising expenditures for the next period in his calculations about his share-of-market merchandising outlays. Will y's profits for the next period be more or less than he expected?

24–7. Are the share elasticity and the size elasticity of merchandising measures usually positive? Why?

24–8. Do the share elasticity and the size elasticity of merchandising measures usually decrease as merchandising expenditures increase? Why?

APPENDIX OF TABLES

TABLE A
Present Value of $1
$$(1 + r)^{-n}$$

n	1%	2%	3%	4%	5%	6%	7%	8%	9%	10%
1	0.9901	0.9804	0.9709	0.9615	0.9524	0.9434	0.9346	0.9259	0.9174	0.9091
2	0.9803	0.9612	0.9426	0.9246	0.9070	0.8900	0.8734	0.8573	0.8417	0.8264
3	0.9706	0.9423	0.9151	0.8890	0.8638	0.8396	0.8163	0.7938	0.7722	0.7513
4	0.9610	0.9238	0.8885	0.8548	0.8227	0.7921	0.7629	0.7350	0.7084	0.6830
5	0.9515	0.9057	0.8626	0.8219	0.7835	0.7473	0.7130	0.6806	0.6499	0.6209
6	0.9420	0.8880	0.8375	0.7903	0.7462	0.7050	0.6663	0.6302	0.5963	0.5645
7	0.9327	0.8706	0.8131	0.7599	0.7107	0.6651	0.6227	0.5835	0.5470	0.5132
8	0.9235	0.8535	0.7894	0.7307	0.6768	0.6274	0.5820	0.5403	0.5019	0.4665
9	0.9143	0.8368	0.7664	0.7026	0.6446	0.5919	0.5439	0.5002	0.4604	0.4241
10	0.9053	0.8203	0.7441	0.6756	0.6139	0.5584	0.5083	0.4632	0.4224	0.3855
11	0.8963	0.8043	0.7224	0.6496	0.5847	0.5268	0.4751	0.4289	0.3875	0.3505
12	0.8874	0.7885	0.7014	0.6246	0.5568	0.4970	0.4440	0.3971	0.3555	0.3186
13	0.8787	0.7730	0.6810	0.6006	0.5303	0.4688	0.4150	0.3677	0.3262	0.2897
14	0.8700	0.7579	0.6611	0.5775	0.5051	0.4423	0.3878	0.3405	0.2992	0.2633
15	0.8613	0.7430	0.6419	0.5553	0.4810	0.4173	0.3624	0.3152	0.2745	0.2394
16	0.8528	0.7284	0.6232	0.5339	0.4581	0.3936	0.3387	0.2919	0.2519	0.2176
17	0.8444	0.7142	0.6050	0.5134	0.4363	0.3714	0.3166	0.2703	0.2311	0.1978
18	0.8360	0.7002	0.5874	0.4936	0.4155	0.3503	0.2959	0.2502	0.2120	0.1799
19	0.8277	0.6864	0.5703	0.4746	0.3957	0.3305	0.2765	0.2317	0.1945	0.1635
20	0.8195	0.6730	0.5537	0.4564	0.3769	0.3118	0.2584	0.2145	0.1784	0.1486
21	0.8114	0.6598	0.5375	0.4388	0.3589	0.2942	0.2415	0.1987	0.1637	0.1351
22	0.8034	0.6468	0.5219	0.4220	0.3418	0.2775	0.2257	0.1839	0.1502	0.1228
23	0.7954	0.6342	0.5067	0.4057	0.3256	0.2618	0.2109	0.1703	0.1378	0.1117
24	0.7876	0.6217	0.4919	0.3901	0.3101	0.2470	0.1971	0.1577	0.1264	0.1015
25	0.7798	0.6095	0.4776	0.3751	0.2953	0.2330	0.1842	0.1460	0.1160	0.0923
26	0.7720	0.5976	0.4637	0.3607	0.2812	0.2198	0.1722	0.1352	0.1064	0.0839
27	0.7644	0.5859	0.4502	0.3468	0.2678	0.2074	0.1609	0.1252	0.0976	0.0763
28	0.7568	0.5744	0.4371	0.3335	0.2551	0.1956	0.1504	0.1159	0.0895	0.0693
29	0.7493	0.5631	0.4243	0.3207	0.2429	0.1846	0.1406	0.1073	0.0822	0.0630
30	0.7419	0.5521	0.4120	0.3083	0.2314	0.1741	0.1314	0.0994	0.0754	0.0573
35	0.7059	0.5000	0.3554	0.2534	0.1813	0.1301	0.0937	0.0676	0.0490	0.0356
40	0.6717	0.4529	0.3066	0.2083	0.1420	0.0972	0.0668	0.0460	0.0318	0.0221
45	0.6391	0.4102	0.2644	0.1712	0.1113	0.0727	0.0476	0.0313	0.0207	0.0137
50	0.6080	0.3715	0.2281	0.1407	0.0872	0.0543	0.0339	0.0213	0.0134	0.0085

TABLE B
The Standardized Normal Distribution Function,* $F(s)$

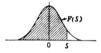

s	0.00	0.01	0.02	0.03	0.04	0.05	0.06	0.07	0.08	0.09
0.0	0.5000	0.5040	0.5080	0.5120	0.5160	0.5199	0.5239	0.5279	0.5319	0.5359
0.1	0.5398	0.5438	0.5478	0.5517	0.5557	0.5596	0.5636	0.5675	0.5714	0.5753
0.2	0.5793	0.5832	0.5871	0.5910	0.5948	0.5987	0.6026	0.6064	0.6103	0.6141
0.3	0.6179	0.6217	0.6255	0.6293	0.6331	0.6368	0.6406	0.6443	0.6480	0.6517
0.4	0.6554	0.6591	0.6628	0.6664	0.6700	0.6736	0.6772	0.6808	0.6844	0.6879
0.5	0.6915	0.6950	0.6985	0.7019	0.7054	0.7088	0.7123	0.7157	0.7190	0.7224
0.6	0.7257	0.7291	0.7324	0.7357	0.7389	0.7422	0.7454	0.7486	0.7517	0.7549
0.7	0.7580	0.7611	0.7642	0.7673	0.7703	0.7734	0.7764	0.7794	0.7823	0.7852
0.8	0.7881	0.7910	0.7939	0.7967	0.7995	0.8023	0.8051	0.8078	0.8106	0.8133
0.9	0.8159	0.8186	0.8212	0.8238	0.8264	0.8289	0.8315	0.8340	0.8365	0.8389
1.0	0.8413	0.8438	0.8461	0.8485	0.8508	0.8531	0.8554	0.8577	0.8599	0.8621
1.1	0.8643	0.8665	0.8686	0.8708	0.8729	0.8749	0.8770	0.8790	0.8810	0.8830
1.2	0.8849	0.8869	0.8888	0.8907	0.8925	0.8944	0.8962	0.8980	0.8997	0.90147
1.3	0.90320	0.90490	0.90658	0.90824	0.90988	0.91149	0.91309	0.91466	0.91621	0.91774
1.4	0.91924	0.92073	0.92220	0.92364	0.92507	0.92647	0.92785	0.92922	0.93056	0.93189
1.5	0.93319	0.93448	0.93574	0.93699	0.93822	0.93943	0.94062	0.94179	0.94295	0.94408
1.6	0.94520	0.94630	0.94738	0.94845	0.94950	0.95053	0.95154	0.95254	0.95352	0.95449
1.7	0.95543	0.95637	0.95728	0.95818	0.95907	0.95994	0.96080	0.96164	0.96246	0.96327
1.8	0.96407	0.96485	0.96562	0.96638	0.96712	0.96784	0.96856	0.96926	0.96995	0.97062
1.9	0.97128	0.97193	0.97257	0.97320	0.97381	0.97441	0.97500	0.97558	0.97615	0.97670
2.0	0.97725	0.97778	0.97831	0.97882	0.97932	0.97982	0.98030	0.98077	0.98124	0.98169
2.1	0.98214	0.98257	0.98300	0.98341	0.98382	0.98422	0.98461	0.98500	0.98537	0.98574
2.2	0.98610	0.98645	0.98679	0.98713	0.98745	0.98778	0.98809	0.98840	0.98870	0.98899
2.3	0.98928	0.98956	0.98983	$0.9^{2}0097$	$0.9^{2}0358$	$0.9^{2}0613$	$0.9^{2}0863$	$0.9^{2}1106$	$0.9^{2}1344$	$0.9^{2}1576$
2.4	$0.9^{2}1802$	$0.9^{2}2024$	$0.9^{2}2240$	$0.9^{2}2451$	$0.9^{2}2656$	$0.9^{2}2857$	$0.9^{2}3053$	$0.9^{2}3244$	$0.9^{2}3431$	$0.9^{2}3613$
2.5	$0.9^{2}3790$	$0.9^{2}3963$	$0.9^{2}4132$	$0.9^{2}4297$	$0.9^{2}4457$	$0.9^{2}4614$	$0.9^{2}4766$	$0.9^{2}4915$	$0.9^{2}5060$	$0.9^{2}5201$
3.0	$0.9^{2}8650$	$0.9^{2}8694$	$0.9^{2}8736$	$0.9^{2}8777$	$0.9^{2}8817$	$0.9^{2}8856$	$0.9^{2}8893$	$0.9^{2}8930$	$0.9^{2}8965$	$0.9^{2}8999$
3.5	$0.9^{3}7674$	$0.9^{3}7759$	$0.9^{3}7842$	$0.9^{3}7922$	$0.9^{3}7999$	$0.9^{3}8074$	$0.9^{3}8146$	$0.9^{3}8215$	$0.9^{3}8282$	$0.9^{3}8347$
4.0	$0.9^{4}6833$	$0.9^{4}6964$	$0.9^{4}7090$	$0.9^{4}7211$	$0.9^{4}7327$	$0.9^{4}7439$	$0.9^{4}7546$	$0.9^{4}7649$	$0.9^{4}7748$	$0.9^{4}7843$

For example: $F(2.41) = .9^{2}2024 = .992024.$

* From A. Hald, *Statistical Tables and Formulas* (New York: John Wiley & Sons, Inc., 1952); reproduced by permission of Professor A. Hald and the publishers.

TABLE C
Continuous Discount Factor—e^{-rt}

rt	e^{-rt}	rt	e^{-rt}	rt	e^{-rt}
.00	1.000	.55	.577	3.40	.033
.01	.990	.60	.549	3.60	.027
.02	.980	.65	.522	3.80	.022
.03	.970	.70	.497	4.00	.018
.04	.961	.75	.472	4.20	.015
.05	.951	.80	.449	4.40	.012
.06	.942	.85	.427	4.60	.010
.07	.932	.90	.407	4.80	.008
.08	.923	.95	.387	5.00	.007
.09	.914	1.00	.368	5.50	.004
.10	.905	1.05	.350	6.00	.002
.11	.896	1.10	.333		
.12	.887	1.15	.317		
.13	.878	1.20	.301		
.14	.869	1.25	.287		
.15	.861	1.30	.273		
.16	.852	1.40	.247		
.17	.844	1.50	.223		
.18	.835	1.60	.202		
.19	.827	1.70	.183		
.20	.819	1.80	.165		
.21	.811	1.90	.150		
.22	.803	2.00	.135		
.23	.795	2.10	.122		
.24	.787	2.20	.111		
.25	.779	2.30	.100		
.26	.771	2.40	.091		
.27	.763	2.50	.082		
.28	.756	2.60	.074		
.29	.748	2.70	.067		
.30	.741	2.80	.061		
.35	.705	2.90	.055		
.40	.670	3.00	.050		
.45	.638	3.10	.045		
.50	.607	3.20	.041		

TABLE D
$N(D)$—Loss Function*

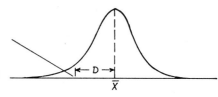

D	.00	.01	.02	.03	.04	.05	.06	.07	.08	.09
.0	.3989	.3940	.3890	.3841	.3793	.3744	.3697	.3649	.3602	.3556
.1	.3509	.3464	.3418	.3373	.3328	.3284	.3240	.3197	.3154	.3111
.2	.3069	.3027	.2986	.2944	.2904	.2863	.2824	.2784	.2745	.2706
.3	.2668	.2630	.2592	.2555	.2518	.2481	.2445	.2409	.2374	.2339
.4	.2304	.2270	.2236	.2203	.2169	.2137	.2104	.2072	.2040	.2009
.5	.1978	.1947	.1917	.1887	.1857	.1828	.1799	.1771	.1742	.1714
.6	.1687	.1659	.1633	.1606	.1580	.1554	.1528	.1503	.1478	.1453
.7	.1429	.1405	.1381	.1358	.1334	.1312	.1289	.1267	.1245	.1223
.8	.1202	.1181	.1160	.1140	.1120	.1100	.1080	.1061	.1042	.1023
.9	.1004	.09860	.09680	.09503	.09328	.09156	.08986	.08819	.08654	.08491
1.0	.08332	.08174	.08019	.07866	.07716	.07568	.07422	.07279	.07138	.06999
1.1	.06862	.06727	.06595	.06465	.06336	.06210	.06086	.05964	.05844	.05726
1.2	.05610	.05496	.05384	.05274	.05165	.05059	.04954	.04851	.04750	.04650
1.3	.04553	.04457	.04363	.04270	.04179	.04090	.04002	.03916	.03831	.03748
1.4	.03667	.03587	.03508	.03431	.03356	.03281	.03208	.03137	.03067	.02998
1.5	.02931	.02865	.02800	.02736	.02674	.02612	.02552	.02494	.02436	.02380
1.6	.02324	.02270	.02217	.02165	.02114	.02064	.02015	.01967	.01920	.01874
1.7	.01829	.01785	.01742	.01699	.01658	.01617	.01578	.01539	.01501	.01464
1.8	.01428	.01392	.01357	.01323	.01290	.01257	.01226	.01195	.01164	.01134
1.9	.01105	.01077	.01049	.01022	$.0^2 9957$	$.0^2 9698$	$.0^2 9445$	$.0^2 9198$	$.0^2 8957$	$.0^2 8721$
2.0	$.0^2 8491$	$.0^2 8266$	$.0^2 8046$	$.0^2 7832$	$.0^2 7623$	$.0^2 7418$	$.0^2 7219$	$.0^2 7024$	$.0^2 6835$	$.0^2 6649$
2.1	$.0^2 6468$	$.0^2 6292$	$.0^2 6120$	$.0^2 5952$	$.0^2 5788$	$.0^2 5628$	$.0^2 5472$	$.0^2 5320$	$.0^2 5172$	$.0^2 5028$
2.2	$.0^2 4887$	$.0^2 4750$	$.0^2 4616$	$.0^2 4486$	$.0^2 4358$	$.0^2 4235$	$.0^2 4114$	$.0^2 3996$	$.0^2 3882$	$.0^2 3770$
2.3	$.0^2 3662$	$.0^2 3556$	$.0^2 3453$	$.0^2 3352$	$.0^2 3255$	$.0^2 3159$	$.0^2 3067$	$.0^2 2977$	$.0^2 2889$	$.0^2 2804$
2.4	$.0^2 2720$	$.0^2 2640$	$.0^2 2561$	$.0^2 2484$	$.0^2 2410$	$.0^2 2337$	$.0^2 2267$	$.0^2 2199$	$.0^2 2132$	$.0^2 2067$
2.5	$.0^2 2005$	$.0^2 1943$	$.0^2 1883$	$.0^2 1826$	$.0^2 1769$	$.0^2 1715$	$.0^2 1662$	$.0^2 1610$	$.0^2 1560$	$.0^2 1511$
3.0	$.0^3 3822$	$.0^3 3689$	$.0^3 3560$	$.0^3 3436$	$.0^3 3316$	$.0^3 3199$	$.0^3 3087$	$.0^3 2978$	$.0^3 2873$	$.0^3 2771$
3.5	$.0^4 5848$	$.0^4 5620$	$.0^4 5400$	$.0^4 5188$	$.0^4 4984$	$.0^4 4788$	$.0^4 4599$	$.0^4 4417$	$.0^4 4242$	$.0^4 4073$
4.0	$.0^5 7145$	$.0^5 6835$	$.0^5 6538$	$.0^5 6253$	$.0^5 5980$	$.0^5 5718$	$.0^5 5468$	$.0^5 5227$	$.0^5 4997$	$.0^5 4777$

* By permission from R. Schlaifer, *Probability and Statistics for Business Decisions* (New York: McGraw-Hill Book Co., Inc., 1959).

TABLE E
Cumulative Binomial Distribution*

$$P(R \geq R | n, p)$$

n = 1

P	01	02	03	04	05	06	07	08	09	10
R										
1	0100	0200	0300	0400	0500	0600	0700	0800	0900	1000

P	11	12	13	14	15	16	17	18	19	20
R										
1	1100	1200	1300	1400	1500	1600	1700	1800	1900	2000

P	21	22	23	24	25	26	27	28	29	30
R										
1	2100	2200	2300	2400	2500	2600	2700	2800	2900	3000

P	31	32	33	34	35	36	37	38	39	40
R										
1	3100	3200	3300	3400	3500	3600	3700	3800	3900	4000

P	41	42	43	44	45	46	47	48	49	50
R										
1	4100	4200	4300	4400	4500	4600	4700	4800	4900	5000

n = 2

P	01	02	03	04	05	06	07	08	09	10
R										
1	0199	0396	0591	0784	0975	1164	1351	1536	1719	1900
2	0001	0004	0009	0016	0025	0036	0049	0064	0081	0100

P	11	12	13	14	15	16	17	18	19	20
R										
1	2079	2256	2431	2604	2775	2944	3111	3276	3439	3600
2	0121	0144	0169	0196	0225	0256	0289	0324	0361	0400

P	21	22	23	24	25	26	27	28	29	30
R										
1	3759	3916	4071	4224	4375	4524	4671	4816	4959	5100
2	0441	0484	0529	0576	0625	0676	0729	0784	0841	0900

P	31	32	33	34	35	36	37	38	39	40
R										
1	5239	5376	5511	5644	5775	5904	6031	6156	6279	6400
2	0961	1024	1089	1156	1225	1296	1369	1444	1521	1600

P	41	42	43	44	45	46	47	48	49	50
R										
1	6519	6636	6751	6864	6975	7084	7191	7296	7399	7500
2	1681	1764	1849	1936	2025	2116	2209	2304	2401	2500

n = 3

P	01	02	03	04	05	06	07	08	09	10
R										
1	0297	0588	0873	1153	1426	1694	1956	2213	2464	2710
2	0003	0012	0026	0047	0073	0104	0140	0182	0228	0280
3				0001	0001	0002	0003	0005	0007	0010

P	11	12	13	14	15	16	17	18	19	20
R										
1	2950	3185	3415	3639	3859	4073	4282	4486	4686	4880
2	0336	0397	0463	0533	0608	0686	0769	0855	0946	1040
3	0013	0017	0022	0027	0034	0041	0049	0058	0069	0080

P	21	22	23	24	25	26	27	28	29	30
R										
1	5070	5254	5435	5610	5781	5948	6110	6268	6421	6570
2	1138	1239	1344	1452	1563	1676	1793	1913	2035	2160
3	0093	0106	0122	0138	0156	0176	0197	0220	0244	0270

* By permission from R. Schlaifer, *Probability and Statistics for Business Decisions* (New York: McGraw-Hill Book Co., Inc., 1959).

TABLE E—Continued

P	31	32	33	34	35	36	37	38	39	40
R										
1	6715	6856	6992	7125	7254	7379	7500	7617	7730	7840
2	2287	2417	2548	2682	2818	2955	3094	3235	3377	3520
3	0298	0328	0359	0393	0429	0467	0507	0549	0593	0640

P	41	42	43	44	45	46	47	48	49	50
R										
1	7946	8049	8148	8244	8336	8425	8511	8594	8673	8750
2	3665	3810	3957	4104	4253	4401	4551	4700	4850	5000
3	0689	0741	0795	0852	0911	0973	1038	1106	1176	1250

$n = 4$

P	01	02	03	04	05	06	07	08	09	10
R										
1	0394	0776	1147	1507	1855	2193	2519	2836	3143	3439
2	0006	0023	0052	0091	0140	0199	0267	0344	0430	0523
3			0001	0002	0005	0008	0013	0019	0027	0037
4									0001	0001

P	11	12	13	14	15	16	17	18	19	20
R										
1	3726	4003	4271	4530	4780	5021	5254	5479	5695	5904
2	0624	0732	0847	0968	1095	1228	1366	1509	1656	1808
3	0049	0063	0079	0098	0120	0144	0171	0202	0235	0272
4	0001	0002	0003	0004	0005	0007	0008	0010	0013	0016

P	21	22	23	24	25	26	27	28	29	30
R										
1	6105	6298	6485	6664	6836	7001	7160	7313	7459	7599
2	1963	2122	2285	2450	2617	2787	2959	3132	3307	3483
3	0312	0356	0403	0453	0508	0566	0628	0694	0763	0837
4	0019	0023	0028	0033	0039	0046	0053	0061	0071	0081

P	31	32	33	34	35	36	37	38	39	40
R										
1	7733	7862	7985	8103	8215	8322	8425	8522	8615	8704
2	3660	3837	4015	4193	4370	4547	4724	4900	5075	5248
3	0915	0996	1082	1171	1265	1362	1464	1569	1679	1792
4	0092	0105	0119	0134	0150	0168	0187	0209	0231	0256

P	41	42	43	44	45	46	47	48	49	50
R										
1	8788	8868	8944	9017	9085	9150	9211	9269	9323	9375
2	5420	5590	5759	5926	6090	6252	6412	6569	6724	6875
3	1909	2030	2155	2283	2415	2550	2689	2831	2977	3125
4	0283	0311	0342	0375	0410	0448	0488	0531	0576	0625

$n = 5$

P	01	02	03	04	05	06	07	08	09	10
R										
1	0490	0961	1413	1846	2262	2661	3043	3409	3760	4095
2	0010	0038	0085	0148	0226	0319	0425	0544	0674	0815
3			0001	0003	0006	0012	0020	0031	0045	0063
4						0001	0001	0002	0003	0005

P	11	12	13	14	15	16	17	18	19	20
R										
1	4416	4723	5016	5296	5563	5818	6061	6293	6513	6723
2	0965	1125	1292	1467	1648	1835	2027	2234	2424	2627
3	0112	0143	0179	0220	0266	0318	0375	0437	0505	0579
4	0007	0009	0013	0017	0022	0029	0036	0045	0055	0067
5				0001	0001	0001	0001	0002	0002	0003

P	21	22	23	24	25	26	27	28	29	30
R										
1	6923	7113	7293	7464	7627	7781	7927	8065	8196	8319
2	2833	3041	3251	3461	3672	3883	4093	4303	4511	4718
3	0659	0744	0836	0933	1035	1143	1257	1376	1501	1631
4	0081	0097	0114	0134	0156	0181	0208	0238	0272	0308
5	0004	0005	0006	0008	0010	0012	0014	0017	0021	0024

TABLE E—*Continued*

P	31	32	33	34	35	36	37	38	39	40
R										
1	8436	8546	8650	8748	8840	8926	9008	9084	9155	9222
2	4923	5125	5325	5522	5716	5906	6093	6276	6455	6630
3	1766	1905	2050	2199	2352	2509	2670	2835	3003	3174
4	0347	0390	0436	0486	0540	0598	0660	0726	0796	0870
5	0029	0034	0039	0045	0053	0060	0069	0079	0090	0102

P	41	42	43	44	45	46	47	48	49	50
R										
1	9285	9344	9398	9449	9497	9541	9582	9620	9655	9688
2	6801	6967	7129	7286	7438	7585	7728	7865	7998	8125
3	3349	3525	3705	3886	4069	4253	4439	4625	4813	5000
4	0949	1033	1121	1214	1312	1415	1522	1635	1753	1875
5	0116	0131	0147	0165	0185	0206	0229	0255	0282	0313

$$n = 6$$

P	01	02	03	04	05	06	07	08	09	10
R										
1	0585	1142	1670	2172	2649	3101	3530	3936	4321	4686
2	0015	0057	0125	0216	0328	0459	0608	0773	0952	1143
3		0002	0005	0012	0022	0038	0058	0085	0118	0159
4					0001	0002	0003	0005	0008	0013
5										0001

P	11	12	13	14	15	16	17	18	19	20
R										
1	5030	5356	5664	5954	6229	6487	6731	6960	7176	7379
2	1345	1556	1776	2003	2235	2472	2713	2956	3201	3446
3	0206	0261	0324	0395	0473	0560	0655	0759	0870	0989
4	0018	0025	0034	0045	0059	0075	0094	0116	0141	0170
5	0001	0001	0002	0003	0004	0005	0007	0010	0013	0016
6										0001

P	21	22	23	24	25	26	27	28	29	30
R										
1	7569	7748	7916	8073	8220	8358	8487	8607	8719	8824
2	3692	3937	4180	4422	4661	4896	5128	5356	5580	5798
3	1115	1250	1391	1539	1694	1856	2023	2196	2374	2557
4	0202	0239	0280	0326	0376	0431	0492	0557	0628	0705
5	0020	0025	0031	0038	0046	0056	0067	0079	0093	0109
6	0001	0001	0001	0002	0002	0003	0004	0005	0006	0007

P	31	32	33	34	35	36	37	38	39	40
R										
1	8921	9011	9095	9173	9246	9313	9375	9432	9485	9533
2	6012	6220	6422	6619	6809	6994	7172	7343	7508	7667
3	2744	2936	3130	3328	3529	3732	3937	4143	4350	4557
4	0787	0875	0969	1069	1174	1286	1404	1527	1657	1792
5	0127	0148	0170	0195	0223	0254	0288	0325	0365	0410
6	0009	0011	0013	0015	0018	0022	0026	0030	0035	0041

P	41	42	43	44	45	46	47	48	49	50
R										
1	9578	9619	9657	9692	9723	9752	9778	9802	9824	9844
2	7819	7965	8105	8238	8364	8485	8599	8707	8810	8906
3	4764	4971	5177	5382	5585	5786	5985	6180	6373	6563
4	1933	2080	2232	2390	2553	2721	2893	3070	3252	3438
5	0458	0510	0566	0627	0692	0762	0837	0917	1003	1094
6	0048	0055	0063	0073	0083	0095	0108	0122	0138	0156

$$n = 7$$

P	01	02	03	04	05	06	07	08	09	10
R										
1	0679	1319	1920	2486	3017	3515	3983	4422	4832	5217
2	0020	0079	0171	0294	0444	0618	0813	1026	1255	1497
3		0003	0009	0020	0038	0063	0097	0140	0193	0257
4				0001	0002	0004	0007	0012	0018	0027
5								0001	0001	0002

TABLE E—Continued

P	11	12	13	14	15	16	17	18	19	20
R										
1	5577	5913	6227	6521	6794	7049	7286	7507	7712	7903
2	1750	2012	2281	2556	2834	3115	3396	3677	3956	4233
3	0331	0416	0513	0620	0738	0866	1005	1154	1313	1480
4	0039	0054	0072	0094	0121	0153	0189	0231	0279	0333
5	0003	0004	0006	0009	0012	0017	0022	0029	0037	0047
6					0001	0001	0001	0002	0003	0004

P	21	22	23	24	25	26	27	28	29	30
R										
1	8080	8243	8395	8535	8665	8785	8895	8997	9090	9176
2	4506	4775	5040	5298	5551	5796	6035	6266	6490	6706
3	1657	1841	2033	2231	2436	2646	2861	3081	3304	3529
4	0394	0461	0536	0617	0706	0802	0905	1016	1134	1260
5	0058	0072	0088	0107	0129	0153	0181	0213	0248	0288
6	0005	0006	0008	0011	0013	0017	0021	0026	0031	0038
7					0001	0001	0001	0001	0002	0002

P	31	32	33	34	35	36	37	38	39	40
R										
1	9255	9328	9394	9454	9510	9560	9606	9648	9686	9720
2	6914	7113	7304	7487	7662	7828	7987	8137	8279	8414
3	3757	3987	4217	4447	4677	4906	5134	5359	5581	5801
4	1394	1534	1682	1837	1998	2167	2341	2521	2707	2898
5	0332	0380	0434	0492	0556	0625	0701	0782	0869	0963
6	0046	0055	0065	0077	0090	0105	0123	0142	0164	0188
7	0003	0003	0004	0005	0006	0008	0009	0011	0014	0016

P	41	42	43	44	45	46	47	48	49	50
R										
1	9751	9779	9805	9827	9848	9866	9883	9897	9910	9922
2	8541	8660	8772	8877	8976	9068	9153	9233	9307	9375
3	6017	6229	6436	6638	6836	7027	7213	7393	7567	7734
4	3094	3294	3498	3706	3917	4131	4346	4563	4781	5000
5	1063	1169	1282	1402	1529	1663	1803	1951	2105	2266
6	0216	0246	0279	0316	0357	0402	0451	0504	0562	0625
7	0019	0023	0027	0032	0037	0044	0051	0059	0068	0078

$$n = 8$$

P	01	02	03	04	05	06	07	08	09	10
R										
1	0773	1492	2163	2786	3366	3904	4404	4868	5297	5695
2	0027	0103	0223	0381	0572	0792	1035	1298	1577	1869
3	0001	0004	0013	0031	0058	0096	0147	0211	0289	0381
4			0001	0002	0004	0007	0013	0022	0034	0050
5							0001	0001	0003	0004

P	11	12	13	14	15	16	17	18	19	20
R										
1	6063	6404	6718	7008	7275	7521	7748	7956	8147	8322
2	2171	2480	2794	3111	3428	3744	4057	4366	4670	4967
3	0487	0608	0743	0891	1052	1226	1412	1608	1815	2031
4	0071	0097	0129	0168	0214	0267	0328	0397	0476	0563
5	0007	0010	0015	0021	0029	0038	0050	0065	0083	0104
6		0001	0001	0002	0002	0003	0005	0007	0009	0012
7									0001	0001

P	21	22	23	24	25	26	27	28	29	30
R										
1	8483	8630	8764	8887	8999	9101	9194	9278	9354	9424
2	5257	5538	5811	6075	6329	6573	6807	7031	7244	7447
3	2255	2486	2724	2967	3215	3465	3718	3973	4228	4482
4	0659	0765	0880	1004	1138	1281	1433	1594	1763	1941
5	0129	0158	0191	0230	0273	0322	0377	0438	0505	0580
6	0016	0021	0027	0034	0042	0052	0064	0078	0094	0113
7	0001	0002	0002	0003	0004	0005	0006	0008	0010	0013
8									0001	0001

TABLE E—Continued

P	31	32	33	34	35	36	37	38	39	40
R										
1	9486	9543	9594	9640	9681	9719	9752	9782	9808	9832
2	7640	7822	7994	8156	8309	8452	8586	8711	8828	8936
3	4736	4987	5236	5481	5722	5958	6189	6415	6634	6846
4	2126	2319	2519	2724	2936	3153	3374	3599	3828	4059
5	0661	0750	0846	0949	1061	1180	1307	1443	1586	1737
6	0134	0159	0187	0218	0253	0293	0336	0385	0439	0498
7	0016	0020	0024	0030	0036	0043	0051	0061	0072	0085
8	0001	0001	0001	0002	0002	0003	0004	0004	0005	0007

P	41	42	43	44	45	46	47	48	49	50
R										
1	9853	9872	9889	9903	9916	9928	9938	9947	9954	9961
2	9037	9130	9216	9295	9368	9435	9496	9552	9602	9648
3	7052	7250	7440	7624	7799	7966	8125	8276	8419	8555
4	4292	4527	4762	4996	5230	5463	5694	5922	6146	6367
5	1895	2062	2235	2416	2604	2798	2999	3205	3416	3633
6	0563	0634	0711	0794	0885	0982	1086	1198	1318	1445
7	0100	0117	0136	0157	0181	0208	0239	0272	0310	0352
8	0008	0010	0012	0014	0017	0020	0024	0028	0033	0039

$n = 9$

P	01	02	03	04	05	06	07	08	09	10
R										
1	0865	1663	2398	3075	3698	4270	4796	5278	5721	6126
2	0034	0131	0282	0478	0712	0978	1271	1583	1912	2252
3	0001	0006	0020	0045	0084	0138	0209	0298	0405	0530
4			0001	0003	0006	0013	0023	0037	0057	0083
5						0001	0002	0003	0005	0009
6										0001

P	11	12	13	14	15	16	17	18	19	20
R										
1	6496	6835	7145	7427	7684	7918	8131	8324	8499	8658
2	2599	2951	3304	3657	4005	4348	4685	5012	5330	5638
3	0672	0833	1009	1202	1409	1629	1861	2105	2357	2618
4	0117	0158	0209	0269	0339	0420	0512	0615	0730	0856
5	0014	0021	0030	0041	0056	0075	0098	0125	0158	0196
6	0001	0002	0003	0004	0006	0009	0013	0017	0023	0031
7						0001	0001	0002	0002	0003

P	21	22	23	24	25	26	27	28	29	30
R										
1	8801	8931	9048	9154	9249	9335	9411	9480	9542	9596
2	5934	6218	6491	6750	6997	7230	7452	7660	7856	8040
3	2885	3158	3434	3713	3993	4273	4552	4829	5102	5372
4	0994	1144	1304	1475	1657	1849	2050	2260	2478	2703
5	0240	0291	0350	0416	0489	0571	0662	0762	0870	0988
6	0040	0051	0065	0081	0100	0122	0149	0179	0213	0253
7	0004	0006	0008	0010	0013	0017	0022·	0028	0035	0043
8			0001	0001	0001	0001	0002	0003	0003	0004

P	31	32	33	34	35	36	37	38	39	40
R										
1	9645	9689	9728	9762	9793	9820	9844	9865	9883	9899
2	8212	8372	8522	8661	8789	8908	9017	9118	9210	9295
3	5636	5894	6146	6390	6627	6856	7076	7287	7489	7682
4	2935	3173	3415	3662	3911	4163	4416	4669	4922	5174
5	1115	1252	1398	1553	1717	1890	2072	2262	2460	2666
6	0298	0348	0404	0467	0536	0612	0696	0787	0886	0994
7	0053	0064	0078	0094	0112	0133	0157	0184	0215	0250
8	0006	0007	0009	0011	0014	0017	0021	0026	0031	0036
9				0001	0001	0001	0001	0002	0002	0003

P	41	42	43	44	45	46	47	48	49	50
R										
1	9913	9926	9936	9946	9954	9961	9967	9972	9977	9980
2	9372	9442	9505	9563	9615	9662	9704	9741	9775	9805
3	7866	8039	8204	8359	8505	8642	8769	8889	8999	9102
4	5424	5670	5913	6152	6386	6614	6836	7052	7260	7461
5	2878	3097	3322	3551	3786	4024	4265	4509	4754	5000
6	1109	1233	1366	1508	1658	1817	1985	2161	2340	2539
7	0290	0334	0383	0437	0498	0564	0637	0717	0804	0898
8	0046	0055	0065	0077	0091	0107	0125	0145	0169	0195
9	0003	0004	0005	0006	0008	0009	0011	0014	0016	0020

TABLE E—Continued

n = 10

P	01	02	03	04	05	06	07	08	09	10
R										
1	0956	1829	2626	3352	4013	4614	5160	5656	6106	6513
2	0043	0162	0345	0582	0861	1176	1517	1879	2254	2639
3	0001	0009	0028	0062	0115	0188	0283	0401	0540	0702
4			0001	0004	0010	0020	0036	0058	0088	0128
5					0001	0002	0003	0006	0010	0016
6									0001	0001

P	11	12	13	14	15	16	17	18	19	20
R										
1	6882	7215	7516	7787	8031	8251	8448	8626	8784	8926
2	3028	3417	3804	4184	4557	4920	5270	5608	5932	6242
3	0884	1087	1308	1545	1798	2064	2341	2628	2922	3222
4	0178	0239	0313	0400	0500	0614	0741	0883	1039	1209
5	0025	0037	0053	0073	0099	0130	0168	0213	0266	0328
6	0003	0004	0006	0010	0014	0020	0027	0037	0049	0064
7			0001	0001	0001	0002	0003	0004	0006	0009
8									0001	0001

P	21	22	23	24	25	26	27	28	29	30
R										
1	9053	9166	9267	9357	9437	9508	9570	9626	9674	9718
2	6536	6815	7079	7327	7560	7778	7981	8170	8345	8507
3	3526	3831	4137	4442	4744	5042	5335	5622	5901	6172
4	1391	1587	1794	2012	2241	2479	2726	2979	3239	3504
5	0399	0479	0569	0670	0781	0904	1037	1181	1337	1503
6	0082	0104	0130	0161	0197	0239	0287	0342	0404	0473
7	0012	0016	0021	0027	0035	0045	0056	0070	0087	0106
8	0001	0002	0002	0003	0004	0006	0007	0010	0012	0016
9							0001	0001	0001	0001

P	31	32	33	34	35	36	37	38	39	40
R										
1	9755	9789	9818	9843	9865	9885	9902	9916	9929	9940
2	8656	8794	8920	9035	9140	9236	9323	9402	9473	9536
3	6434	6687	6930	7162	7384	7595	7794	7983	8160	8327
4	3772	4044	4316	4589	4862	5132	5400	5664	5923	6177
5	1679	1867	2064	2270	2485	2708	2939	3177	3420	3669
6	0551	0637	0732	0836	0949	1072	1205	1348	1500	1662
7	0129	0155	0185	0220	0260	0305	0356	0413	0477	0548
8	0020	0025	0032	0039	0048	0059	0071	0086	0103	0123
9	0002	0003	0003	0004	0005	0007	0009	0011	0014	0017
10								0001	0001	0001

P	41	42	43	44	45	46	47	48	49	50
R										
1	9949	9957	9964	9970	9975	9979	9983	9986	9988	9990
2	9594	9645	9691	9731	9767	9799	9827	9852	9874	9893
3	8483	8628	8764	8889	9004	9111	9209	9298	9379	9453
4	6425	6665	6898	7123	7340	7547	7745	7933	8112	8281
5	3922	4178	4436	4696	4956	5216	5474	5730	5982	6230
6	1834	2016	2207	2407	2616	2832	3057	3288	3526	3770
7	0626	0712	0806	0908	1020	1141	1271	1410	1560	1719
8	0146	0172	0202	0236	0274	0317	0366	0420	0480	0547
9	0021	0025	0031	0037	0045	0054	0065	0077	0091	0107
10	0001	0002	0002	0003	0003	0004	0005	0006	0008	0010

n = 11

P	01	02	03	04	05	06	07	08	09	10
R										
1	1047	1993	2847	3618	4312	4937	5499	6004	6456	6862
2	0052	0195	0413	0692	1019	1382	1772	2181	2601	3026
3	0002	0012	0037	0083	0152	0248	0370	0519	0695	0896
4			0002	0007	0016	0030	0053	0085	0129	0185
5					0001	0003	0005	0010	0017	0028
6								0001	0002	0003

TABLE E—Continued

P	11	12	13	14	15	16	17	18	19	20
R										
1	7225	7549	7839	8097	8327	8531	8712	8873	9015	9141
2	3452	3873	4286	4689	5078	5453	5811	6151	6474	6779
3	1120	1366	1632	1915	2212	2521	2839	3164	3494	3826
4	0256	0341	0442	0560	0694	0846	1013	1197	1397	1611
5	0042	0061	0087	0119	0159	0207	0266	0334	0413	0504
6	0005	0008	0012	0018	0027	0037	0051	0068	0090	0117
7		0001	0001	0002	0003	0005	0007	0010	0014	0020
8							0001	0001	0002	0002

P	21	22	23	24	25	26	27	28	29	30
R										
1	9252	9350	9436	9511	9578	9636	9686	9730	9769	9802
2	7065	7333	7582	7814	8029	8227	8410	8577	8730	8870
3	4158	4488	4814	5134	5448	5753	6049	6335	6610	6873
4	1840	2081	2333	2596	2867	3146	3430	3719	4011	4304
5	0607	0723	0851	0992	1146	1313	1493	1685	1888	2103
6	0148	0186	0231	0283	0343	0412	0490	0577	0674	0782
7	0027	0035	0046	0059	0076	0095	0119	0146	0179	0216
8	0003	0005	0007	0009	0012	0016	0021	0027	0034	0043
9			0001	0001	0001	0002	0002	0003	0004	0006

P	31	32	33	34	35	36	37	38	39	40
R										
1	9831	9856	9878	9896	9912	9926	9938	9948	9956	9964
2	8997	9112	9216	9310	9394	9470	9537	9597	9650	9698
3	7183	7361	7587	7799	7999	8186	8360	8522	8672	8811
4	4598	4890	5179	5464	5744	6019	6286	6545	6796	7037
5	2338	2563	2807	3059	3317	3581	3850	4122	4397	4672
6	0901	1031	1171	1324	1487	1661	1847	2043	2249	2465
7	0260	0309	0366	0430	0501	0581	0670	0768	0876	0994
8	0054	0067	0082	0101	0122	0148	0177	0210	0249	0293
9	0008	0010	0013	0016	0020	0026	0032	0039	0048	0059
10	0001	0001	0001	0002	0002	0003	0004	0005	0006	0007

P	41	42	43	44	45	46	47	48	49	50
R										
1	9970	9975	9979	9983	9986	9989	9991	9992	9994	9995
2	9739	9776	9808	9836	9861	9882	9900	9916	9930	9941
3	8938	9055	9162	9260	9348	9428	9500	9564	9622	9673
4	7269	7490	7700	7900	8089	8266	8433	8588	8733	8867
5	4940	5223	5495	5764	6029	6288	6541	6787	7026	7256
6	2690	2924	3166	3414	3669	3929	4193	4460	4729	5000
7	1121	1260	1408	1568	1738	1919	2110	2312	2523	2744
8	0343	0399	0461	0532	0610	0696	0791	0895	1009	1133
9	0072	0087	0104	0125	0148	0175	0206	0241	0282	0327
10	0009	0012	0014	0018	0022	0027	0033	0040	0049	0059
11	0001	0001	0001	0001	0002	0002	0002	0003	0004	0005

$n = 12$

P	01	02	03	04	05	06	07	08	09	10
R										
1	1136	2153	3062	3873	4596	5241	5814	6323	6775	7176
2	0062	0231	0486	0809	1184	1595	2033	2487	2948	3410
3	0002	0015	0048	0107	0196	0316	0468	0652	0866	1109
4		0001	0003	0010	0022	0043	0075	0120	0180	0256
5				0001	0002	0004	0009	0016	0027	0043
6							0001	0002	0003	0005
7										0001

P	11	12	13	14	15	16	17	18	19	20
R										
1	7530	7843	8120	8363	8578	8766	8931	9076	9202	9313
2	3867	4314	4748	5166	5565	5945	6304	6641	6957	7251
3	1377	1667	1977	2303	2642	2990	3344	3702	4060	4417
4	0351	0464	0597	0750	0922	1114	1324	1552	1795	2054
5	0065	0095	0133	0181	0239	0310	0393	0489	0600	0726
6	0009	0014	0022	0033	0046	0065	0088	0116	0151	0194
7	0001	0002	0003	0004	0007	0010	0015	0021	0029	0039
8					0001	0001	0002	0003	0004	0006
9										0001

TABLE E—Continued

P / R	21	22	23	24	25	26	27	28	29	30
1	9409	9493	9566	9629	9683	9730	9771	9806	9836	9862
2	7524	7776	8009	8222	8416	8594	8755	8900	9032	9150
3	4768	5114	5450	5778	6093	6397	6687	6963	7225	7472
4	2326	2610	2904	3205	3512	3824	4137	4452	4765	5075
5	0866	1021	1192	1377	1576	1790	2016	2254	2504	2763
6	0245	0304	0374	0453	0544	0646	0760	0887	1026	1178
7	0052	0068	0089	0113	0143	0178	0219	0267	0322	0386
8	0008	0011	0016	0021	0028	0036	0047	0060	0076	0095
9	0001	0001	0002	0003	0004	0005	0007	0010	0013	0017
10						0001	0001	0001	0002	0002

P / R	31	32	33	34	35	36	37	38	39	40
1	9884	9902	9918	9932	9943	9953	9961	9968	9973	9978
2	9256	9350	9435	9509	9576	9634	9685	9730	9770	9804
3	7704	7922	8124	8313	8487	8648	8795	8931	9054	9166
4	5381	5681	5973	6258	6533	6799	7053	7296	7528	7747
5	3032	3308	3590	3876	4167	4459	4751	5043	5332	5618
6	1343	1521	1711	1913	2127	2352	2588	2833	3087	3348
7	0458	0540	0632	0734	0846	0970	1106	1253	1411	1582
8	0118	0144	0176	0213	0255	0304	0359	0422	0493	0573
9	0022	0028	0036	0045	0056	0070	0086	0104	0127	0153
10	0003	0004	0005	0007	0008	0011	0014	0018	0022	0028
11				0001	0001	0001	0001	0002	0002	0003

P / R	41	42	43	44	45	46	47	48	49	50
1	9982	9986	9988	9990	9992	9994	9995	9996	9997	9998
2	9834	9860	9882	9901	9917	9931	9943	9953	9961	9968
3	9266	9358	9440	9513	9579	9637	9688	9733	9773	9807
4	7953	8147	8329	8498	8655	8801	8934	9057	9168	9270
5	5899	6175	6443	6704	6956	7198	7430	7652	7862	8062
6	3616	3889	4167	4448	4731	5014	5297	5577	5855	6128
7	1765	1959	2164	2380	2607	2843	3089	3343	3604	3872
8	0662	0760	0869	0988	1117	1258	1411	1575	1751	1938
9	0183	0218	0258	0304	0356	0415	0481	0555	0638	0730
10	0035	0043	0053	0065	0079	0095	0114	0137	0163	0193
11	0004	0005	0007	0009	0011	0014	0017	0021	0026	0032
12				0001	0001	0001	0001	0001	0002	0002

$$n = 13$$

P / R	01	02	03	04	05	06	07	08	09	10
1	1225	2310	3270	4118	4867	5526	6107	6617	7065	7458
2	0072	0270	0564	0932	1354	1814	2298	2794	3293	3787
3	0003	0020	0062	0135	0245	0392	0578	0799	1054	1339
4		0001	0005	0014	0031	0060	0103	0163	0242	0342
5				0001	0003	0007	0013	0024	0041	0065
6						0001	0001	0003	0005	0009
7									0001	0001

P / R	11	12	13	14	15	16	17	18	19	20
1	7802	8102	8364	8592	8791	8963	9113	9242	9354	9450
2	4270	4738	5186	5614	6017	6396	6751	7080	7384	7664
3	1651	1985	2337	2704	3080	3463	3848	4231	4611	4983
4	0464	0609	0776	0967	1180	1414	1667	1939	2226	2527
5	0097	0139	0193	0260	0342	0438	0551	0681	0827	0991
6	0015	0024	0036	0053	0075	0104	0139	0183	0237	0300
7	0002	0003	0005	0008	0013	0019	0027	0038	0052	0070
8			0001	0001	0002	0003	0004	0006	0009	0012
9								0001	0001	0002

TABLE E—Continued

P	21	22	23	24	25	26	27	28	29	30
R										
1	9533	9604	9666	9718	9762	9800	9833	9860	9883	9903
2	7920	8154	8367	8559	8733	8889	9029	9154	9265	9363
3	5347	5699	6039	6364	6674	6968	7245	7505	7749	7975
4	2839	3161	3489	3822	4157	4493	4826	5155	5478	5794
5	1173	1371	1585	1816	2060	2319	2589	2870	3160	3457
6	0375	0462	0562	0675	0802	0944	1099	1270	1455	1654
7	0093	0120	0154	0195	0243	0299	0365	0440	0527	0624
8	0017	0024	0032	0043	0056	0073	0093	0118	0147	0182
9	0002	0004	0005	0007	0010	0013	0018	0024	0031	0040
10			0001	0001	0001	0002	0003	0004	0005	0007
11									0001	0001

P	31	32	33	34	35	36	37	38	39	40
R										
1	9920	9934	9945	9955	9963	9970	9975	9980	9984	9987
2	9450	9527	9594	9653	9704	9749	9787	9821	9849	9874
3	8185	8379	8557	8720	8868	9003	9125	9235	9333	9421
4	6101	6398	6683	6957	7217	7464	7698	7917	8123	8314
5	3760	4067	4376	4686	4995	5301	5603	5899	6188	6470
6	1867	2093	2331	2581	2841	3111	3388	3673	3962	4356
7	0733	0854	0988	1135	1295	1468	1654	1853	2065	2288
8	0223	0271	0326	0390	0462	0544	0635	0738	0851	0977
9	0052	0065	0082	0102	0126	0154	0187	0225	0270	0321
10	0009	0012	0015	0020	0025	0032	0040	0051	0063	0078
11	0001	0001	0002	0003	0003	0005	0006	0008	0010	0013
12							0001	0001	0001	0001

P	41	42	43	44	45	46	47	48	49	50
R										
1	9990	9992	9993	9995	9996	9997	9997	9998	9998	9999
2	9895	9912	9928	9940	9951	9960	9967	9974	9979	9983
3	9499	9569	9630	9684	9731	9772	9808	9838	9865	9888
4	8492	8656	8807	8945	9071	9185	9288	9381	9464	9539
5	6742	7003	7254	7493	7721	7935	8137	8326	8502	8666
6	4552	4849	5146	5441	5732	6019	6299	6573	6838	7095
7	2524	2770	3025	3290	3563	3842	4127	4415	4707	5000
8	1114	1264	1426	1600	1788	1988	2200	2424	2659	2905
9	0379	0446	0520	0605	0698	0803	0918	1045	1183	1334
10	0096	0117	0141	0170	0203	0242	0287	0338	0396	0461
11	0017	0021	0027	0033	0041	0051	0063	0077	0093	0112
12	0002	0002	0003	0004	0005	0007	0009	0011	0014	0017
13							0001	0001	0001	0001

$n = 14$

P	01	02	03	04	05	06	07	08	09	10
R										
1	1313	2464	3472	4353	5123	5795	6380	6888	7330	7712
2	0084	0310	0645	1059	1530	2037	2564	3100	3632	4154
3	0003	0025	0077	0167	0301	0478	0698	0958	1255	1584
4		0001	0006	0019	0042	0080	0136	0214	0315	0441
5				0002	0004	0010	0020	0035	0059	0092
6						0001	0002	0004	0008	0015
7									0001	0002

P	11	12	13	14	15	16	17	18	19	20
R										
1	8044	8330	8577	8789	8972	9129	9264	9379	9477	9560
2	4658	5141	5599	6031	6433	6807	7152	7469	7758	8021
3	1939	2315	2708	3111	3521	3932	4341	4744	5138	5519
4	0594	0774	0979	1210	1465	1742	2038	2351	2679	3018
5	0137	0196	0269	0359	0467	0594	0741	0907	1093	1298
6	0024	0038	0057	0082	0115	0157	0209	0273	0349	0439
7	0003	0006	0009	0015	0022	0032	0046	0064	0087	0116
8		0001	0001	0002	0003	0005	0008	0012	0017	0024
9						0001	0001	0002	0003	0004

TABLE E—Continued

P\R	21	22	23	24	25	26	27	28	29	30
1	9631	9691	9742	9786	9822	9852	9878	9899	9917	9932
2	8259	8473	8665	8837	8990	9126	9246	9352	9444	9525
3	5887	6239	6574	6891	7189	7467	7727	7967	8188	8392
4	3366	3719	4076	4432	4787	5136	5479	5813	6137	6448
5	1523	1765	2023	2297	2585	2884	3193	3509	3832	4158
6	0543	0662	0797	0949	1117	1301	1502	1718	1949	2195
7	0152	0196	0248	0310	0383	0467	0563	0673	0796	0933
8	0033	0045	0060	0079	0103	0132	0167	0208	0257	0315
9	0006	0008	0011	0016	0022	0029	0038	0050	0065	0083
10	0001	0001	0002	0002	0003	0005	0007	0009	0012	0017
11						0001	0001	0001	0002	0002

P\R	31	32	33	34	35	36	37	38	39	40
1	9945	9955	9963	9970	9976	9981	9984	9988	9990	9992
2	9596	9657	9710	9756	9795	9828	9857	9881	9902	9919
3	8577	8746	8899	9037	9161	9271	9370	9457	9534	9602
4	6747	7032	7301	7556	7795	8018	8226	8418	8595	8757
5	4486	4813	5138	5458	5773	6080	6378	6666	6943	7207
6	2454	2724	3006	3297	3595	3899	4208	4519	4831	5141
7	1084	1250	1431	1626	1836	2059	2296	2545	2805	3075
8	0381	0458	0545	0643	0753	0876	1012	1162	1325	1501
9	0105	0131	0163	0200	0243	0294	0353	0420	0497	0583
10	0022	0029	0037	0048	0060	0076	0095	0117	0144	0175
11	0003	0005	0006	0008	0011	0014	0019	0024	0031	0039
12		0001	0001	0001	0001	0002	0003	0003	0005	0006
13										0001

P\R	41	42	43	44	45	46	47	48	49	50
1	9994	9995	9996	9997	9998	9998	9999	9999	9999	9999
2	9934	9946	9956	9964	9971	9977	9981	9985	9988	9991
3	9661	9713	9758	9797	9830	9858	9883	9903	9921	9935
4	8905	9039	9161	9270	9368	9455	9532	9601	9661	9713
5	7459	7697	7922	8132	8328	8510	8678	8833	8974	9102
6	5450	5754	6052	6344	6627	6900	7163	7415	7654	7880
7	3355	3643	3937	4236	4539	4843	5148	5451	5751	6047
8	1692	1896	2113	2344	2586	2840	3105	3380	3663	3953
9	0680	0789	0910	1043	1189	1348	1520	1707	1906	2120
10	0212	0255	0304	0361	0426	0500	0583	0677	0782	0898
11	0049	0061	0076	0093	0114	0139	0168	0202	0241	0287
12	0008	0010	0013	0017	0022	0027	0034	0042	0053	0065
13	0001	0001	0001	0002	0003	0003	0004	0006	0007	0009
14										0001

$$n = 15$$

P\R	01	02	03	04	05	06	07	08	09	10
1	1399	2614	3667	4579	5367	6047	6633	7137	7570	7941
2	0096	0353	0730	1191	1710	2262	2832	3403	3965	4510
3	0004	0030	0094	0203	0362	0571	0829	1130	1469	1841
4		0002	0008	0024	0055	0104	0175	0273	0399	0556
5			0001	0002	00·06	0014	0028	0050	0082	0127
6					0001	0001	0003	0007	0013	0022
7								0001	0002	0003

P\R	11	12	13	14	15	16	17	18	19	20
1	8259	8530	8762	8959	9126	9269	9389	9490	9576	9648
2	5031	5524	5987	6417	6814	7179	7511	7813	8085	8329
3	2238	2654	3084	3520	3958	4392	4819	5234	5635	6020
4	0742	0959	1204	1476	1773	2092	2429	2782	3146	3518
5	0187	0265	0361	0478	0617	0778	0961	1167	1394	1642
6	0037	0057	0084	0121	0168	0227	0300	0387	0490	0611
7	0006	0010	0015	0024	0036	0052	0074	0102	0137	0181
8	0001	0001	0002	0004	0006	0010	0014	0021	0030	0042
9					0001	0001	0002	0003	0005	0008
10									0001	0001

TABLE E—Continued

P	21	22	23	24	25	26	27	28	29	30
R										
1	9709	9759	9802	9837	9866	9891	9911	9928	9941	9953
2	8547	8741	8913	9065	9198	9315	9417	9505	9581	9647
3	6385	6731	7055	7358	7639	7899	8137	8355	8553	8732
4	3895	4274	4650	5022	5387	5742	6086	6416	6732	7031
5	1910	2195	2495	2810	3135	3469	3810	4154	4500	4845
6	0748	0905	1079	1272	1484	1713	1958	2220	2495	2784
7	0234	0298	0374	0463	0566	0684	0817	0965	1130	1311
8	0058	0078	0104	0135	0173	0219	0274	0338	0413	0500
9	0011	0016	0023	0031	0042	0056	0073	0094	0121	0152
10	0002	0003	0004	0006	0008	0011	0015	0021	0028	0037
11			0001	0001	0001	0002	0002	0003	0005	0007
12									0001	0001

P	31	32	33	34	35	36	37	38	39	40
R										
1	9962	9969	9975	9980	9984	9988	9990	9992	9994	9995
2	9704	9752	9794	9829	9858	9883	9904	9922	9936	9948
3	8893	9038	9167	9281	9383	9472	9550	9618	9678	9729
4	7314	7580	7829	8060	8273	8469	8649	8813	8961	9095
5	5187	5523	5852	6171	6481	6778	7062	7332	7587	7827
6	3084	3393	3709	4032	4357	4684	5011	5335	5654	5968
7	1509	1722	1951	2194	2452	2722	3003	3295	3595	3902
8	0599	0711	0837	0977	1132	1302	1487	1687	1902	2131
9	0190	0236	0289	0351	0422	0504	0597	0702	0820	0950
10	0048	0062	0079	0099	0124	0154	0190	0232	0281	0338
11	0009	0012	0016	0022	0028	0037	0047	0059	0075	0093
12	0001	0002	0003	0004	0005	0006	0009	0011	0015	0019
13					0001	0001	0001	0002	0002	0003

P	41	42	43	44	45	46	47	48	49	50
R										
1	9996	9997	9998	9998	9999	9999	9999	9999	10000	10000
2	9958	9966	9973	9979	9983	9987	9991	9992	9994	9995
3	9773	9811	9843	9870	9893	9913	9929	9943	9954	9963
4	9215	9322	9417	9502	9576	9641	9697	9746	9788	9824
5	8052	8261	8454	8633	8796	8945	9080	9201	9310	9408
6	6274	6570	6856	7131	7392	7641	7875	8095	8301	8491
7	4214	4530	4847	5164	5478	5789	6095	6394	6684	6964
8	2374	2630	2898	3176	3465	3762	4065	4374	4686	5000
9	1095	1254	1427	1615	1818	2034	2265	2510	2767	3036
10	0404	0479	0565	0661	0769	0890	1024	1171	1333	1509
11	0116	0143	0174	0211	0255	0305	0363	0430	0506	0592
12	0025	0032	0040	0051	0063	0079	0097	0119	0145	0176
13	0004	0005	0007	0009	0011	0014	0018	0023	0029	0037
14			0001	0001	0001	0002	0002	0003	0004	0005

n = 16

P	01	02	03	04	05	06	07	08	09	10
R										
1	1485	2762	3857	4796	5599	6284	6869	7366	7789	8147
2	0109	0399	0818	1327	1892	2489	3098	3701	4289	4853
3	0005	0037	0113	0242	0429	0673	0969	1311	1694	2108
4		0002	0011	0032	0070	0132	0221	0342	0496	0684
5			0001	0003	0009	0019	0038	0068	0111	0170
6					0001	0002	0005	0010	0019	0033
7							0001	0001	0003	0005
8										0001

P	11	12	13	14	15	16	17	18	19	20
R										
1	8450	8707	8923	9105	9257	9386	9493	9582	9657	9719
2	5386	5885	6347	6773	7161	7513	7830	8115	8368	8593
3	2545	2999	3461	3926	4386	4838	5277	5698	6101	6482
4	0907	1162	1448	1763	2101	2460	2836	3223	3619	4019
5	0248	0348	0471	0618	0791	0988	1211	1458	1727	2018
6	0053	0082	0120	0171	0235	0315	0412	0527	0662	0817
7	0009	0015	0024	0038	0056	0080	0112	0153	0204	0267
8	0001	0002	0004	0007	0011	0016	0024	0036	0051	0070
9			0001	0001	0002	0003	0004	0007	0010	0015
10							0001	0001	0002	0002

TABLE E—Continued

P \ R	21	22	23	24	25	26	27	28	29	30
1	9770	9812	9847	9876	9900	9919	9935	9948	9958	9967
2	8791	8965	9117	9250	9365	9465	9550	9623	9686	9739
3	6839	7173	7483	7768	8029	8267	8482	8677	8851	9006
4	4418	4814	5203	5583	5950	6303	6640	6959	7260	7541
5	2327	2652	2991	3341	3698	4060	4425	4788	5147	5501
6	0992	1188	1405	1641	1897	2169	2458	2761	3077	3402
7	0342	0432	0536	0657	0796	0951	1125	1317	1526	1753
8	0095	0127	0166	0214	0271	0340	0420	0514	0621	0744
9	0021	0030	0041	0056	0075	0098	0127	0163	0206	0257
10	0004	0006	0008	0012	0016	0023	0031	0041	0055	0071
11	0001	0001	0001	0002	0003	0004	0006	0008	0011	0016
12						0001	0001	0001	0002	0003

P \ R	31	32	33	34	35	36	37	38	39	40
1	9974	9979	9984	9987	9990	9992	9994	9995	9996	9997
2	9784	9822	9854	9880	9902	9921	9936	9948	9959	9967
3	9144	9266	9374	9467	9549	9620	9681	9734	9778	9817
4	7804	8047	8270	8475	8661	8830	8982	9119	9241	9349
5	5846	6181	6504	6813	7108	7387	7649	7895	8123	8334
6	3736	4074	4416	4759	5100	5438	5770	6094	6408	6712
7	1997	2257	2531	2819	3119	3428	3746	4070	4398	4728
8	0881	1035	1205	1391	1594	1813	2048	2298	2562	2839
9	0317	0388	0470	0564	0671	0791	0926	1076	1242	1423
10	0092	0117	0148	0185	0229	0280	0341	0411	0491	0583
11	0021	0028	0037	0048	0062	0079	0100	0125	0155	0191
12	0004	0005	0007	0010	0013	0017	0023	0030	0038	0049
13		0001	0001	0001	0002	0003	0004	0005	0007	0009
14								0001	0001	0001

P \ R	41	42	43	44	45	46	47	48	49	50
1	9998	9998	9999	9999	9999	9999	10000	10000	10000	10000
2	9974	9979	9984	9987	9990	9992	9994	9995	9997	9997
3	9849	9876	9899	9918	9934	9947	9958	9966	9973	9979
4	9444	9527	9600	9664	9719	9766	9806	9840	9869	9894
5	8529	8707	8869	9015	9147	9265	9370	9463	9544	9616
6	7003	7280	7543	7792	8024	8241	8441	8626	8795	8949
7	5058	5387	5711	6029	6340	6641	6932	7210	7476	7728
8	3128	3428	3736	4051	4371	4694	5019	5343	5665	5982
9	1619	1832	2060	2302	2559	2829	3111	3405	3707	4018
10	0687	0805	0936	1081	1241	1416	1607	1814	2036	2272
11	0234	0284	0342	0409	0486	0574	0674	0786	0911	1051
12	0062	0078	0098	0121	0149	0183	0222	0268	0322	0384
13	0012	0016	0021	0027	0035	0044	0055	0069	0086	0106
14	0002	0002	0003	0004	0006	0007	0010	0013	0016	0021
15					0001	0001	0001	0001	0002	0003

$$n = 17$$

P \ R	01	02	03	04	05	06	07	08	09	10
1	1571	2907	4042	5004	5819	6507	7088	7577	7988	8332
2	0123	0446	0909	1465	2078	2717	3362	3995	4604	5182
3	0006	0044	0134	0286	0503	0782	1118	1503	1927	2382
4		0003	0014	0040	0088	0164	0273	0419	0603	0826
5			0001	0004	0012	0026	0051	0089	0145	0221
6					0001	0003	0007	0015	0027	0047
7							0001	0002	0004	0008
8										0001

P \ R	11	12	13	14	15	16	17	18	19	20
1	8621	8862	9063	9230	9369	9484	9579	9657	9722	9775
2	5723	6223	6682	7099	7475	7813	8113	8379	8613	8818
3	2858	3345	3836	4324	4802	5266	5711	6133	6532	6904
4	1087	1383	1710	2065	2444	2841	3251	3669	4091	4511
5	0321	0446	0598	0778	0987	1224	1487	1775	2087	2418
6	0075	0114	0166	0234	0319	0423	0548	0695	0864	1057
7	0014	0023	0037	0056	0083	0118	0163	0220	0291	0377
8	0002	0004	0007	0011	0017	0027	0039	0057	0080	0109
9		0001	0001	0002	0003	0005	0008	0012	0018	0026
10						0001	0001	0002	0003	0005
11										0001

TABLE E—Continued

P	21	22	23	24	25	26	27	28	29	30
R										
1	9818	9854	9882	9906	9925	9940	9953	9962	9970	9977
2	8996	9152	9285	9400	9499	9583	9654	9714	9765	9807
3	7249	7567	7859	8123	8363	8578	8771	8942	9093	9226
4	4927	5333	5728	6107	6470	6814	7137	7440	7721	7981
5	2766	3128	3500	3879	4261	4643	5023	5396	5760	6113
6	1273	1510	1770	2049	2347	2661	2989	3329	3677	4032
7	0479	0598	0736	0894	1071	1268	1485	1721	1976	2248
8	0147	0194	0251	0320	0402	0499	0611	0739	0884	1046
9	0037	0051	0070	0094	0124	0161	0206	0261	0326	0403
10	0007	0011	0016	0022	0031	0042	0057	0075	0098	0127
11	0001	0002	0003	0004	0006	0009	0013	0018	0024	0032
12				0001	0001	0002	0002	0003	0005	0007
13									0001	0001

P	31	32	33	34	35	36	37	38	39	40
R										
1	9982	9986	9989	9991	9993	9995	9996	9997	9998	9998
2	9843	9872	9896	9917	9933	9946	9957	9966	9973	9979
3	9343	9444	9532	9608	9673	9728	9775	9815	9849	9877
4	8219	8437	8634	8812	8972	9115	9241	9353	9450	9536
5	6453	6778	7087	7378	7652	7906	8142	8360	8559	8740
6	4390	4749	5105	5458	5803	6139	6465	6778	7077	7361
7	2536	2838	3153	3479	3812	4152	4495	4839	5182	5522
8	1227	1426	1642	1877	2128	2395	2676	2971	3278	3595
9	0492	0595	0712	0845	0994	1159	1341	1541	1757	1989
10	0162	0204	0254	0314	0383	0464	0557	0664	0784	0919
11	0043	0057	0074	0095	0120	0151	0189	0234	0286	0348
12	0009	0013	0017	0023	0030	0040	0051	0066	0084	0106
13	0002	0002	0003	0004	0006	0008	0011	0015	0019	0025
14				0001	0001	0001	0002	0002	0003	0005
15										0001

P	41	42	43	44	45	46	47	48	49	50
R										
1	9999	9999	9999	9999	10000	10000	10000	10000	10000	10000
2	9984	9987	9990	9992	9994	9996	9997	9998	9998	9999
3	9900	9920	9935	9948	9959	9968	9975	9980	9985	9988
4	9610	9674	9729	9776	9816	9849	9877	9901	9920	9936
5	8904	9051	9183	9301	9404	9495	9575	9644	9704	9755
6	7628	7879	8113	8330	8529	8712	8878	9028	9162	9283
7	5856	6182	6499	6805	7098	7377	7641	7890	8122	8338
8	3920	4250	4585	4921	5257	5590	5918	6239	6552	6855
9	2238	2502	2780	3072	3374	3687	4008	4335	4667	5000
10	1070	1236	1419	1618	1834	2066	2314	2577	2855	3145
11	0430	0503	0597	0705	0826	0962	1112	1279	1462	1662
12	0133	0165	0203	0248	0301	0363	0434	0517	0611	0717
13	0033	0042	0054	0069	0086	0108	0134	0165	0202	0245
14	0006	0008	0011	0014	0019	0024	0031	0040	0050	0064
15	0001	0001	0002	0002	0003	0004	0005	0007	0009	0012
16							0001	0001	0001	0001

$n = 18$

P	01	02	03	04	05	06	07	08	09	10
R										
1	1655	3049	4220	5204	6028	6717	7292	7771	8169	8499
2	0138	0495	1003	1607	2265	2945	3622	4281	4909	5497
3	0007	0052	0157	0333	0581	0898	1275	1702	2168	2662
4		0004	0018	0050	0109	0201	0333	0506	0723	0982
5			0002	0006	0015	0034	0067	0116	0186	0282
6				0001	0002	0005	0010	0021	0038	0064
7							0001	0003	0006	0012
8									0001	0002

P	11	12	13	14	15	16	17	18	19	20
R										
1	8773	8998	9185	9338	9464	9566	9651	9719	9775	9820
2	6042	6540	6992	7398	7759	8080	8362	8609	8824	9009
3	3173	3690	4206	4713	5203	5673	6119	6538	6927	7287
4	1282	1618	1986	2382	2798	3229	3669	4112	4554	4990
5	0405	0558	0743	0959	1206	1482	1787	2116	2467	2836

TABLE E—Continued

P	11	12	13	14	15	16	17	18	19	20
R										
6	0102	0154	0222	0310	0419	0551	0708	0889	1097	1329
7	0021	0034	0054	0081	0118	0167	0229	0306	0400	0513
8	0003	0006	0011	0017	0027	0041	0060	0086	0120	0163
9		0001	0002	0003	0005	0008	0013	0020	0029	0043
10					0001	0001	0002	0004	0006	0009
11								0001	0001	0002

P	21	22	23	24	25	26	27	28	29	30
R										
1	9856	9886	9909	9928	9944	9956	9965	9973	9979	9984
2	9169	9306	9423	9522	9605	9676	9735	9784	9824	9858
3	7616	7916	8187	8430	8647	8839	9009	9158	9288	9400
4	5414	5825	6218	6591	6943	7272	7578	7860	8119	8354
5	3220	3613	4012	4414	4813	5208	5594	5968	6329	6673
6	1586	1866	2168	2488	2825	3176	3538	3907	4281	4656
7	0645	0799	0974	1171	1390	1630	1891	2171	2469	2783
8	0217	0283	0363	0458	0569	0699	0847	1014	1200	1407
9	0060	0083	0112	0148	0193	0249	0316	0395	0488	0596
10	0014	0020	0028	0039	0054	0073	0097	0127	0164	0210
11	0003	0004	0006	0009	0012	0018	0025	0034	0046	0061
12		0001	0001	0002	0002	0003	0005	0007	0010	0014
13						0001	0001	0001	0002	0003

P	31	32	33	34	35	36	37	38	39	40
R										
1	9987	9990	9993	9994	9996	9997	9998	9998	9999	9999
2	9886	9908	9927	9942	9954	9964	9972	9978	9983	9987
3	9498	9581	9652	9713	9764	9807	9843	9873	9897	9918
4	8568	8759	8931	9083	9217	9335	9439	9528	9606	9672
5	7001	7309	7598	7866	8114	8341	8549	8737	8907	9058
6	5029	5398	5759	6111	6450	6776	7086	7379	7655	7912
7	3111	3450	3797	4151	4509	4867	5224	5576	5921	6257
8	1633	1878	2141	2421	2717	3027	3349	3681	4021	4366
9	0720	0861	1019	1196	1391	1604	1835	2084	2350	2632
10	0264	0329	0405	0494	0597	0714	0847	0997	1163	1347
11	0080	0104	0133	0169	0212	0264	0325	0397	0480	0576
12	0020	0027	0036	0047	0062	0080	0102	0130	0163	0203
13	0004	0005	0008	0011	0014	0019	0026	0034	0044	0058
14	0001	0001	0001	0002	0003	0004	0005	0007	0010	0013
15						0001	0001	0001	0002	0002

P	41	42	43	44	45	46	47	48	49	50
R										
1	9999	9999	10000	10000	10000	10000	10000	10000	10000	10000
2	9990	9992	9994	9996	9997	9998	9998	9999	9999	9999
3	9934	9948	9959	9968	9975	9981	9985	9989	9991	9993
4	9729	9777	9818	9852	9880	9904	9923	9939	9952	9962
5	9193	9313	9418	9510	9589	9658	9717	9767	9810	9846
6	8151	8372	8573	8757	8923	9072	9205	9324	9428	9519
7	6582	6895	7193	7476	7742	7991	8222	8436	8632	8811
8	4713	5062	5408	5750	6085	6412	6728	7032	7322	7597
9	2928	3236	3556	3885	4222	4562	4906	5249	5591	5927
10	1549	1768	2004	2258	2527	2812	3110	3421	3742	4073
11	0686	0811	0951	1107	1280	1470	1677	1902	2144	2403
12	0250	0307	0372	0449	0537	0658	0753	0883	1028	1189
13	0074	0094	0118	0147	0183	0225	0275	0334	0402	0481
14	0017	0022	0029	0038	0049	0063	0079	0100	0125	0154
15	0003	0004	0006	0007	0010	0013	0017	0023	0029	0038
16		0001	0001	0001	0001	0002	0003	0004	0005	0007
17									0001	0001

n = 19

P	01	02	03	04	05	06	07	08	09	10
R										
1	1738	3188	4394	5396	6226	6914	7481	7949	8334	8649
2	0153	0546	1100	1751	2453	3171	3879	4560	5202	5797
3	0009	0061	0183	0384	0665	1021	1439	1908	2415	2946
4		0005	0022	0061	0132	0243	0398	0602	0953	1150
5			0002	0007	0020	0044	0085	0147	0235	0352
6				0001	0002	0006	0014	0029	0051	0086
7						0001	0002	0004	0009	0017
8								0001	0001	0003

TABLE E—Continued

P / R	11	12	13	14	15	16	17	18	19	20
1	8908	9119	9291	9431	9544	9636	9710	9770	9818	9856
2	6342	6835	7277	7669	8015	8318	8581	8809	9004	9171
3	3488	4032	4568	5089	5587	6059	6500	6910	7287	7631
4	1490	1867	2275	2708	3159	3620	4085	4549	5005	5449
5	0502	0685	0904	1158	1444	1762	2107	2476	2864	3267
6	0135	0202	0290	0401	0537	0700	0891	1110	1357	1631
7	0030	0048	0076	0113	0163	0328	0310	0411	0532	0676
8	0005	0009	0016	0026	0041	0061	0089	0126	0173	0233
9	0001	0002	0003	0005	0008	0014	0021	0032	0047	0067
10				0001	0001	0002	0004	0007	0010	0016
11							0001	0001	0002	0003

P / R	21	22	23	24	25	26	27	28	29	30
1	9887	9911	9930	9946	9958	9967	9975	9981	9985	9989
2	9313	9434	9535	9619	9690	9749	9797	9837	9869	9896
3	7942	8222	8471	8692	8887	9057	9205	9333	9443	9538
4	5877	6285	6671	7032	7369	7680	7965	8224	8458	8668
5	3681	4100	4520	4936	5346	5744	6129	6498	6848	7178
6	1929	2251	2592	2950	3322	3705	4093	4484	4875	5261
7	0843	1034	1248	1487	1749	2032	2336	2657	2995	3345
8	0307	0396	0503	0629	0775	0941	1129	1338	1568	1820
9	0093	0127	0169	0222	0287	0366	0459	0568	0694	0839
10	0023	0034	0047	0066	0089	0119	0156	0202	0258	0326
11	0005	0007	0011	0016	0023	0032	0044	0060	0080	0105
12	0001	0001	0002	0003	0005	0007	0010	0015	0021	0028
13				0001	0001	0001	0002	0003	0004	0006
14									0001	0001

P / R	31	32	33	34	35	36	37	38	39	40
1	9991	9993	9995	9996	9997	9998	9998	9999	9999	9999
2	9917	9935	9949	9960	9969	9976	9981	9986	9989	9992
3	9618	9686	9743	9791	9830	9863	9890	9913	9931	9945
4	8856	9022	9169	9297	9409	9505	9588	9659	9719	9770
5	7486	7773	8037	8280	8500	8699	8878	9038	9179	9304
6	5641	6010	6366	6707	7032	7339	7627	7895	8143	8371
7	3705	4073	4445	4818	5188	5554	5913	6261	6597	6919
8	2091	2381	2688	3010	3344	3690	4043	4401	4762	5122
9	1003	1186	1389	1612	1855	2116	2395	2691	3002	3325
10	0405	0499	0608	0733	0875	1035	1213	1410	1626	1861
11	0137	0176	0223	0280	0347	0426	0518	0625	0747	0885
12	0038	0051	0068	0089	0114	0146	0185	0231	0287	0352
13	0009	0012	0017	0023	0031	0041	0054	0070	0091	0116
14	0002	0002	0003	0005	0007	0009	0013	0017	0023	0031
15			0001	0001	0001	0002	0002	0003	0005	0006
16									0001	0001

P / R	41	42	43	44	45	46	47	48	49	50
1	10000	10000	10000	10000	10000	10000	10000	10000	10000	10000
2	9994	9995	9996	9997	9998	9999	9999	9999	9999	10000
3	9957	9967	9974	9980	9985	9988	9991	9993	9995	9996
4	9813	9849	9878	9903	9923	9939	9952	9963	9971	9978
5	9413	9508	9590	9660	9720	9771	9814	9850	9879	9904
6	8579	8767	8937	9088	9223	9342	9446	9537	9615	9682
7	7226	7515	7787	8039	8273	8488	8684	8862	9022	9165
8	5480	5832	6176	6509	6831	7138	7430	7706	7964	8204
9	3660	4003	4353	4706	5060	5413	5762	6105	6439	6762
10	2114	2385	2672	2974	3290	3617	3954	4299	4648	5000
11	1040	1213	1404	1613	1841	2087	2351	2631	2928	3238
12	0429	0518	0621	0738	0871	1021	1187	1372	1575	1796
13	0146	0183	0227	0280	0342	0415	0500	0597	0709	0835
14	0040	0052	0067	0086	0109	0137	0171	0212	0261	0318
15	0009	0012	0016	0021	0028	0036	0046	0060	0076	0096
16	0001	0002	0003	0004	0005	0007	0010	0013	0017	0022
17				0001	0001	0001	0001	0002	0003	0004

TABLE E—Continued

$$n = 20$$

P	01	02	03	04	05	06	07	08	09	10
R										
1	1821	3324	4562	5580	6415	7099	7658	8113	8484	8784
2	0169	0599	1198	1897	2642	3395	4131	4831	5484	6083
3	0010	0071	0210	0439	0755	1150	1610	2121	2666	3231
4		0006	0027	0074	0159	0290	0471	0706	0993	1330
5			0003	0010	0026	0056	0107	0183	0290	0432
6				0001	0003	0009	0019	0038	0068	0113
7						0001	0003	0006	0013	0024
8								0001	0002	0004
9										0001

P	11	12	13	14	15	16	17	18	19	20
R										
1	9028	9224	9383	9510	9612	9694	9759	9811	9852	9885
2	6624	7109	7539	7916	8244	8529	8773	8982	9159	9308
3	3802	4369	4920	5450	5951	6420	6854	7252	7614	7939
4	1710	2127	2573	3041	3523	4010	4496	4974	5439	5886
5	0610	0827	1083	1375	1702	2059	2443	2849	3271	3704
6	0175	0260	0370	0507	0673	0870	1098	1356	1643	1958
7	0041	0067	0103	0153	0219	0304	0409	0537	0689	0867
8	0008	0014	0024	0038	0059	0088	0127	0177	0241	0321
9	0001	0002	0005	0008	0013	0021	0033	0049	0071	0100
10			0001	0001	0002	0004	0007	0011	0017	0026
11							0001	0001	0002	0004	0006
12									0001	0001

P	21	22	23	24	25	26	27	28	29	30
R										
1	9910	9931	9946	9959	9968	9976	9982	9986	9989	9992
2	9434	9539	9626	9698	9757	9805	9845	9877	9903	9924
3	8230	8488	8716	8915	9087	9237	9365	9474	9567	9645
4	6310	6711	7085	7431	7748	8038	8300	8534	8744	8929
5	4142	4580	5014	5439	5852	6248	6625	6981	7315	7625
6	2297	2657	3035	3427	3828	4235	4643	5048	5447	5836
7	1071	1301	1557	1838	2142	2467	2810	3169	3540	3920
8	0419	0536	0675	0835	1018	1225	1455	1707	1982	2277
9	0138	0186	0246	0320	0409	0515	0640	0784	0948	1133
10	0038	0054	0075	0103	0139	0183	0238	0305	0385	0480
11	0009	0013	0019	0028	0039	0055	0074	0100	0132	0171
12	0002	0003	0004	0006	0009	0014	0019	0027	0038	0051
13			0001	0001	0002	0003	0004	0006	0009	0013
14							0001	0001	0002	0003

P	31	32	33	34	35	36	37	38	39	40
R										
1	9994	9996	9997	9998	9998	9999	9999	9999	9999	10000
2	9940	9953	9964	9972	9979	9984	9988	9991	9993	9995
3	9711	9765	9811	9848	9879	9904	9924	9940	9953	9964
4	9092	9235	9358	9465	9556	9634	9700	9755	9802	9840
5	7911	8173	8411	8626	8818	8989	9141	9274	9390	9490
6	6213	6574	6917	7242	7546	7829	8090	8329	8547	8744
7	4305	4693	5079	5460	5834	6197	6547	6882	7200	7500
8	2591	2922	3268	3624	3990	4361	4735	5108	5478	5841
9	1340	1568	1818	2087	2376	2683	3005	3341	3688	4044
10	0591	0719	0866	1032	1218	1424	1650	1897	2163	2447
11	0220	0279	0350	0434	0532	0645	0775	0923	1090	1275
12	0069	0091	0119	0154	0196	0247	0308	0381	0466	0565
13	0018	0025	0034	0045	0060	0079	0102	0132	0167	0210
14	0004	0006	0008	0011	0015	0021	0028	0037	0049	0065
15	0001	0001	0001	0002	0003	0004	0006	0009	0012	0016
16						0001	0001	0002	0002	0003

P	41	42	43	44	45	46	47	48	49	50
R										
1	10000	10000	10000	10000	10000	10000	10000	10000	10000	10000
2	9996	9997	9998	9998	9999	9999	9999	10000	10000	10000
3	9972	9979	9984	9988	9991	9993	9995	9996	9997	9998
4	9872	9898	9920	9937	9951	9962	9971	9977	9983	9987
5	9577	9651	9714	9767	9811	9848	9879	9904	9924	9941

TABLE E—Continued

P R	41	42	43	44	45	46	47	48	49	50
6	8921	9078	9217	9340	9447	9539	9619	9687	9745	9793
7	7780	8041	8281	8501	8701	8881	9042	9186	9312	9423
8	6196	6539	6868	7183	7480	7759	8020	8261	8482	8684
9	4406	4771	5136	5499	5857	6207	6546	6873	7186	7483
10	2748	3064	3394	3736	4086	4443	4804	5166	5525	5881
11	1480	1705	1949	2212	2493	2791	3104	3432	3771	4119
12	0679	0810	0958	1123	1308	1511	1734	1977	2238	2517
13	0262	0324	0397	0482	0580	0694	0823	0969	1133	1316
14	0084	0107	0136	0172	0214	0265	0326	0397	0480	0577
15	0022	0029	0038	0050	0064	0083	0105	0133	0166	0207
16	0004	0006	0008	0011	0015	0020	0027	0035	0046	0059
17	0001	0001	0001	0002	0003	0004	0005	0007	0010	0013
18						0001	0001	0001	0001	0002

INDEX

449

This book has been set on the Monotype in 11 point Modern 8A, leaded 2 points and 10 point Modern 8A, leaded 1 point. Chapter numbers are in 18 point Bulmer and 42 point Weiss Series I; chapter titles are in 18 point Bulmer. The size of the type page is 27 by 46½ picas.